Other Titles in This Series

(Continued in the back of this publication)

Ten Lectures
on the Interface
Between Analytic Number
Theory and Harmonic Analysis

Conference Board of the Mathematical Sciences

CBMS

Regional Conference Series in Mathematics

Number 84

Ten Lectures on the Interface Between Analytic Number Theory and Harmonic Analysis

Hugh L. Montgomery

Published for the
Conference Board of the Mathematical Sciences
by the
American Mathematical Society
Providence, Rhode Island
with support from the
National Science Foundation

Expository Lectures
from the NSF-CBMS Regional Conference
held at Kansas State University, Manhattan, Kansas
May 22–25, 1990

Research partially supported by
National Science Foundation Grant DMS 8912917

1991 *Mathematics Subject Classification*. Primary 11–02, 42–02;
Secondary 11K06, 11K38, 11K70, 11L03, 11L07, 11L15, 11M20, 11M26, 11N05, 11N25,
11N30, 11N69, 11R06, 41A30, 42A05, 42A10.

Library of Congress Cataloging-in-Publication Data
Montgomery, Hugh L. (Hugh Lowell), 1944–
    Ten lectures on the interface between analytic number theory and harmonic analysis/Hugh L.
Montgomery.
        p.   cm. — (Regional conference series in mathematics, ISSN 0160-7642; no. 84)
    "Expository lectures from the NSF-CBMS regional conference held at Kansas State University,
Manhattan, May 22-25, 1990"—T.p. verso.
    Includes bibliographical references.
    ISBN 0-8218-0737-4
    1. Number theory—Congresses.   2. Harmonic analysis—Congresses.   I. Title.   II. Series.
QA1.R33   no. 84
[QA241]
510 s—dc20   94-26864
[512′73]   CIP

♾ The paper used in this book is acid-free and falls within the guidelines
established to ensure permanence and durability.
♻ Printed on recycled paper.
This volume was printed directly from copy prepared by the author using $\mathcal{A}\mathcal{M}\mathcal{S}$-TEX,
the American Mathematical Society's TEX macro system.

10 9 8 7 6 5 4 3 2   99 98 97 96

Contents

Preface

Todd Cochrane and Robert Dressler noted the common interests of number theorists and harmonic analysts in their department, and proposed an NSF–CBMS conference whose purpose would be to further the cross-fertilization between these two areas. The conference took place during the week May 21–25, 1990, on the campus of Kansas State University, in Manhattan ("The Little Apple"), Kansas. The conference was funded by NSF Grant DMS-8912917. In addition, NSA Grant MDS-904-90-14-4018 provided the travel expenses of a number of graduates students, enabling them to attend the conference.

In addition to the lectures reported upon in this volume, the conference featured the following nine major addresses:

Speaker	Title
J. Beck (Rutgers U.)	*New Applications of the Roth-Halász Method in Irregularities of Distribution*
P. X. Gallagher (Columbia U.)	*Duality for long second Moments of Short Interval Densities*
H. Iwaniec (Rutgers U.)	*Estimates for coefficients of L-functions*
T. W. Körner (Cambridge U.)	*Universal Fourier Series*
J.-F. Méla (U. Paris XIII)	*Remarkable Subgroups of the Circle*
I. Z. Ruzsa (MTA, Budapest)	*Nouveaux sets of Trigonometric Polynomials: Halfway between Random and Regular*
B. Saffari (U. Paris XI)	*An Account of extremal Problems on Polynomials with restricted Coefficients*
G. Tenenbaum (U. Nancy)	*Fourier Transforms of Divisor Distributions: A Survey of Applications*
R. C. Vaughan (Imperial College)	*The Upper Bound for $G(k)$ in Waring's Problem*

Even during the conference, the cross-fertilization paid dividends: Beck, after hearing Saffari's talk, realized that he had tools at his disposal that enabled him to contribute to an old problem concerning trigonometric polynomials (see the commentary on Problem **55.** on p. 206).

The conference was enhanced by several social events, including an invigorating excursion to the Konza Prairie. On behalf of the 88 participants, it is my pleasure to thank the organizers for their fine work, and the mathematicians at KSU for their hospitality.

Most of the material in this volume is found in the research literature, and does not originate from the present author. Original results published here for the first time were obtained with the support from the National Science Foundation, particularly NSF Grant DMS-9107605.

The author sought and received assistance concerning the contents of this volume from many associates. For their suggestions, large or small, the author is indebted to them all, most especially to R. C. Baker, P. T. Bateman, J. Beck, J. Bourgain, P. Bundschuh, T. Cochrane, J. B. Conrey, R. Cook, R. E. Dressler, P. Enflo, J. B. Friedlander, S. W. Graham, G. Halász, P. R. Halmos, G. Harman, H. Iwaniec, T. W. Körner, R. Lyons, M. Mendes-France, R. Nair, A. D. Pollington, J. B. Rauch, I. Z. Ruzsa, B. Saffari, J. W. Sander, A. Schinzel, J.-P. Serre, G. Tenenbaum, R. C. Vaughan, E. Wirsing, and T. D. Wooley.

Hugh L. Montgomery
Ann Arbor
13 May, 1994

Notation

The harmonic analysis pursued here involves the real line $\mathbb{R}$, the circle group $\mathbb{T} = \mathbb{R}/\mathbb{Z}$, or the finite Fourier transform (called "additive characters" by number theorists). We let

$$e(x) = e^{2\pi i x}$$

denote the complex exponential with period 1, so that if $f \in L^1(\mathbb{T})$ then its Fourier coefficients are given by the formula

$$\widehat{f}(k) = \int_{\mathbb{T}} f(x) e(-kx)\, dx.$$

Similarly, the Fourier coefficients of a Borel measure μ on $\mathbb{T}$ we take to be

$$\widehat{\mu}(k) = \int_{\mathbb{T}} e(-kx)\, d\mu(x).$$

We let $[x]$ and $\{x\}$ denote the integral part of x and the fractional part of x, respectively. Thus $x = [x] + \{x\}$ with $[x] \in \mathbb{Z}$ and $0 \leq \{x\} < 1$. In addition, we let $\|x\|$ denote the distance from x to the nearest integer, $\|x\| = \min_{n \in \mathbb{Z}} |x - n|$. Thus $\|x\|$ is the natural norm on $\mathbb{T}$.

The relation $f \ll g$ means exactly the same thing as $f = O(g)$; that is, there is an absolute constant C such that $|f| \leq Cg$ for all values of the free variables under consideration. If the implicit constant C is allowed to depend on a parameter k, then such dependence may be indicated by writing $f \ll_k g$ or $f = O_k(g)$.

More specialized notation, appropriate to various topics, is developed in individual chapters. Such notation should not be expected to be consistent from one chapter to another. For example, δ in Chapter 1 is quite different from δ in Chapter 2.

Chapter 1. Uniform Distribution

1. Qualitative theory. We let $\mathbb{T}$ denote the circle group, $\mathbb{T} = \mathbb{R}/\mathbb{Z}$. Suppose that we are given a sequence $\{u_n\}$ of points of $\mathbb{T}$. For $0 \leq \alpha \leq 1$ put

$$Z(N;\alpha) = \operatorname{card}\{n \in \mathbb{Z} : 1 \leq n \leq N, 0 \leq u_n \leq \alpha \pmod{1}\}.$$

We say that the sequence $\{u_n\}$ is *uniformly distributed* if

$$(1) \qquad \lim_{N \to \infty} \frac{1}{N} Z(N;\alpha) = \alpha$$

for every α, $0 \leq \alpha \leq 1$. Let U_N denote the measure that places unit point-masses at the points $u_1, u_2, \ldots, u_N$. The Fourier transform of this measure is defined to be

$$\widehat{U}_N(k) = \int_{\mathbb{T}} e(-k\alpha)\, dU_N$$

$$(2) \qquad \qquad = \sum_{n=1}^{N} e(-ku_n).$$

Here $e(\theta) = e^{2\pi i\theta}$ denotes the complex exponential with period 1. Weyl [**13**, **14**] characterized uniformly distributed sequences as follows.

WEYL'S CRITERION. *The following assertions concerning the sequence $\{u_n\}$ are equivalent:*

(a) *The sequence $\{u_n\}$ is uniformly distributed;*
(b) *For each integer $k \neq 0$, $\widehat{U}_N(k) = o(N)$ as $N \to \infty$;*
(c) *If F is properly Riemann-integrable on $\mathbb{T}$ then*

$$(3) \qquad \lim_{N \to \infty} \frac{1}{N} \sum_{n=1}^{N} F(u_n) = \int_{\mathbb{T}} F(\alpha)\, d\alpha.$$

By a simple compactness argument it may be seen that if $\{u_n\}$ is uniformly distributed then the limit (1) is attained uniformly in α. For $0 \leq \alpha \leq 1$ we put

$$D(N;\alpha) = Z(N;\alpha) - N\alpha.$$

Then the *discrepancy* of the sequence is

(4) $$D^*(N) = \sup_{\alpha \in [0,1]} |D(N;\alpha)|.$$

Thus the conditions (a)–(c) above are equivalent to

(d) $D^*(N) = o(N)$ *as* $N \to \infty$.

The discrepancy $D^*(N)$ is not invariant under translation, which is regrettable since $\mathbb{T}$ is a homogeneous space. The usual method used to overcome this defect involves counting the number $Z(N;\alpha,\beta)$ of n for which $u_n \in [\alpha,\beta] \pmod 1$. We put

(5) $$D(N;\alpha,\beta) = Z(N;\alpha,\beta) - (\beta-\alpha)N,$$

assuming that $\alpha \leq \beta \leq \alpha+1$, and then we set

(6) $$D(N) = \sup_{\alpha,\beta} |D(N;\alpha,\beta)|.$$

Equivalently, we may put

(7) $$D(N) = \sup_{\alpha} D(N;\alpha) - \inf_{\alpha} D(N;\alpha),$$

and it is evident that

(8) $$D^*(N) \leq D(N) \leq 2D^*(N).$$

This new discrepancy D is translation-invariant, but it is more complicated than necessary. To construct an alternative approach, let $s(x)$ denote the saw-tooth function

(9) $$s(x) = \begin{cases} \{x\} - 1/2 & x \notin \mathbb{Z}, \\ 0 & x \in \mathbb{Z}. \end{cases}$$

Here $\{x\}$ denotes the fractional part of x, $\{x\} = x - [x]$. Let

(10) $$\delta(N;\alpha) = \sum_{n=1}^{N} s(u_n - \alpha).$$

That is, $\delta(N;\alpha) = \int_{\mathbb{T}} s(x-\alpha)\,dZ(N;\alpha)$. We put

(11) $$\delta(N) = \sup_{\alpha} |\delta(N;\alpha)|.$$

If $x \neq 0, x \neq \alpha \pmod 1$, then $\chi_{[0,\alpha]}(x) = \alpha + s(x-\alpha) - s(x)$ where $\chi_{\mathcal{S}}$ denotes the characteristic function of the set $\mathcal{S}$. We set $x = u_n$, sum over n, and subtract $N\alpha$ to see that

$$D^*(N;\alpha) = \delta(N;\alpha) - \delta(N;0)$$

at points of continuity. Thus $\delta(N;\alpha)$ differs from $D^*(N;\alpha)$ by an additive constant. In the case of $D^*(N;\alpha)$, the additive constant is chosen so that

$D^*(N; 1^-) = 0$, while for $\delta(N; \alpha)$ the constant is chosen so that $\int_{\mathbb{T}} \delta(N; \alpha)\, d\alpha = 0$. Similarly

$$D(N; \alpha, \beta) = \delta(N; \beta) - \delta(N; \alpha)$$

whenever α and β are chosen so as not to coincide with any u_n. Hence

$$D(N) = \sup_\beta \delta(N; \beta) - \inf_\alpha \delta(N; \alpha).$$

From this it is evident that

(12) $$\delta(N) \le D(N) \le 2\delta(N).$$

2. Quantitative relations. We now consider the possibility of constructing quantitative relations between the assertions (a)–(d) of Weyl's criterion.

Suppose that F is of bounded variation on $\mathbb{T}$, and that F is continuous at the points u_n. Then

$$\sum_{n=1}^N F(u_n) = \int_{\mathbb{T}} F(\alpha)\, dZ(N; \alpha).$$

On subtracting $N \int_{\mathbb{T}} F(\alpha)\, d\alpha$ from both sides, we deduce that

$$\sum_{n=1}^N F(u_n) - N \int_{\mathbb{T}} F(\alpha)\, d\alpha = \int_{\mathbb{T}} F(\alpha)\, dD(N; \alpha).$$

Put

$$\Delta(N; \alpha) = D(N; \alpha) - \frac{1}{2} \sup_\beta D(N; \beta) - \frac{1}{2} \inf_\beta D(N; \beta).$$

Thus $\sup_\alpha \Delta(N; \alpha) = \frac{1}{2} D(N)$ and $\inf_\alpha \Delta(N; \alpha) = -\frac{1}{2} D(N)$. But $\Delta(N; \alpha)$ differs from $D(N; \alpha)$ by a constant, so the integral on the right above is

$$= \int_{\mathbb{T}} F(\alpha)\, d\Delta(N; \alpha).$$

By integrating by parts it follows that this is

$$= -\int_{\mathbb{T}} \Delta(N; \alpha)\, dF(\alpha).$$

This integral has absolute value not exceeding

$$\frac{1}{2} D(N) \int_{\mathbb{T}} 1\, |dF(\alpha)| = \frac{1}{2} D(N) \mathrm{Var}_{\mathbb{T}}(F).$$

That is,

(13) $$\left| \sum_{n=1}^N F(u_n) - N \int_{\mathbb{T}} F(\alpha)\, d\alpha \right| \le \frac{1}{2} D(N) \mathrm{Var}_{\mathbb{T}}(F).$$

Although the class of Riemann-integrable functions includes functions not of bounded variation, for practical purposes the inequality above meets our needs in passing from (d) to (c) in Weyl's criterion.

On taking $F(x) = e(-kx)$ in (13), we see at once that $|\widehat{U}_N(k)| \leq \pi|k|D(N)$ for $k \neq 0$. Here the constant can be improved by taking a little more care. Express the complex number $\widehat{U}_N(k)$ in polar coordinates, $\widehat{U}_N(k) = \rho e(\theta)$ where $\rho = |\widehat{U}_N(k)|$. Then

$$|\widehat{U}_N(k)| = e(-\theta)\widehat{U}_N(k) = \sum_{n=1}^{N} e(-ku_n - \theta).$$

Since this sum is real, it suffices to consider the real parts of the summands. Thus

$$|\widehat{U}_N(k)| = \sum_{n=1}^{N} \cos 2\pi(ku_n + \theta).$$

On taking $F(x) = \cos 2\pi(kx + \theta)$ in (13), we deduce that

(14) $$|\widehat{U}_N(k)| \leq 2|k|D(N)$$

for all $k \neq 0$. If we take $u_n = n/k$ then $\widehat{U}_N(k) = N$ and $D(N) \sim N/k$. Thus the upper bound is within a constant factor of being best possible. On the other hand, for any given sequence u_n there are not many values of k for which $|\widehat{U}_N(k)|$ is this large. To show this we first note that

$$\widehat{\delta}(N;k) = -\widehat{U}_N(k)\widehat{s}(k) = \frac{\widehat{U}_N(k)}{2\pi i k}$$

for $k \neq 0$. Since $\widehat{\delta}(0) = 0$, and since $\widehat{U}_N(-k) = \overline{\widehat{U}_N(k)}$, it follows by Parseval's identity that

(15) $$\sum_{k=1}^{\infty} \frac{|\widehat{U}_N(k)|^2}{k^2} = 2\pi^2 \int_{\mathbb{T}} \delta(N;\alpha)^2 \, d\alpha.$$

Hence in particular,

$$\sum_{k=1}^{K} |\widehat{U}_N(k)|^2 \ll K^2 D(N)^2,$$

so that there are at most boundedly many k, $1 \leq k \leq K$ for which $|\widehat{U}_N(k)|$ is of the order of $KD(N)$. (In the above we have employed Vinogradov's $\ll$ notation, which is synonymous with the Big-O notation popularized by Hardy and Landau. Precisely, we write $f \ll g$ or $f = O(g)$ if there is an absolute constant A such that $|f| \leq Ag$ uniformly for all values of the free variables under consideration. The constant A is referred to as the *implicit constant*.) The relations (14) and (15) provide good quantitative passage from (d) to (b).

The usual derivation of (a) from (b) involves the existence of trigonometric polynomials $T^-(x), T^+(x)$ such that

$$T^-(x) \leq \chi_{[0,\alpha]}(x) \leq T^+(x)$$

for all x, and

$$\int_{\mathbb{T}} T^+(x) - T^-(x)\, dx < \epsilon.$$

To put this in quantitative form we need to know how small we may take ϵ as a function of the degrees of the trigonometric polynomials $T^{\pm}(x)$. Since the characteristic function of an interval can be expressed in terms of the saw-tooth function $s(x)$, we begin by considering one-sided approximations to $s(x)$.

We recall that Fejér's kernel $\Delta_K(x)$ is given by the formulæ

$$(16) \qquad \Delta_K(x) = \sum_{-K}^{K} \left(1 - \frac{|k|}{K}\right) e(kx) = \frac{1}{K}\left(\frac{\sin \pi K x}{\sin \pi x}\right)^2.$$

Then *Vaaler's polynomial* is

$$(17) \qquad \begin{aligned} V_K(x) = {} & \frac{1}{K+1}\sum_{k=1}^{K}\left(\frac{k}{K+1} - \frac{1}{2}\right)\Delta_{K+1}\left(x - \frac{k}{K+1}\right) \\ & + \frac{1}{2\pi(K+1)}\sin 2\pi(K+1)x - \frac{1}{2\pi}\Delta_{K+1}(x)\sin 2\pi x. \end{aligned}$$

Since $\Delta_{K+1}(x)$ is a trigonometric polynomial of degree K, the sum is of degree at most K. The last two terms are trigonometric polynomials of degree $K+1$, but the coefficients of $e(\pm(K+1)x)$ cancel, so that the combined contribution of the last two terms is a trigonometric polynomial of degree at most K. By an elementary calculation it may be shown that

$$(18) \qquad V_K(x) = \frac{1}{K+1}\sum_{k=1}^{K} f(k/(K+1))\sin 2\pi kx$$

where $f(u) = -(1-u)\cot \pi u - /\pi$, and one could take this to be the definition of V_K, but the most interesting properties of $V_K(x)$ follow more readily from the definition (17).

The function $V_K(x)$ provides a good approximation to the saw-tooth function $s(x)$. Like $s(x)$, the function $V_K(x)$ is odd. Indeed, it may be shown that

$$(19) \qquad V_K(x) = s(x) + O\left(\min\left(1, \frac{1}{K^3\|x\|^3}\right)\right).$$

Here $\|x\|$ denotes the natural metric on $\mathbb{T}$, namely $\|x\| = \min_{n\in\mathbb{Z}}|x - n|$. While $V_K(x)$ is presumably not quite the best L^1 approximation to $s(x)$, it lends itself to constructing the best majorant, which is given by the *Beurling polynomial*

$$(20) \qquad B_K(x) = V_K(x) + \frac{1}{2(K+1)}\Delta_{K+1}(x).$$

The relations among these functions is described in the following fundamental result, which we refer to as

VAALER'S LEMMA. *If $0 \leq x \leq 1/2$ then $s(x) \leq V_K(x) \leq B_K(x)$, while if $1/2 \leq x \leq 1$ then $V_K(x) \leq s(x) \leq B_K(x)$. If $T(x)$ is a trigonometric polynomial of degree $\leq K$ such that $T(x) \geq s(x)$ for all x then $\int_{\mathbb{T}} T(x)\,dx \geq \frac{1}{2(K+1)}$ with equality if and only if $T(x) = B_K(x)$.*

We postpone the proof of this to the next section, and consider here the applications of this to uniform distribution.

Let $\mathfrak{I} = [\alpha, \beta]$ be an arc of $\mathbb{T}$, with $\alpha \leq \beta \leq \alpha + 1$. From Vaaler's Lemma we know that $-B_K(-x) \leq s(x) \leq B_K(x)$ for all x. Since

$$\chi_{\mathfrak{I}}(x) = \beta - \alpha + s(x - \beta) + s(\alpha - x)$$

except when x coincides with one of the endpoints of $\mathfrak{I}$, we put

$$(21^+) \qquad S_K^+(x) = \beta - \alpha + B_K(x - \beta) + B_K(\alpha - x)$$

and

$$(21^-) \qquad S_K^-(x) = \beta - \alpha - B_K(\beta - x) - B_K(x - \alpha).$$

These are the *Selberg polynomials*. It is at once evident that $S_K^\pm(x)$ is a trigonometric polynomial of degree at most K, that $S_K^-(x) \leq \chi_{\mathfrak{I}}(x) \leq S_K^+(x)$ for all x, and that $\int_{\mathbb{T}} S_K^\pm(x)\,dx = \beta - \alpha \pm \frac{1}{K+1}$. Hence

$$Z(N; \alpha, \beta) \leq \sum_{n=1}^{N} S_K^+(u_n)$$

$$= \sum_{n=1}^{N} \sum_{-K}^{K} \widehat{S}_K^+(k)e(ku_n).$$

On inverting the order of summation we see that this is

$$= \sum_{-K}^{K} \widehat{S}_K^+(k)\widehat{U}_N(-k).$$

Since $\widehat{U}_N(0) = N$ and $\widehat{S}_K^+(0) = \beta - \alpha + \frac{1}{K+1}$, it follows that

$$D(N; \alpha, \beta) \leq \frac{N}{K+1} + \sum_{0 < |k| \leq K} \widehat{S}_K^+(k)\widehat{U}_N(-k).$$

We now require an estimate for $|\widehat{S}_K^+(k)|$. Since $S_K^+(x)$ has been explicitly defined, one might argue directly, but a serviceable estimate is obtained by applying the inequality $|\widehat{f}(k)| \leq \|f\|_{L^1}$ to the function $f(x) = S_K^+(x) - \chi_{\mathfrak{I}}(x)$. Hence

$$|\widehat{S}_K^+(k) - \widehat{\chi}_{\mathfrak{I}}(k)| \leq \|S_K^+ - \chi_{\mathfrak{I}}\|_{L^1} = \frac{1}{K+1}.$$

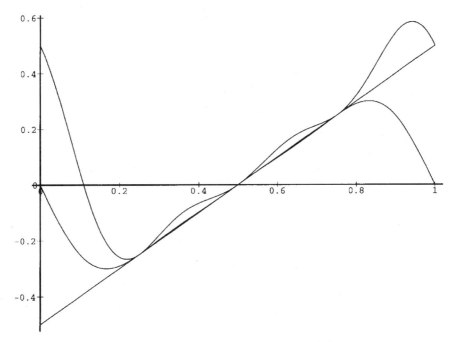

FIGURE 1. The functions $s(x)$, $V_3(x)$, and $B_3(x)$ for $0 \le x \le 1$.

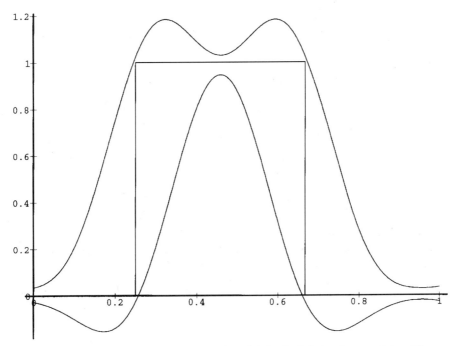

FIGURE 2. The functions $\chi_{\mathfrak{J}}(x)$, $S_3^+(x)$, $S_3^-(x)$ for $0 \le x \le 1$, with $\mathfrak{J} = [1/4, 2/3]$.

Moreover, $\widehat{s}(k) = -1/(2\pi i k)$ for $k \neq 0$, so that

$$\widehat{\chi}_{\mathfrak{I}}(k) = (e(k\alpha) - e(k\beta))/(2\pi i k).$$

Hence

$$|\widehat{\chi}_{\mathfrak{I}}(k)| = \left|\frac{\sin \pi k(\beta - \alpha)}{\pi k}\right| \leq \min\left(\beta - \alpha, \frac{1}{\pi|k|}\right)$$

when $k \neq 0$. On combining these inequalities we find that

$$(22) \qquad |\widehat{S}_K^+(k)| \leq \frac{1}{K+1} + \min\left(\beta - \alpha, \frac{1}{\pi|k|}\right)$$

for $0 < |k| \leq K$, and hence that

$$D(N; \alpha, \beta) \leq \frac{N}{K+1} + 2\sum_{k=1}^{K}\left(\frac{1}{K+1} + \min\left(\beta - \alpha, \frac{1}{\pi k}\right)\right)|\widehat{U}_N(k)|.$$

Since a lower bound for $D(N; \alpha, \beta)$ may be similarly derived using $S_K^-(x)$, we arrive at the following result.

THEOREM 1. *Let $\{u_n\}_{n=1}^N$ be a sequence of points of $\mathbb{T}$, let $\mathfrak{I} = [\alpha, \beta]$ be an arc of $\mathbb{T}$ with $\alpha \leq \beta \leq \alpha + 1$, and let $D(N; \alpha, \beta)$ be the discrepancy given in (5). Then*

$$(23) \quad |D(N; \alpha, \beta)| \leq \frac{N}{K+1} + 2\sum_{k=1}^{K}\left(\frac{1}{K+1} + \min\left(\beta - \alpha, \frac{1}{\pi k}\right)\right)\left|\sum_{n=1}^{N} e(ku_n)\right|$$

for any positive integers N and K.

Since $\frac{1}{K+1} + \frac{1}{\pi k} < \frac{3}{2k}$, we obtain the following familiar estimate.

COROLLARY 1.1. (The Erdős-Turán inequality) *For any positive integer K,*

$$(24) \qquad D(N) \leq \frac{N}{K+1} + 3\sum_{k=1}^{K}\frac{1}{k}\left|\sum_{n=1}^{N} e(ku_n)\right|.$$

The advantage of the Theorem over the Corollary is that the coefficients on the right hand side are smaller if the interval $\mathfrak{I}$ is short. Thus the Theorem not only yields an estimate of discrepancy, but also allows us to estimate the maximum gap in the sequence u_n, in terms of the exponential sums $\widehat{U}_N(k)$.

COROLLARY 1.2. *Suppose that K is a positive integer chosen so that*

$$(25) \qquad \sum_{k=1}^{K}\left|\sum_{n=1}^{N} e(ku_n)\right| < N/10.$$

Then every arc $\mathfrak{I} = [\alpha, \beta]$ of $\mathbb{T}$ of length $\beta - \alpha \geq \frac{4}{K+1}$ contains at least $\frac{1}{2}N(\beta - \alpha)$ of the points u_n, $1 \leq n \leq N$.

PROOF. It suffices to show that $D(N; \alpha, \beta) \leq \frac{1}{2} N(\beta - \alpha)$. From the Theorem we see that

$$D(N; \alpha, \beta) \leq \frac{N}{K+1} + 2\left(\frac{1}{K+1} + \beta - \alpha\right) \sum_{k=1}^{K} \left| \sum_{n=1}^{N} e(k u_n) \right|,$$

which by hypothesis is

$$\leq \left(\frac{1}{K+1} + \frac{1}{5}\left(\frac{1}{K+1} + \beta - \alpha\right)\right) N.$$

Since $\frac{1}{K+1} \leq (\beta - \alpha)/4$, this gives the desired bound.

Let $E_K(N)$ denote the right hand side of (24), and put $E(N) = \min_K E_K(N)$. Thus $E(N)$ is the best upper bound for $D^*(N)$ that can be derived from the Erdős-Turán inequality. An alternative upper bound for $D(N)$ has been given by LeVeque [7], namely

$$(26) \qquad D(N) \leq \left(\frac{6}{\pi^2} N \sum_{k=1}^{\infty} |\widehat{U}_N(k)|^2 / k^2\right)^{1/3}.$$

Let $L(N)$ denote the right hand side above. We now show that $E(N) \ll L(N)$, so that the bound provided by the Erdős-Turán inequality is always the better of the two, apart from a constant factor.

THEOREM 2. *Let $E(N)$ and $L(N)$ be the upper bounds for the discrepancy $D(N)$ provided by the Erdős-Turán and LeVeque inequalities. Then*

$$(27) \qquad D(N) \ll E(N) \ll L(N) \ll N^{1/3} D(N)^{2/3}.$$

PROOF. The first inequality is the Erdős-Turán inequality (24). To prove the second inequality, take $K = [2N/E(N)]$. Then $\frac{N}{K+1} < \frac{1}{2} E(N)$, so that

$$E(N) \ll \sum_{k=1}^{K} \frac{1}{k} |\widehat{U}_N(k)|.$$

By Cauchy's inequality this is

$$\leq K^{1/2} \left(\sum_{k=1}^{K} \frac{1}{k^2} |\widehat{U}_N(k)|^2\right)^{1/2}$$

$$\ll \left(\frac{N}{E(N)}\right)^{1/2} \left(\sum_{k=1}^{\infty} \frac{1}{k^2} |\widehat{U}_N(k)|^2\right)^{1/2}.$$

That is,

$$E(N)^{3/2} \ll \left(N \sum_{k=1}^{\infty} \frac{1}{k^2} |\widehat{U}_N(k)|^2\right)^{1/2},$$

which gives the stated result.

The final inequality is derived by observing that (15) and (12) give the inequalities

$$L(N) \ll \left(N \int_{\mathbb{T}} \delta(N;\alpha)^2 \, d\alpha \right)^{1/3} \ll \left(N D(N)^2 \right)^{1/3}.$$

As regards to the relative sizes of the quantities in the chain of inequalities (27), it is instructive to consider some examples.

EXAMPLE 1. It can be shown that if $u_n = n\theta$ where $\theta = (1 + \sqrt{5})/2$ then $1 \ll D(N) \ll \log N$, $E(N) \approx (\log N)^2$, and $L(N) \approx N^{1/3}$. The tools needed to derive these estimates will be developed in Chapters 3 and 6. The discrepancy of this sequence is as small as can occur, yet the estimate provided by the Erdős-Turán inequality is not much larger. LeVeque's inequality, on the other hand, gives an inferior result. Indeed, that the inequality $\int_{\mathbb{T}} \delta(N;\alpha)^2 \, d\alpha \gg 1$ holds for any sequence u_n. Hence from (15) and (26) we see that $L(N) \gg N^{1/3}$ for any sequence u_n. Thus LeVeque's inequality is incapable of providing the precise bounds that one may obtain from the Erdős-Turán inequality.

EXAMPLE 2. Take $u_n = n^2/p$ where p is an odd prime. Then the exponential sums $\widehat{U}_p(k)$ are Gauss sums, and hence

$$|\widehat{U}_p(k)| = \begin{cases} \sqrt{p} & k \not\equiv 0 \pmod{p}, \\ p & k \equiv 0 \pmod{p}. \end{cases}$$

Consequently $E(p) \approx p^{1/2} \log p$, so that the Erdős-Turán inequality gives the estimate $D(p) \ll p^{1/2} \log p$, which is a special case of the Pólya-Vinogradov inequality for character sums. Moreover, from (15) we deduce that $\int_{\mathbb{T}} \delta(p,\alpha)^2 \, d\alpha \approx p$, which implies that $D(p) \gg p^{1/2}$. We note that also in this example, the bound provided by the Erdős-Turán inequality is close to best possible. On the other hand, $L(p) \approx p^{2/3}$, so that LeVeque's inequality is again inferior.

EXAMPLE 3. Suppose that $1 \le M \le N$, and that

$$u_n = \begin{cases} 0 & 1 \le n \le M, \\ n/N & M < n \le N. \end{cases}$$

Then $D(N) \approx E(N) \approx M$ while $L(N) \approx M + N^{1/3}$. More generally, it may be observed that the bound provided by LeVeque's inequality is of the correct order of magnitude precisely when $\max |\delta(N;\alpha)|$ is attained at a peak whose L^2-mass is a positive proportion of the total L^2-mass of $\delta(N;\alpha)$.

3. Trigonometric approximation. We now prove Vaaler's Lemma, which was formulated in the preceding section. The first step is to show that $V_K(x) \ge s(x)$ for $0 \le x \le 1/2$. Since $\Delta_{K+1}(\frac{r}{K+1}) = 0$ for $1 \le r \le K$, and since $\Delta_{K+1}(0) = K + 1$, we see at once from the definition (17) of $V_K(x)$ that $V_K(\frac{r}{K+1}) = s(\frac{r}{K+1})$ for all integers r. Since $\Delta'_K(\frac{r}{K+1}) = 0$ for all integral r, we see also that $V_K'(\frac{r}{K+1}) = 1$ for $1 \leq r \leq K$. Let $0 < x_1 < x_2 < \ldots < x_L < 1$ denote the distinct points in $(0, 1)$ for which

$$(28) \qquad\qquad V_K(x) = s(x),$$

and let L' denote the number of solutions in $(0, 1)$ of the equation

$$(29) \qquad\qquad V_K'(x) = 1.$$

By the mean value theorem of differential calculus, each interval (x_l, x_{l+1}) contains at least one root of (29), for $l = 1, 2, \ldots, L - 1$. Moreover, the K points $\frac{r}{K+1}$, $1 \leq r \leq K$, which form a subsequence of the points $\{x_l\}$, are also roots of (29). Thus (29) has at least $K + L - 1$ solutions in $(0, 1)$. But the trigonometric polynomial $V_K'(x) - 1$, whose degree is at most K, can have at most $2K$ zeros in $(0, 1)$. Hence $K + L - 1 \leq 2K$, which is to say that $L \leq K + 1$. Since $V_K(x)$ and $s(x)$ are odd functions, we have $V_K(1/2) = s(1/2) = 0$, so that the point $1/2$ lies among the x_l. If K is even then the point $1/2$ together with the K points $\frac{r}{K+1}$ give $K + 1$ points, and we see that (28) has no other solutions. If K is odd then the point $1/2$ lies among the x_l. However, if the set $\{x_l\}$ includes a point x' not of the form $\frac{r}{K+1}$ then it also contains the point $1 - x'$, giving a total of at least $K + 2$ solutions of (28). Since this is impossible, we deduce that (28) has precisely the K solutions $\frac{r}{K+1}$ when K is odd.

To complete the proof that $V_K(x) \geq s(x)$ for $0 \leq x \leq 1/2$, it now suffices to show that

$$(30) \qquad\qquad V_K''(\frac{r}{K+1}) > 0$$

for $1 \leq r < \frac{K+1}{2}$. By direct calculation we find that

$$(31) \quad V_K''(\frac{r}{K+1}) = \frac{1}{K+1} \sum_{k=0}^{K} s(\frac{k}{K+1}) \Delta_{K+1}''(\frac{r-k}{K+1}) - 2\pi(K+1) \cot \frac{\pi r}{K+1}.$$

We note that if $T(x)$ is a trigonometric polynomial then

$$\sum_{m=1}^{M} T\left(\frac{m}{M}\right) = M \sum_{k \equiv 0 \pmod{M}} \widehat{T}(k).$$

Hence if the degree of $T(x)$ is $\leq K$ then

$$(32) \qquad\qquad \sum_{k=1}^{K+1} T\left(\frac{k}{K+1}\right) = (K+1)\widehat{T}(0).$$

By applying this with $T(x) = \Delta_{K+1}''(\frac{r}{K+1} - x)$ we deduce that

$$\sum_{k=0}^{K} \Delta_{K+1}''\left(\frac{r-k}{K+1}\right) = 0.$$

We multiply this by $s(\frac{r}{K+1})$ and subtract from the former identity to see that the first term on the right in (31) is

$$\frac{1}{K+1} \sum_{k=0}^{K} \left(s\left(\frac{k}{K+1}\right) - s\left(\frac{r}{K+1}\right) \right) \Delta''_{K+1}\left(\frac{r-k}{K+1}\right).$$

On writing $k = r + i$, we see that this is

(33)
$$= \frac{1}{K+1} \sum_{i=1}^{K} \left(s\left(\frac{r+i}{K+1}\right) - s\left(\frac{r}{K+1}\right) \right) \Delta''_{K+1}\left(\frac{i}{K+1}\right).$$

By direct calculation from (16) we find that

$$\Delta''_{K+1}\left(\frac{i}{K+1}\right) = 2\pi^2(K+1)\left(\sin\frac{\pi i}{K+1}\right)^{-2}$$

for $1 \leq i \leq K$. We insert this, and pair i with $K+1-i$ to see that the expression (33) is

$$= \pi^2 \sum_{i=1}^{K} \left(s\left(\frac{r+i}{K+1}\right) + s\left(\frac{r-i}{K+1}\right) \right) \left(\sin\frac{\pi i}{K+1}\right)^{-2}.$$

Suppose now that $0 < r < (K+1)/2$. Then the linear combination of the sawtooth function is

$$= \begin{cases} 0 & \text{for } 0 < i < r, \\ 1/2 & \text{for } i = r, \\ 1 & \text{for } r < i < K+1-r, \\ 1/2 & \text{for } i = K+1-r, \\ 0 & \text{for } K+1-r < i < K+1. \end{cases}$$

Since $(\sin\frac{\pi x}{K+1})^{-2}$ is convex for $r \leq x \leq K+1-r$, the sum above, which approximates an integral by trapezoids, is larger than the integral

$$\pi^2 \int_r^{K+1-r} \left(\sin\frac{\pi x}{K+1}\right)^{-2} dx = 2\pi(K+1)\cot\frac{\pi r}{K+1}.$$

Since this is precisely the second term in (31), we have established (30).

We have proved that $V_K(x) \geq s(x)$ for $0 \leq x \leq 1/2$. Since $V_K(x)$ and $s(x)$ are odd functions, it follows that $V_K(x) \leq s(x)$ for $1/2 \leq x \leq 1$. Since $\Delta_K(x) \geq 0$ for all x, it also follows that $B_K(x) \geq s(x)$ for $0 \leq x \leq 1/2$. We now prove that $B_K(x) \geq s(x)$ for $1/2 \leq x \leq 1$. Arguing as we did for $V_K(x)$, we find that the equation $B_K(x) = x - 1/2$ has at most $K+1$ roots in $(0,1]$. Since it has the $K+1$ roots $\frac{r}{K+1}$, $1 \leq r \leq K+1$, it follows that there are no others. Thus it suffices to prove that

(34)
$$B''_K\left(\frac{r}{K+1}\right) > 0$$

for $(K+1)/2 < r \leq K$. Arguing as we did for $V_K''(\frac{r}{K+1})$, we find that

$$B_K''\left(\frac{r}{K+1}\right) = -\pi^2 \sum_{i=K+2-r}^{r-1} \left(\sin \frac{\pi i}{K+1}\right)^{-2} - 2\pi \cot \frac{\pi r}{K+1}$$

for $(K+2)/2 \leq r \leq K$. If K is even and $r = (K+2)/2$ then the sum is empty and $B_K''(\frac{r}{K+1}) = -2\pi \cot \frac{r}{K+1} > 0$. Thus we may suppose that $(K+3)/2 \leq r \leq K$. We remark that if f is a concave function then $f(0) \geq \int_{-1/2}^{1/2} f(x)\,dx$. Applying this to the functions $f(x) = -\pi^2 \left(\sin \frac{\pi}{K+1}(i+x)\right)^{-2}$, we deduce that the expression above is

$$\geq \pi^2 \int_{K+1-r+1/2}^{r-1/2} \left(\sin \frac{\pi x}{K+1}\right)^{-2} dx - 2\pi \cot \frac{\pi r}{K+1}$$

$$= 2\pi \left(\cot \frac{\pi(r-1/2)}{K+1} - \cot \frac{\pi r}{K+1}\right).$$

This quantity is positive, since $\cot \pi x$ is decreasing for $0 < x < 1$. Thus we have (34), so the proof that $B_K(x) \geq s(x)$ is complete.

It remains to demonstrate that $B_K(x)$ is the unique extremal polynomial. Suppose that $T(x)$ is a trigonometric polynomial of degree not exceeding K, and that $T(x) \geq s(x)$ for all x. Since $T(0) = T(0^-) \geq s(0^-) = 1/2$, it follows that

$$(35) \qquad \sum_{k=0}^{K} T\left(\frac{k}{K+1}\right) \geq \frac{1}{2} + \sum_{k=1}^{K} s\left(\frac{k}{K+1}\right) = \frac{1}{2}.$$

Hence by (32) we see that $\int_{\mathbb{T}} T(x)\,dx \geq \frac{1}{2(K+1)}$. If equality holds here, then equality holds in (35), and hence $T(\frac{k}{K+1}) = s(\frac{k}{K+1})$ for $1 \leq k \leq K+1$, and $T(0) = 1/2$. Moreover, since $T(x) \geq s(x)$ for x in a neighborhood of $\frac{k}{K+1}$, we must also have $T'(\frac{k}{K+1}) = 1$. Since $B_K(x)$ also has these properties, we deduce that $T(x) - B_K(x)$ has zeros of multiplicity at least 2 at each of the K points $\frac{k}{K+1}$, $1 \leq k \leq K$, and a further zero at 0. This gives a total of at least $2K+1$ zeros. Since a non-trivial trigonometric polynomial of degree at most K can have at most $2K$ zeros, it follows that $T(x) \equiv B_K(x)$.

The proof of Vaaler's Lemma is now complete. It may be further remarked that, by applying (32) to $B_K'(x)$, it follows that $B_K'(0) = -K$.

4. Notes. §1. The measure U_N is the sum of N point-masses, but in our discussion we have only needed to know that U_N is non-negative with known total mass. Thus Weyl's criterion extends to sequences of probability measures tending to Lebesgue measure. More generally, a similar criterion can be developed to describe a sequence of probability measures μ_N tending weakly to a limiting measure μ. This generalization provides an important tool for establishing limit laws in probability theory. For a more extensive discussion of uniform distribution, see Kuipers & Niederreiter [6]. Simple expositions of Weyl's criterion have been given by Cassels [1, Chapter 4] and by Chandrasekharan [2, Chapter 8].

§2. Inequality (13) is known as Koksma's inequality; see Koksma [5] and Kuipers & Neiderreiter [6, pp. 147, 157–158].

Our proof of the Erdős-Turán inequality follows the original conceptual approach of Erdős & Turán [3], but they gave an *ad hoc* construction of one-sided approximations $T^{\pm}$ whereas we have used the more precise construction of Selberg.

Corollary 1.2 casts in sharp quantitative form the obvious observation that a uniformly distributed sequence can not have large gaps. The traditional technique used in this connection is Vinogradov's "method of little glasses" (see Vinogradov [12, pp. 32–34] or Karatsuba [4, p. 6]), which involves constructing a peak function by convolving the characteristic function of a short interval with itself many times. Corollary 1.2 was derived by the author some years ago, and is found in the survey of Vaaler [11, Corollary 21].

The second and third inequalities of Theorem 2 seem to be new. In particular, Theorem 2 provides a new proof of LeVeque's inequality, apart from the value of the implicit constant. It seems that the inequality $E(N) \ll N^{1/3} D^*(N)^{2/3}$ of Theorem 2 is sharp; in response to these lectures Ruzsa [9] has shown that there exist sequences $\{u_n\}$ with $D_N^* \ll 1$ and $E(N) \approx N^{1/3}$. Ruzsa [8] has also shown that if positive numbers $C_1, C_2, \ldots, C_K$ are given, then there exists a sequence $\{u_n\}$ such that

$$\left| \sum_{n=1}^{N} e(ku_n) \right| \le C_k + O\left(\frac{k \log k}{\sqrt{N}} \right)$$

for $1 \le k \le K$, but the discrepancy of the sequence satisfies the inequality $D(N) > c(N/K + \sum_{k=1}^{K} C_k/k)$ where c is some positive absolute constant. Thus the bound provided by the Erdős-Turán inequality is essentially the best bound for $D(N)$ that can be deduced, if upper bounds for $|\widehat{U}_N(k)|$ is all that is used.

§3. The terms *Vaaler's polynomial, Beurling's polynomial, Selberg's polynomials* are not necessarily standard. Initially, Beurling (unpublished) constructed a function $b(x)$ such that $b(x) \ge \operatorname{sgn}(x)$ for all real x, such that $\widehat{b}(t) = 0$ when $|t| > 1$, and with $\int_{\mathbb{R}} b(x) - \operatorname{sgn}(x)\, dx$ as small as possible, namely $= 1$. Beurling also showed that his function is the unique extremal function. Many years later, Selberg [10, pp. 213–218] used Beurling's function to construct a majorant s^+ and a minorant s^- of the characteristic function of an interval $[a, b]$ of the real line, with the property that $\operatorname{supp} \widehat{s}^{\pm} \subseteq [-\delta, \delta]$, and also $\int_{\mathbb{R}} s^{\pm}(x)\, dx = b - a \pm 1/\delta$. For an interesting historical account of this topic see Selberg [10, pp. 225–226]. The analogue for $\mathbb{T}$ is can be derived by applying the Poisson summation formula: $S^{\pm}(x) = \sum_{n \in \mathbb{Z}} s^{\pm}(n + x)$. Since our present interest is in the circle group $\mathbb{T}$, we have taken a more direct approach that avoids the Poisson summation formula. We have also avoided a somewhat challenging technical point relating to $b(x)$: Since $b(x)$ is not absolutely integrable over $\mathbb{R}$, the Fourier transform

$\widehat{b}(t)$ is not immediately defined. Vaaler [11] added a nice touch by defining the function $v(x) = b(x) - \left(\frac{\sin \pi x}{\pi x}\right)^2$. Vaaler noted that this function is odd, that $0 \le v(x) \le 1$ for $x \ge 0$, and that $\operatorname{supp} \widehat{v} \subseteq [-1, 1]$. The function $V(x)$ that we have taken to be fundamental, is the analogue for $\mathbb{T}$ of Vaaler's function $v(x)$ on the real line. Vaaler [11] has given an extensive discussion of the properties of these functions, with diverse applications.

References

1. J. W. S. Cassels, *An Introduction to Diophantine Approximation*, Cambrdige Tracts no. 45, Cambridge University Press, London, 1957.

2. K. Chandrasekharan, *Introduction to Analytic Number Theory*, Grundlehren math. Wiss. 148, Springer-Verlag, New York, 1968.

3. P. Erdős and P. Turán, *On a problem in the theory of uniform distribution I*, Nederl. Akad. Wetensch. Proc. **51** (1948), 1146–1154; *II*, 1262–1269, (= Indag. Math. **10** (1948), 370–378; 406–413).

4. A. A. Karatsuba, *Basic Analytic Number Theory*, Springer-Verlag, Berlin, 1993.

5. J. F. Koksma, *Een algemeene stelling uit de theorie der gelijkmatige verdeeling modulo 1*, Mathematica B (Zutphen) **11** (1942/43), 7–11.

6. L. Kuipers and H. Niederreiter, *Uniform Distribution of Sequences*, John Wiley & Sons, New York, 1974.

7. W. J. LeVeque, *An inequality connected with Weyl's criterion for uniform distribution*, Proc. Symp. Pure Math., Vol. VIII, Amer. Math. Soc., Providence, RI, 1965, pp. 22–30.

8. I. Z. Ruzsa, *On an inequality of Erdős and Turán concerning uniform distribution modulo one, I*, Sets, Graphs and Numbers (Budapest, 1991), Coll. Math. Soc. J. Bolyai 60, 1992, pp. 621–630.

9. _____, *On an inequality of Erdős and Turán concerning uniform distribution modulo one, II*, J. Number Theory (to appear).

10. A. Selberg, *Collected Papers*, Volume II, Springer-Verlag, Berlin, 1991.

11. J. D. Vaaler, *Some extremal functions in Fourier analysis*, Bull. Amer. Math. Soc. **12** (1985), 183–216.

12. I. M. Vinogradov, *The Method of Trigonometrical Sums in the Theory of Numbers*; translated by A. Davenport & K. F. Roth, Interscience, London, 1954.

13. H. Weyl, *Über ein Problem aus dem Gebiete der diophantischen Approximationen*, Nachr. Ges. Wiss. Göttingen, Math.-phys. Kl. (1914), 234–244; Gesammelte Abhandlungen, Band I, Springer-Verlag, Berlin-Heidelberg-New York, 1968, pp. 487–497.

14. _____ , *Über die Gleichverteilung von Zahlen mod. Eins*, Math. Ann. **77** (1916), 313–352; Gesammelte Abhandlungen, Band I, Springer-Verlag, Berlin-Heidelberg-New York, 1968, pp. 563–599; Selecta Hermann Weyl, Birkhäuser Verlag, Basel-Stuttgart, 1956, pp. 111–147.

Chapter 2. van der Corput Sets

1. Introduction. Weyl not only gave a useful criterion for determining whether a sequence is uniformly distributed, he also used his criterion to show that if $P(x)$ is a polynomial with real coefficients at least one of which is irrational (other than the constant term), then the sequence of numbers $\{P(n)\}$ is uniformly distributed modulo 1. In proving this, Weyl introduced a second very important idea: Write

$$\left| \sum_{n=1}^{N} e(kP(n)) \right|^2 = \sum_{m=1}^{N} \sum_{n=1}^{N} e\big(k(P(m) - P(n))\big),$$

and then put $h = m - n$, to see that this is

$$= \sum_{n=1}^{N} \sum_{h=1-n}^{N-n} e\big(k(P(n+h) - P(n))\big).$$

On inverting the order of summation, we see that this is

$$= \sum_{h=-N+1}^{N-1} \sum_{\substack{1 \le n \le N \\ 1-h \le n \le N-h}} e\big(k(P(n+h) - P(n))\big).$$

When $h = 0$ the inner sum is N. On combining h with $-h$, we see that the above is

(1)
$$= N + 2\Re \sum_{h=1}^{N-1} \sum_{n=1}^{N-h} e\big(k(P(n+h) - P(n))\big).$$

This manipulation is known as 'Weyl differencing.' Since $P(x + h) - P(x)$ is a polynomial of degree one less than that of $P(x)$, the possibility of inducting on $\deg P$ arises. Weyl's argument was made more complicated by the fact that the differencing parameter h runs all the way to N. However, a few years later, J. G. van der Corput [6] found a way to limit the size of h. His basic result, whose proof involves one (clever) application of Cauchy's inequality, is as follows.

VAN DER CORPUT'S LEMMA. *Let H be a positive integer. Then for any complex numbers $y_1, y_2, \ldots, y_N$,*

$$(2) \quad \left| \sum_{n=1}^{N} y_n \right|^2 \le \frac{N+H}{H+1} \sum_{n=1}^{N} |y_n|^2 + \frac{2(N+H)}{H+1} \sum_{h=1}^{H} \left(1 - \frac{h}{H+1}\right) \left| \sum_{n=1}^{N-h} y_{n+h} \overline{y_n} \right|.$$

When $H \longrightarrow \infty$ this is substantially the same as (1), but the opportunity to take H smaller than N offers a distinct advantage. For example, by using the above with $y_n = e(ku_n)$ in conjunction with Weyl's criterion, it is a simple matter to prove

VAN DER CORPUT'S THEOREM. *If for each positive integer h the sequence $\{u_{n+h} - u_n\}$ is uniformly distributed* (mod 1), *then the sequence $\{u_n\}$ is uniformly distributed* (mod 1).

The converse of van der Corput's Theorem is false, for if θ is an irrational real number then the sequence $u_n = n\theta$ is uniformly distributed, but $u_{n+h} - u_n = h\theta$ is constant, and hence not uniformly distributed. Using van der Corput's Theorem, it is not difficult to prove Weyl's theorem concerning the uniform distribution (mod 1) of polynomial sequences $\{P(n)\}$.

Only within recent years has it been recognized that van der Corput's Theorem may be strengthened by weakening the hypothesis: Instead of assuming that $u_{n+h} - u_n$ is uniformly distributed for *every* positive integer h, it is enough to know that this is true for every $h \in \mathcal{H}$, where $\mathcal{H}$ is a suitable subset of the positive integers. Our object—only partly achieved—is to characterize those subsets $\mathcal{H}$ that may be used in this way.

DEFINITION. A set $\mathcal{H}$ of positive integers is called a *van der Corput set* if the sequence $\{u_n\}$ is uniformly distributed (mod 1) whenever the differenced sequence $\{u_{n+h} - u_n\}$ is uniformly distributed (mod 1) for all $h \in \mathcal{H}$.

In this terminology, van der Corput's original theorem asserts that the set $\mathbb{Z}^+$ of positive integers is a van der Corput set.

The coefficients in the sum on the right hand side of (2) are suggestive of the Fejér kernel (recall (1.16)). By introducing a small wrinkle we obtain a generalization of van der Corput's Lemma in which this connection is more obvious.

LEMMA 1. (Generalized van der Corput Lemma) *Suppose that*

$$(3) \qquad\qquad T(x) = a_0 + \sum_{h=1}^{H} a_h \cos 2\pi h x,$$

that $T(x) \ge 0$ for all x, and that $T(0) = 1$. Then for any complex numbers $y_1, y_2, \ldots, y_N$,

$$\left| \sum_{n=1}^{N} y_n \right|^2 \le (N+H) \left(a_0 \sum_{n=1}^{N} |y_n|^2 + \sum_{h=1}^{H} |a_h| \left| \sum_{n=1}^{N-h} y_{n+h} \overline{y_n} \right| \right).$$

PROOF. To simplify the task of keeping track of the endpoints of summation, we set $y_n = 0$ when $n < 1$ or $n > N$. By a classical theorem of Fejér, there exist complex numbers $\alpha_0, \alpha_1, \ldots, \alpha_H$ such that

$$(4) \qquad T(x) = \left| \sum_{m=0}^{H} \alpha_m e(mx) \right|^2.$$

Since $T(0) = 1$, by multiplying the α_m by a suitable unimodular constant we may suppose that $\sum_{m=0}^{H} \alpha_m = 1$. Then

$$\sum_n y_n = \left(\sum_m \alpha_m \right) \left(\sum_n y_n \right) = \sum_m \alpha_m \sum_n y_{m+n}$$

$$= \sum_{n=-H+1}^{N} \sum_m \alpha_m y_{m+n}.$$

Thus by Cauchy's inequality,

$$\left| \sum_n y_n \right|^2 \leq (N + H) \sum_n \left| \sum_m \alpha_m y_{m+n} \right|^2.$$

On expanding and taking the sum over n inside, we see that this is

$$= (N + H) \sum_{m_1} \sum_{m_2} \alpha_{m_1} \overline{\alpha_{m_2}} \sum_n y_{m_1+n} \overline{y_{m_2+n}}.$$

We reindex, putting $m = m_2$, $h = m_1 - m_2$, so that the triple sum above is

$$\sum_h \sum_m \alpha_{m+h} \overline{\alpha_m} \sum_n y_{m+h+n} \overline{y_{m+n}}.$$

Here the value of the innermost sum depends only on the difference h between the indices. Thus the above is

$$= \sum_h \left(\sum_m \alpha_{m+h} \overline{\alpha_m} \right) \left(\sum_n y_{n+h} \overline{y_n} \right).$$

From (4) we see that

$$\sum_m \alpha_{m+h} \overline{\alpha_m} = \widehat{T}(h).$$

We write the term corresponding to $h = 0$ separately, and observe that the contribution of $-h$ is the complex conjugate of that of h. Hence

$$\left| \sum_n y_n \right|^2 \leq (N + H) \left(\widehat{T}(0) \sum_n |y_n|^2 + 2 \sum_{h=1}^{H} |\widehat{T}(h)| \left| \sum_n y_{n+h} \overline{y_n} \right| \right),$$

which gives the stated result.

If we take $T(x) = \frac{1}{H+1} \Delta_{H+1}(x)$ in Lemma 1, then $a_0 = \frac{1}{H+1}$, $a_h = (1 - \frac{h}{H+1})/(H + 1)$ for $1 \leq h \leq H$, and Lemma 1 reduces to van der Corput's Lemma. Indeed, if we start by taking $\alpha_0 = \alpha_1 = \ldots = \alpha_H = \frac{1}{H+1}$ in the above

argument, then the appeal to Fejér's theorem is superfluous and we have the
original proof of van der Corput's Lemma.

Suppose that $\mathcal{H}$ is a set of positive integers, and let $\mathcal{T} = \mathcal{T}(\mathcal{H})$ denote the
collection of those cosine polynomials $T(x)$ as in (3) such that $T(x) \geq 0$ for
all x, $T(0) = 1$, and such that $a_h \neq 0$ only when $h \in \mathcal{H}$. When we use such
trigonometric polynomials in Lemma 1 it is important that the constant term
a_0 be small. Accordingly, put

$$(5) \qquad\qquad \delta = \delta(\mathcal{H}) = \inf_{T \in \mathcal{T}} a_0.$$

This allows us to formulate a natural generalization of van der Corput's Theorem.

THEOREM 1. (Generalized van der Corput Theorem) *Suppose that $\mathcal{H}$ is a set
of positive integers such that $\delta(\mathcal{H}) = 0$. Then $\mathcal{H}$ is a van der Corput set.*

We shall show presently that the converse of this is also true.

PROOF. We follow van der Corput, except that we substitute Lemma 1 where
van der Corput used his Lemma. Let u_n be a sequence such that $u_{n+h} - u_n$ is
uniformly distributed (mod 1) for each $h \in \mathcal{H}$. by Weyl's criterion, the sequence
u_n is uniformly distributed if $\sum_{n=1}^{N} e(ku_n) = o(N)$ as $N \longrightarrow \infty$, for each given
positive integer k. Choose $T \in \mathcal{T}$, and put $y_n = e(ku_n)$ in Lemma 1. Then

$$\left| \sum_{n=1}^{N} e(ku_n) \right|^2 \leq a_0 N(N+H) + (N+H) \sum_{h=1}^{H} |a_h| \left| \sum_{n=1}^{N-h} e\big(k(u_{n+h} - u_n)\big) \right|.$$

Since $a_h \neq 0$ only when $h \in \mathcal{H}$, and since for these h the sequence $\{u_{n+h} - u_n\}$
is uniformly distributed, it follows by Weyl's criterion that the inner sum on the
right hand side above is $o(N)$ as $N \longrightarrow \infty$, whenever $a_h \neq 0$. Hence

$$\limsup_{N \to \infty} \frac{1}{N} \left| \sum_{n=1}^{N} e(ku_n) \right| \leq \sqrt{a_0}.$$

Since we may choose $T \in \mathcal{T}$ with a_0 arbitrarily small, this give the desired result.

We observe that for any given set $\mathcal{H}$, the set $\mathcal{T}(\mathcal{H})$ is convex. That is, if
$T_i \in \mathcal{T}$ for $i = 1, 2$, then $tT_1 + (1-t)T_2 \in \mathcal{T}$ for $0 \leq t \leq 1$. With the idea of
linear programming in mind, it is not surprising that the extremal problem of
determining δ can be associated with a dual extremal problem. This runs as
follows.

Let μ be a probability measure on $\mathbb{T}$. For $k \in \mathbb{Z}$ we define the Fourier coefficients of μ to be the numbers

$$\widehat{\mu}(k) = \int_{\mathbb{T}} e(-kx) \, d\mu(x).$$

Let $\mathcal{M}$ denote the class of those probability measures μ on $\mathbb{T}$ such that $\widehat{\mu}(k) \neq 0$
only when $|k| \notin \mathcal{H}$. Since $\widehat{\mu}(-k) = \overline{\widehat{\mu}(k)}$, this is the same thing as saying that
supp $\widehat{\mu}$ and $\mathcal{H}$ are disjoint. The measures $\mu \in \mathcal{M}$ are not necessarily continuous.

Indeed, we are interested in the possibility that μ may have a large point mass at 0. Let

$$(6) \qquad\qquad \gamma = \sup_{\mu \in \mathcal{M}} \mu(\{0\}).$$

We show now that

$$(7) \qquad\qquad \gamma \leq \delta.$$

To see this, suppose that $T \in \mathcal{T}$ and that $\mu \in \mathcal{M}$. Then

$$\mu(\{0\}) \leq \int_{\mathbb{T}} T(x)\, d\mu(x)$$

since T is continuous, non-negative, and $T(0) = 1$. The integral here is

$$\sum_h \widehat{T}(h)\widehat{\mu}(-h),$$

and from the definitions of $\mathcal{T}$ and $\mathcal{M}$, the only integer h for which $\widehat{T}(h)$ and $\widehat{\mu}(-h)$ are both non-zero is $h = 0$. Thus this expression is $\widehat{T}(0)\widehat{\mu}(0) = a_0$. Since $\mu(\{0\}) \leq a_0$ whenever $T \in \mathcal{T}$ and $\mu \in \mathcal{M}$, we have (7). In §2 we use ideas of linear programming to show that $\gamma = \delta$. This provides a powerful method for determining whether a set is a van der Corput set, and in §5 we show that the set of perfect squares is a van der Corput set (see Corollary 9). So which sets are not van der Corput sets? The following negative result is illuminating.

THEOREM 2. *Let m be a fixed positive integer, take*

$$\mathcal{H} = \{1, 2, \ldots, m-1\},$$

and put

$$\mathcal{K} = \{h \in \mathbb{Z}^+ : m \nmid h\}.$$

Then $\delta(\mathcal{H}) = \gamma(\mathcal{H}) = \delta(\mathcal{K}) = \gamma(\mathcal{K}) = 1/m$.

Thus, using the results that will be established in the next two sections, the set of primes is not a van der Corput set (because it contains no multiple of 4). Similarly, the set of numbers $n^2 + 1$ is not a van der Corput set (because it contains no multiple of 3).

PROOF. We prove that

$$(8) \qquad\qquad \frac{1}{m} \leq \gamma(\mathcal{K}) \leq \gamma(\mathcal{H}) \leq \delta(\mathcal{H}) \leq \frac{1}{m}$$

and also that

$$(9) \qquad\qquad \frac{1}{m} \leq \gamma(\mathcal{K}) \leq \delta(\mathcal{K}) \leq \delta(\mathcal{H}) \leq \frac{1}{m}.$$

Let $\mu = \frac{1}{m}\sum_{a=1}^{m}\delta_{a/m}$, where δ_{α} denotes the probability measure (Dirac measure) that places a unit point mass at α. Then

$$\widehat{\mu}(k) = \frac{1}{m}\sum_{a=1}^{m}e\left(\frac{-ak}{m}\right) = \begin{cases} 1 & \text{if } m|k, \\ 0 & \text{otherwise.} \end{cases}$$

Thus $\mu \in \mathcal{M}(\mathcal{K})$. As $\mu(\{0\}) = 1/m$, it follows that $\gamma(\mathcal{K}) \geq 1/m$. This is the first inequality in (8), and also in (9).

Since $\mathcal{H} \subseteq \mathcal{K}$, we see that $\mathcal{T}(\mathcal{H}) \subseteq \mathcal{T}(\mathcal{K})$, and that $\mathcal{M}(\mathcal{K}) \subseteq \mathcal{M}(\mathcal{H})$, and hence that $\delta(\mathcal{K}) \leq \delta(\mathcal{H})$ and $\gamma(\mathcal{K}) \leq \gamma(\mathcal{H})$. This gives the second inequality in (8), and the third in (9). The third inequality in (8) and the second in (9) are provided by (7).

Take $T(x) = \frac{1}{m}\Delta_m(x)$. Then $T \in \mathcal{T}(\mathcal{H})$. As $a_0 = 1/m$, we deduce that $\delta(\mathcal{H}) \leq 1/m$. This gives the final inequality in (8), and also in (9). The proof is complete.

Suppose that a set $\mathcal{H}$ of positive integers is given. Let $\mathcal{U} = \mathcal{U}(\mathcal{H})$ denote the collection of infinite sequences $\{u_n\}$ such that $\{u_{n+h} - u_n\}$ is uniformly distributed (mod 1) for every $h \in \mathcal{H}$. Put

$$(10) \qquad \alpha = \sup_{\{u_n\}\in\mathcal{U}} \limsup_{N\to\infty} \frac{1}{N}D^*(N).$$

Thus $\alpha = 0$ if and only if $\mathcal{H}$ is a van der Corput set. We now indicate how α, γ, and δ are related. With Lemma 1 in mind, we let $\mathcal{Y}_2$ denote the set of infinite sequence $\{y_n\}$ of complex numbers such that

$$(11) \qquad \limsup_{N\to\infty} \frac{1}{N}\sum_{n=1}^{N}|y_n|^2 \leq 1,$$

and such that

$$(12) \qquad \sum_{n=1}^{N}y_{n+h}\overline{y_n} = o(N)$$

as $N \longrightarrow \infty$, whenever $h \in \mathcal{H}$. We put

$$(13) \qquad \beta_2 = \sup_{\{y_n\}\in\mathcal{Y}_2} \limsup_{N\to\infty} \frac{1}{N}\left|\sum_{n=1}^{N}y_n\right|.$$

In the application of Lemma 1 that we made in proving Theorem 1, we were not able to use the full power of the lemma because our y_n were constrained to be unimodular. To reflect this, let $\mathcal{Y}_\infty$ denote the class of those infinite sequences $\{y_n\}$ of complex numbers such that $|y_n| \leq 1$ for all n, and such that (12) holds as $N \longrightarrow \infty$, for all $h \in \mathcal{H}$. We put

$$(14) \qquad \beta_\infty = \sup_{\{y_n\}\in\mathcal{Y}_\infty} \limsup_{N\to\infty} \frac{1}{N}\left|\sum_{n=1}^{N}y_n\right|.$$

In §2 we show that

(15) $\beta_2^2 = \gamma = \delta,$

and in §3 we show that

(16) $\beta_2^2 \leq \beta_\infty \leq \beta_2,$

and that

(17) $\beta_\infty \ll \alpha \ll \beta_\infty \log \dfrac{2}{\beta_\infty}.$

From these relations we see that if one of α, β_∞, β_2, γ, δ vanishes then all the others do, in which case $\mathcal{H}$ is a van der Corput set. In §4 we use this equivalence to establish several properties of van der Corput sets.

Since the set of perfect squares is a van der Corput set, it follows that a van der Corput set need not have positive density, although it is to be expected that the multiples of m must have positive relative density in $\mathcal{H}$, for every positive integer m. On the other hand, a van der Corput set cannot be extremely sparse. Suppose that $0 < h_1 < h_2 < \ldots$, and that there is a constant $\lambda > 1$ such that $h_{r+1} > \lambda h_r$ (i.e. the set $\mathcal{H}$ has 'Hadamard gaps'). Then by using finite Riesz products it is easy to show that $\delta(\mathcal{H}) > 0$, so that $\mathcal{H}$ is not a van der Corput set. We might interpret this by saying that the elements of $\mathcal{H}$ are not sufficiently linearly dependent. Roughly speaking, we expect that if the elements of a set $\mathcal{H}$ of positive integers are highly linearly dependent, and if $\mathcal{H}$ contains a good supply of multiples of m, for every positive integer m, then we expect $\mathcal{H}$ to be a van der Corput set. We lack a general theorem to this effect, but in §5 we establish a useful sufficient condition that allows us to demonstrate that the set of perfect squares is a van der Corput set. In §§6, 7 we consider the relation between van der Corput sets and other classes of sets, called *intersective sets* and *Heilbronn sets*, respectively.

2. Extremal measures. We now show that the inequality (7) can be replaced by equality.

THEOREM 3. *For any set $\mathcal{H}$ of positive integers, $\gamma(\mathcal{H}) = \delta(\mathcal{H})$, and there is a measure $\mu \in \mathcal{M}$ such that $\mu(\{0\}) = \gamma$.*

If $\mathcal{H}$ is finite then by compactness there is a $T \in \mathcal{T}(\mathcal{H})$ whose constant term a_0 attains the minimal value $\delta(\mathcal{H})$. On the other hand, if $\mathcal{H}$ is infinite, the infimum (5) is not in general attained; in particular, if $\mathcal{H}$ is a van der Corput set then it cannot be attained. Though the supremum in (6) is always attained, the extremal measure is not always unique; see Example 2 in §4.

PROOF. We observe first that if $\mathcal{H}$ is empty then $\mathcal{T}$ contains only the constant function $T(x) \equiv 1$, so that $\delta = 1$. On the other hand, $\delta_0 \in \mathcal{M}$, and hence $\gamma = 1$ in this case. In what follows, we suppose that $\mathcal{H}$ is non-empty. Our argument is in the nature of a mini-max theorem for a Banach space. Let B be the Banach space of continuous functions on $\mathbb{T}$ with the uniform norm, $\|f\| = \max_{x \in \mathbb{T}} |f(x)|$. Let

$$\mathcal{P} = \{f \in B : f(x) > 0 \text{ for all } x \in \mathbb{T}\},$$
$$\mathcal{Q} = \{T(x) = \delta + \sum_{h \in \mathcal{H}} a_h \cos 2\pi hx : T \text{ is a trig. poly.}, T(0) = 1\}.$$

If $T \in \mathcal{Q}$ then $\min T(x) \leq 0$; hence $\mathcal{P}$ and $\mathcal{Q}$ are disjoint. Also, $\mathcal{P}$ and $\mathcal{Q}$ are convex, and $\mathcal{P}$ is open. Hence there is a linear functional $L \in B^*$ that separates $\mathcal{P}$ and $\mathcal{Q}$. That is, there is a number c such that $L(f) \geq c$ for all $f \in \mathcal{P}$, $L(T) \leq c$ for all $T \in \mathcal{Q}$, and $L \not\equiv 0$. (See Schaefer [18], Chapter 9] for substantiation of this point.) Since $\mathcal{P}$ is a cone (i.e., $f \in \mathcal{P}$, $a > 0$ implies that $af \in \mathcal{P}$), it follows that $c \leq 0$, and hence we may assume that $c = 0$. By the Riesz representation theorem there is a Borel measure μ_0 such that $L(f) = \int_{\mathbb{T}} f(x) \, d\mu_0(x)$. Since $L(f) \geq 0$ for all $f \in \mathcal{P}$, and since $L \not\equiv 0$, we deduce that $\int_{\mathbb{T}} d\mu_0 > 0$. By normalizing, we may suppose that this integral is 1, so that μ_0 is a probability measure. We may define a new probability measure μ_1 by putting $\mu_1(\mathcal{S}) = \frac{1}{2}\mu_0(\mathcal{S}) + \frac{1}{2}\mu_0(-\mathcal{S})$. Then μ_1 is a probability measure, the linear functional $\int_{\mathbb{T}} f(x) \, d\mu_1(x)$ separates $\mathcal{P}$ and $\mathcal{Q}$, and μ_1 is even. From now on, we suppose that our linear functional $L(f)$ is obtained by integrating f against the measure μ_1. Since μ_1 is even, we see that $\widehat{\mu_1}(n) = \widehat{\mu_1}(-n) = \int_{\mathbb{T}} \cos 2\pi nx \, d\mu_1(x)$. Suppose that $T \in \mathcal{Q}$ and that $h \in \mathcal{H}$, $h' \in \mathcal{H}$. Then for any real number k,

$$T_1(x) = T(x) + k(\cos 2\pi hx - \cos 2\pi h'x) \in \mathcal{Q},$$

and hence $L(T_1) \leq 0$. That is,

$$L(T) + k\big(L(\cos 2\pi hx) - L(\cos 2\pi h'x)\big) \leq 0$$

for any real number k. Hence there is a number d such that $L(\cos 2\pi hx) = d$ for all $h \in \mathcal{H}$. Since $\delta + (1 - \delta) \cos 2\pi hx \in \mathcal{Q}$, we see that

(18) $$\delta + (1 - \delta)d \leq 0.$$

Moreover, $(1 + \cos 2\pi hx)/2 \in \mathcal{T}$, so that $0 \leq \delta \leq 1/2$. Hence $d < 0$. Let

(19) $$\mu = \frac{1}{1 - d}\mu_1 + \frac{-d}{1 - d}\delta_0.$$

This is a probability measure, since it is a convex combination of two two such measures. Moreover,

$$\widehat{\mu}(\pm h) = \frac{1}{1 - d}\widehat{\mu_1}(h) + \frac{-d}{1 - d}\widehat{\delta_0}(h) = \frac{d}{1 - d} + \frac{-d}{1 - d} = 0$$

for all $h \in \mathcal{H}$, so that $\mu \in \mathcal{M}$. Finally, by (19) and (18) we observe that

$$\mu(\{0\}) \geq \frac{-d}{1 - d} \geq \delta.$$

Hence $\gamma \geq \delta$. Taken with the inequality (7), we deduce that $\gamma = \delta$. Moreover, the measure μ that we have constructed is an example of an extremal measure. This completes the proof.

We now relate β_2 to γ and δ.

THEOREM 4. *Let $\mathcal{H}$ be a fixed set of positive integers, and let β_2 be defined as in (13) above. Then $\beta_2^2 = \gamma = \delta$.*

PROOF. The inequality $\beta_2^2 \leq \delta$ is an immediate consequence of Lemma 1. Thus it remains to show that $\gamma \leq \beta_2^2$.

Let $\mu \in \mathcal{M}$ be extremal, so that $\mu(\{0\}) = \gamma$. Consider the trigonometric polynomial

$$T(x) = N \int_{\mathbb{T}} \Delta_N(x+y)\,d\mu(y)$$
$$= \sum_{|n|<N} (N - |n|)\widehat{\mu}(n)e(nx).$$

Since $T(x) \geq 0$ for all x, by Fejér's theorem there exist z_k such that

$$\left|\sum_{k=1}^{N} z_k e(kx)\right|^2 = T(x).$$

Thus $\sum_{k=1}^{N} |z_k|^2 = N$ and $\sum_{1 \leq k \leq N-h} z_k \overline{z_{k+h}} = 0$ for all $h \in \mathcal{H}$. Finally we note that $\left|\sum_{k=1}^{N} z_k\right|^2 = T(0) \geq N^2\gamma$, so that $\left|\sum_{k=1}^{N} z_k\right| \geq \gamma^{1/2}N$. By multiplying the z_k by a unimodular factor, we may assume that $\sum_{k=1}^{N} z_k \geq \gamma^{1/2}N$. This gives an arbitrarily long finite sequence of the desired sort. To obtain an infinite sequence with the desired properties, we note that every natural number n is uniquely of the form $n = m^3 + k$, $1 \leq k \leq 3m^2 + 3m + 1$. We take $N = 3m^2 + 2m + 1$ in the above construction, and put

$$y_n = y_{m^3+k} = \begin{cases} z_k & \text{if } 1 \leq k \leq 3m^2 + 2m + 1, \\ 0 & \text{if } 3m^2 + 2m + 1 < k \leq 3m^2 + 3m + 1. \end{cases}$$

The advantage of having $y_n = 0$ at the end of each block is that in estimating $\sum y_n \overline{y_{n+h}}$, the terms for which n and $n+h$ come from different blocks all vanish from some point on. It is evident that $\{y_n\} \in \mathcal{Y}_2$, and that

$$\limsup_{N\to\infty} \frac{1}{N}\left|\sum_{n=1}^{N} y_n\right| \geq \gamma^{1/2}.$$

Hence $\beta_2 \geq \gamma^{1/2}$, and the proof is complete.

3. Relations between α, β_∞, β_2. We begin by establishing a connection between β_2 and β_∞.

THEOREM 5. *Let $\mathcal{H}$ be a fixed set of positive integers, and let β_2 and β_∞ be defined by* (13) *and* (14), *respectively. Then $\beta_2^2 \leq \beta_\infty \leq \beta_2$.*

PROOF. Since $\mathcal{Y}_\infty \subseteq \mathcal{Y}_2$, it is trivial that $\beta_\infty \leq \beta_2$. To establish an inequality in the opposite direction, put $\mathcal{H}(m) = \{h \in \mathcal{H} : h \leq m\}$. Since $\mathcal{H}(m)$ is finite, the set $\mathcal{T}(\mathcal{H}(m))$ is compact, and hence the minimum in (5) is attained, say by $T(x)$. We let δ_m denote this minimum. First we show that $\max_{x \in \mathbb{T}} T(x) = T(0) = 1$. Let x_0 be fixed, $x_0 \in \mathbb{T}$, and put $T_1(x) = (T(x + x_0) + T(x - x_0))/(2T(x_0))$. Then $T_1 \in \mathcal{T}(\mathcal{H}(m))$, and hence $a_0(T_1) \geq \delta_m$. But $a_0(T_1) = \delta_m/T(x_0)$, so it follows that $T(x_0) \leq 1$.

By Theorem 3 there is an extremal measure $\mu \in \mathcal{M}(\mathcal{H}(m))$ such that $\mu(\{0\}) = \gamma_m = \delta_m$. Since

$$\int_{\mathbb{T}} T(x)\, d\mu(x) = \gamma_m,$$

it follows that μ must have all its mass at zeros of $T(x)$, apart from its mass at 0. That is, μ is of the form

$$\mu = \gamma_m \delta_0 + \sum_{r=1}^{R} m_r \delta_{x_r}$$

where $m_r \geq 0$, $\gamma_m + \sum m_r = 1$, and $T(x_r) = 0$ for all r. Since T is of degree not exceeding m, it has at most $2m$ zeros in $\mathbb{T}$. Each zero is of even multiplicity, so there are at most m distinct points at which T vanishes: $R \leq m$. By an inequality of Bernstein (Theorem 3.13 in Chapter 10 of Zygmund [20]) we know that $\|T'\|_{L^\infty} \ll m\|T\|_{L^\infty}$. Since $\|T\|_{L^\infty} = 1$ and $T(x_r) = 0$, we deduce that $\|x_r\| \gg 1/m$. (Here $\|x\| = \min_{n \in \mathbb{Z}} |x - n|$.) We now define $z_1, z_2, \ldots, z_N$ as follows: For the first $[\gamma_m N]$ values of k put $z_k = 1$. For the next $[m_1 N]$ values of k put $z_k = e(kx_1)$. For the next $[m_2 N]$ values of k put $z_k = e(kx_2)$. Continue in the manner, until $z_k = e(kx_R)$ for $[m_R N]$ values of k. There are $\leq R$ values of k for which z_k has not yet been determined; put $z_k = 0$ for these last values of k. Since

$$\sum_{K_1 \leq k < K_2} e(kx) = \frac{e(K_2 x) - e(K_1 x)}{e(x) - 1} \ll \frac{1}{\|x\|},$$

it follows that

$$\sum_{k=1}^{N} z_k = \gamma_m N + O(1) + \sum_r O\left(\frac{1}{\|x_r\|}\right)$$

(20) $$= \gamma_m N + O(m^2).$$

For $h \in \mathcal{H}(m)$ we have

$$\sum_{k=1}^{N-h} z_k \overline{z_{k+h}} = \gamma_m N + O(h) + \sum_{r=1}^{R} m_r N e(-hx_r) + O(h)$$

$$= N\widehat{\mu}(h) + O(mh)$$

(21) $$\ll mh.$$

To form an infinite sequence, we observe that every natural number n can be uniquely written in the form $n = m^4 + k$ with $1 \leq k \leq 4m^3 + 6m^2 + 4m$. We take $N = 4m^3 + 6m^2 + 4m$ in the above, and put $y_n = z_{m^4+k} = z_k$. From (21) we see that $\{y_n\} \in \mathcal{Y}_\infty$. Since $\gamma_m \longrightarrow \gamma$ as $m \longrightarrow \infty$, from (20) we deduce that $\beta_\infty \geq \gamma$. In Theorem 4 we established the identity $\gamma = \beta_2^2$, so the proof is complete.

Finally we relate α to β_∞.

THEOREM 6. *Let $\mathcal{H}$ be a fixed set of positive integers, let α be defined as in (10), and let β_∞ be defined as in (14). Then $\beta_\infty \ll \alpha \ll \beta_\infty \log(2/\beta_\infty)$.*

PROOF. We establish the upper bound for α first. Suppose that $\{u_n\} \in \mathcal{U}$, and let k be a positive integer. From the definitions of $\mathcal{U}$ and $\mathcal{Y}_\infty$, together with Weyl's criterion, we see that $\{e(ku_n)\} \in \mathcal{Y}_\infty$. Hence by the definition of β_∞ we deduce that

$$(22) \qquad \limsup_{N \to \infty} \frac{1}{N} \left| \sum_{n=1}^{N} e(ku_n) \right| \leq \beta_\infty.$$

By the Erdős-Turán inequality (Corollary 1.1 in Chapter 1),

$$D(N) \ll \frac{N}{K+1} + \sum_{k=1}^{K} \frac{1}{k} \left| \sum_{n=1}^{N} e(ku_n) \right|.$$

Hence by (22) we deduce that

$$\limsup_{N \to \infty} \frac{D(N)}{N} \ll \frac{1}{K+1} + \beta_\infty \log 2K.$$

If $\beta_\infty > 0$ then we take $K = [1/\beta_\infty]$; otherwise we take K to be arbitrarily large. In either case we deduce that $\alpha \ll \beta_\infty \log 2/\beta_\infty$.

To demonstrate that $\beta_\infty \ll \alpha$ we argue probabilistically. Let $\{y_n\} \in \mathcal{Y}_\infty$. Suppose that $\theta_1, \theta_2, \ldots$ are independent random variables in $\mathbb{T}$ such that θ_n has density function $1 + \Re y_n e(-x)$. Since $|y_n| \leq 1$, this is a density function. Moreover,

$$\mathbf{E}\big(e(\theta_n)\big) = \int_\mathbb{T} e(x)\big(1 + \Re y_n e(-x)\big)\,dx = \frac{1}{2}y_n,$$

and for $k > 1$,

$$\mathbf{E}\big(e(k\theta_n)\big) = \int_\mathbb{T} e(kx)\big(1 + \Re y_n e(-x)\big)\,dx = 0.$$

By the strong law of large numbers it follows that

$$\sum_{n=1}^{N} e(\theta_n) = \frac{1}{2} \sum_{n=1}^{N} y_n + o(N) \qquad \text{a.s.,}$$

and that for each fixed $k > 1$,

$$\sum_{n=1}^{N} e(k\theta_n) = o(N) \qquad \text{a.s.}$$

Moreover,

$$\mathbf{E}\left(e\big(k(\theta_n - \theta_{n+h})\big)\right) = \begin{cases} \frac{1}{4} y_n \overline{y_{n+h}} & \text{if } k = 1, \\ 0 & \text{if } k > 1, \end{cases}$$

so that

$$\sum_{n=1}^{N} e\big(k(\theta_n - \theta_{n+h})\big) = o(N) \qquad \text{a.s.}$$

for each $k \neq 0$. Hence the sequences $\theta_n - \theta_{n+h}$ are almost surely uniformly distributed. By taking $u_n = \theta_n$ in Koksma's inequality (recall (1.14)) we find that

$$\left| \sum_{n=1}^{N} e(\theta_n) \right| \leq 4D(N).$$

Thus

$$D(N) \geq \frac{1}{8} \left| \sum_{n=1}^{N} y_n \right| - o(N) \qquad \text{a.s.}$$

Hence $\alpha \geq \frac{1}{8} \beta_\infty$, and the proof is complete.

4. Corollaries. We now use Theorems 2–6 to gain further insights into van der Corput sets.

COROLLARY 1. *Let $\mathcal{H}$ be a set of positive integers, let q be a positive integer, and put $q\mathcal{H} = \{qh : h \in \mathcal{H}\}$. Then $\delta(q\mathcal{H}) = \delta(\mathcal{H})$. Hence if $q\mathcal{H}$ is a van der Corput set for some q, then it is for all q.*

PROOF. Let T be a cosine polynomial, and put $T_q(x) = T(qx)$. It is clear that $T \in \mathcal{T}(\mathcal{H})$ if and only if $T_q \in \mathcal{T}(q\mathcal{H})$. Moreover, $\widehat{T}(0) = \widehat{T_q}(0)$.

COROLLARY 2. *Let $\mathcal{H}$ be a set of positive integers, let q be a positive integer, and put $\mathcal{H}_q = \{h \in \mathcal{H} : q|h\}$. Then $\delta(\mathcal{H}_q) \leq q\delta(\mathcal{H})$. Hence if $\mathcal{H}_q$ is empty then $\delta(\mathcal{H}) \geq 1/q$.*

PROOF. Suppose that $T \in \mathcal{T}(\mathcal{H})$, $T(x) = a_0 + \sum_h a_h \cos 2\pi h x$, and put

(23)
$$U(x) = \frac{1}{q} \sum_{a=1}^{q} T(x + a/q).$$

Thus

$$U(x) = a_0 + \sum_{\substack{h \\ q|h}} a_h \cos 2\pi h x.$$

Put $V(x) = U(x)/U(0)$. Then $V \in \mathcal{T}(\mathcal{H}_q)$. Moreover, from (23) we see that $U(0) \geq T(0)/q = 1/q$. Hence

$$\widehat{V}(0) = \frac{\widehat{U}(0)}{U(0)} = \frac{a_0}{U(0)} \leq qa_0.$$

We now exhibit an example in which the extremal measure $\mu \in \mathcal{M}(\mathcal{H})$, whose existence is guaranteed by Theorem 3, is not unique.

EXAMPLE 1. Let $\mathcal{H} = \{1, 2, \dots, m-1\}$; this set was considered in Theorem 2. Let $q\mathcal{H}$ be defined as in Corollary 1 above. By combining these two results we see that $\delta(q\mathcal{H}) = 1/m$. However, the extremal measure $\mu \in \mathcal{M}(q\mathcal{H})$ is not unique if $q > 1$. To see this, let $\mathcal{C}$ be a complete residue system modulo m with $\mathcal{C} \subseteq \{1, 2, \dots, qm\}$, and put

$$\mu = \frac{1}{m} \sum_{c \in \mathcal{C}} \delta_{c/(qm)}.$$

This is an extremal measure in $\mathcal{M}(q\mathcal{H})$. Since distinct choices of $\mathcal{C}$ give rise to distinct measures, there are many such measures. Not all these measures are even, but several of them are. Once two extremal measures have been constructed, any convex combination of them is also extremal, and hence there are infinitely many extremal measures.

In contrast, the extremal measure in $\mathcal{M}(\mathcal{H})$ *is* unique. To see this, suppose that μ is extremal. We know that $T(x) = \frac{1}{m}\Delta_m(x)$ is an extremal member of $\mathcal{T}(\mathcal{H})$. On examining the proof of (7), we realize that for equality to occur in (7) the measure μ must place all its mass at zeros of $T(x)$, apart from the mass $1/m$ at 0. But (recall (1.16)) the zeros of $T(x)$ are the points a/m, $0 < a < m$. Hence μ is of the form

$$\mu = \sum_{a=1}^{m} w(a)\delta_{a/m}$$

where $w(0) = 1/m$, $w(a) \geq 0$ for all a, and $\sum_a w(a) = 1$. Hence

$$\widehat{\mu}(k) = \sum_{a=1}^{m} w(a)e\left(\frac{-ak}{m}\right),$$

and consequently

$$w(a) = \sum_{k=0}^{m-1} \widehat{\mu}(k)\left(\frac{ak}{m}\right).$$

But $\widehat{\mu}(0) = 1$, and $\widehat{\mu}(k) = 0$ for $0 < k < m$ since $\mu \in \mathcal{M}(\mathcal{H})$. Hence $w(a) = 1/m$ for all a, $1 \leq a \leq m$, and μ is the measure already used in the proof of Theorem 2.

Suppose that a set $\mathcal{H}$ of positive integers is given, and that a cosine polynomial $T \in \mathcal{T}(\mathcal{H})$ and a measure $\mu \in \mathcal{M}(\mathcal{H})$ can be found so that $\widehat{T}(0) = \mu(\{0\})$. Then this common value must be $\delta(\mathcal{H})$, as we see from the proof of the inequality (7). We use this approach in the following example.

EXAMPLE 2. Let $\mathcal{H} = \{2,3\}$. Then

$$\delta(\mathcal{H}) = \frac{\cos \pi/5}{1 + \cos \pi/5} = 0.44721\ldots.$$

To prove this it suffices to note that

$$T(x) = \frac{\cos \pi/5}{1 + \cos \pi/5} + \frac{3}{5(1 + \cos \pi/5)} \cos 4\pi x + \frac{2}{5(1 + \cos \pi/5)} \cos 6\pi x$$

$$= \frac{8}{5(1 + \cos \pi/5)} (\cos 2\pi x - \cos 2\pi/5)^2 (\cos 2\pi x + 3/4 + 2\cos 2\pi/5)$$

is a member of $\mathcal{T}(\mathcal{H})$, and that

$$\mu = \frac{\cos \pi/5}{1 + \cos \pi/5} \delta_0 + \frac{1}{2(1 + \cos \pi/5)} \left(\delta_{1/5} + \delta_{4/5} \right)$$

is a member of $\mathcal{M}(\mathcal{H})$.

COROLLARY 3. *If $\mathcal{H}_1$ and $\mathcal{H}_2$ are sets of positive integers, and if $\mathcal{H} = \mathcal{H}_1 \cup \mathcal{H}_2$, then $\delta(\mathcal{H}) \geq \delta(\mathcal{H}_1)\delta(\mathcal{H}_2)$. Hence if $\mathcal{H}$ is a van der Corput set then at least one of $\mathcal{H}_1$, $\mathcal{H}_2$ is also a van der Corput set.*

PROOF. Let $\mu_i \in \mathcal{M}(\mathcal{H}_i)$ be the extremal measures whose existence is guaranteed by Theorem 3, and put $\mu = \mu_1 * \mu_2$. Then $\mu \in \mathcal{M}(\mathcal{H})$, and $\mu(\{0\}) \geq \mu_1(\{0\})\mu_2(\{0\})$.

COROLLARY 4. *If $\mathcal{H}_1$ and $\mathcal{H}_2$ are disjoint subsets of $\{1, 2, \ldots, N\}$, then*

$$\delta(\mathcal{H}_1)\delta(\mathcal{H}_2) \geq \frac{1}{2N}.$$

PROOF. Let $T_i \in \mathcal{T}(\mathcal{H}_i)$ be extremal cosine polynomials, and put $T(x) = T_1(x)T_2(x)$. Then $T(0) = 1$. Moreover, $\widehat{T}(0) = \delta(\mathcal{H}_1)\delta(\mathcal{H}_2)$ since $\mathcal{H}_1$ and $\mathcal{H}_2$ are disjoint. We observe that T has degree at most $2N - 1$. We now take $m = 2N$ in Theorem 2, and adopt the notation of that theorem. Thus we find that $T \in \mathcal{T}(\mathcal{H})$, and hence $\widehat{T}(0) \geq \delta(\mathcal{H}) = 1/(2N)$.

COROLLARY 5. *If $\mathcal{H}_1$ and $\mathcal{H}_2$ partition the set $\{1, 2, \ldots, N\}$ then*

$$\frac{1}{2N} \leq \delta(\mathcal{H}_1)\delta(\mathcal{H}_2) \leq \frac{1}{N+1}.$$

PROOF. The lower bound follows from the preceding corollary. For the upper bound, let $\mathcal{H}$ be defined as in Theorem 2 with $m = N + 1$. Then by Corollary 3 and Theorem 2 we see that $\delta(\mathcal{H}_1)\delta(\mathcal{H}_2) \leq \delta(\mathcal{H}) = 1/(N + 1)$.

Let $\mathcal{H}$ be a van der Corput set, and put $\mathcal{H}_N = \{h \in \mathcal{H} : h \leq N\}$. Then $\mathcal{H}_N$ is not a van der Corput set, but we know that $\delta(\mathcal{H}_N) \longrightarrow 0$ as $N \longrightarrow \infty$. It would be useful to know how rapidly this limit is approached in special cases, such as when $\mathcal{H}$ is the set of positive perfect squares. Such problems seem to be very difficult in general, but we are able to determine the size of $\delta(\mathcal{H}_N)$ for one very special set $\mathcal{H}$, as follows.

COROLLARY 6. *Let* $\mathcal{H} = \{h > 0 : 2^a \| h, a \text{ even}\}$, *and put* $\mathcal{H}_N = \{h \in \mathcal{H} : h \leq N\}$. *Then* $\delta(\mathcal{H}_N) \approx N^{-1/2}$.

PROOF. Let $\mathcal{K} = \{h > 0 : 2^a \| h, a \text{ odd}\}$, and put $\mathcal{K}_N = \{h \in \mathcal{K} : h \leq N\}$. Let $T \in \mathcal{T}(\mathcal{H}_N)$ be extremal. Then $T(2x) \in \mathcal{T}(\mathcal{K}_{2N})$, and hence $\delta(\mathcal{K}_{2N}) \leq \delta(\mathcal{H}_N)$. Thus

$$\delta(\mathcal{H}_N)^2 \geq \delta(\mathcal{H}_N)\delta(\mathcal{H}_{2N}) \geq \delta(\mathcal{K}_{2N})\delta(\mathcal{H}_{2N}).$$

By Corollary 3, the last expression on the right is $\gg 1/N$, and so $\delta(\mathcal{H}_N) \gg N^{-1/2}$. By reversing the roles of $\mathcal{H}$ and $\mathcal{K}$, we see similarly that $\delta(\mathcal{K}_N) \gg N^{-1/2}$. Hence by the preceding corollary we see that $\delta(\mathcal{H}_N) \ll 1/(N\delta(\mathcal{K}_N)) \ll N^{-1/2}$.

COROLLARY 7. *Let* $\mathcal{H}$ *be a van der Corput set. Then* $\mathcal{H}$ *can be partitioned into infinitely many disjoint subsets* $\mathcal{H}_i$ *so that each* $\mathcal{H}_i$ *is a van der Corput set.*

PROOF. First we show that it is possible to construct finite pairwise disjoint subsets $\mathcal{S}_k$ of $\mathcal{H}$, so that $\delta(\mathcal{S}_k) \leq 1/k$. Suppose that $\mathcal{S}_j$ has been determined for all $j \leq k$, and put $\mathcal{R}_k = \mathcal{H} \setminus \bigcup_{j=1}^{k} \mathcal{S}_j$. By Corollary 3, $\mathcal{R}_k$ is a van der Corput set. Hence there is a finite set $\mathcal{S}_{k+1} \subseteq \mathcal{R}_k$ with $\delta(\mathcal{S}_{k+1}) \leq 1/(k+1)$. With the $\mathcal{S}_k$ constructed in this way, it is easy to determine the $\mathcal{H}_i$ so that each one includes infinitely many of the $\mathcal{S}_k$.

COROLLARY 8. *Let* $\mathcal{H}$ *be a set of positive integers, and suppose that* $\mathcal{H}$ *contains arbitrarily long blocks of consecutive numbers. Then* $\mathcal{H}$ *is a van der Corput set.*

PROOF. For each positive integer N put $F_N(x) = \frac{1}{N} \sum_{n=M+1}^{M+N} e(nx)$ where $M = M(N)$ is chosen so that all the frequencies of F_N lie in $\mathcal{H}$. Thus if $\mu \in \mathcal{M}(\mathcal{H})$ then $\int_{\mathbb{T}} F_N \, d\mu = 0$. But $F_N(0) = 1$, $|F_N(x)| \leq 1$ for all x, and $F_N(x) \longrightarrow 0$ as $N \longrightarrow \infty$, for any fixed $x \notin \mathbb{Z}$. Hence by the Lebesgue dominated convergence theorem,

$$0 = \lim_{N \to \infty} \int_{\mathbb{T}} F_N(x) \, d\mu = \int_{\mathbb{T}} \lim_{N \to \infty} F_N(x) \, d\mu = \mu(\{0\}).$$

Since this holds for all $\mu \in \mathcal{M}(\mathcal{H})$, it follows that $\gamma(\mathcal{H}) = 0$, and hence that $\mathcal{H}$ is a van der Corput set.

5. A sufficient condition. We now establish a useful criterion that allows us to prove that various sets are van der Corput. Among the applications is the result that the set of perfect squares forms a van der Corput set.

THEOREM 7. *Let* $\mathcal{H}$ *be a set of positive integers, and put*

$$\mathcal{H}_q = \{h \in \mathcal{H} : q! | h\}.$$

If there are infinitely many positive integers q *such that for each fixed irrational real number* x *the sequence* $\mathcal{H}_q x$ *is uniformly distributed* (mod 1), *then* $\mathcal{H}$ *is a van der Corput set.*

PROOF. Suppose that $\mu \in \mathcal{M}(\mathcal{H})$, and let

$$\mathcal{Q} = \{q \in \mathbb{Z}^+ : \mathcal{H}_q x \text{ u. d. } \forall x \in \mathbb{R} \setminus \mathbb{Q}\}.$$

Furthermore, put

$$A(H; q) = \sum_{\substack{1 \leq h \leq H \\ h \in \mathcal{H}_q}} 1,$$

and set

$$f_H(x; q) = \frac{1}{A(H; q)} \sum_{\substack{1 \leq h \leq H \\ h \in \mathcal{H}_q}} \cos 2\pi h x.$$

If $q \in \mathcal{Q}$ and x is an irrational real number, then

$$\lim_{H \to \infty} f_H(x; q) = 0$$

by Weyl's criterion. Now pick a rational number x_1, and suppose that $x = x_1$. The sequence $f_H(x_1; q)$ may not converge as $H \longrightarrow \infty$. However, $|f_H(x_1; q)| \leq 1$ for all H, and hence there is a subsequence that converges, say

$$\lim_{\substack{H \to \infty \\ h \in \mathcal{N}_1}} f_H(x_1; q) = f_q(x_1).$$

Now pick a second rational number, x_2. The sequence $\{f_H(x_2; q)\}_{H \in \mathcal{N}_1}$ may not converge, but there is a subsequence that converges, say

$$\lim_{\substack{H \to \infty \\ H \in \mathcal{N}_2}} f_H(x_2; q) = f_q(x_2)$$

where $\mathcal{N}_2 \subseteq \mathcal{N}_1$. Suppose that $\{x_j\}$ is an enumeration of the rational numbers. Continuing in this way, we construct a sequence of subsequences, $\mathcal{N}_1 \supseteq \mathcal{N}_2 \supseteq \ldots$ with the property that the numbers $f_H(x_j; q)$ converge to a limit $f_q(x_j)$ as $H \longrightarrow \infty$, $H \in \mathcal{N}_j$. Let n_{ij} denote the ith member of $\mathcal{N}_j$, and form a sequence $\mathcal{N} = \{n_i\}$ by setting $n_i = n_{ii}$. For each j, all but finitely many members of $\mathcal{N}$ lie in $\mathcal{N}_j$. Hence

$$\lim_{\substack{H \to \infty \\ H \in \mathcal{N}}} f_H(x_j; q) = f_q(x_j)$$

for all rational numbers x_j. (This construction is known as "Helly selection.") By setting $f_q(x) = 0$ if x is irrational, we find that

$$\lim_{\substack{H \to \infty \\ H \in \mathcal{N}}} f_H(x; q) = f_q(x)$$

for all real numbers x. Moreover, $|f_q(x)| \leq 1$ for all x. Now $\widehat{\mu}(\pm h) = 0$ for all $h \in \mathcal{H}$ since $\mu \in \mathcal{M}(\mathcal{H})$, and hence $\int_{\mathbb{T}} f_H(x; q) \, d\mu = 0$. Consequently by the

Lebesgue dominated convergence theorem,

$$0 = \lim_{\substack{H \to \infty \\ H \in \mathcal{N}}} \int_{\mathbb{T}} f_H(x;q)\,d\mu = \int_{\mathbb{T}} \lim_{\substack{H \to \infty \\ H \in \mathcal{N}}} f_H(x;q)\,d\mu$$

$$= \int_{\mathbb{T}} f_q(x)\,d\mu = \sum_{r=1}^{\infty} \sum_{\substack{a=1 \\ (a,r)=1}}^{r} f_q(a/r)\mu(\{a/r\}).$$

Since $f_q(a/r) = 1$ if $r|q!$, and $|f_q(a/r)| \le 1$ otherwise, we may rewrite the above as

$$0 = \sum_{r|q!} \sum_{\substack{a=1 \\ (a,r)=1}}^{r} \mu(\{a/r\}) + \theta \sum_{r \nmid q!} \sum_{\substack{a=1 \\ (a,r)=1}}^{r} \mu(\{a/r\})$$

where $|\theta| \le 1$. The numbers $\mu(\{a/r\})$ are non-negative, and have sum not exceeding 1. Hence for any $\epsilon > 0$ there is a q such that the second double sum on the right is $< \epsilon$. But the first double sum includes the term $\mu(\{0\})$, and hence we conclude that $\mu(\{0\}) \le \epsilon$. Since ϵ may be arbitrarily small, we deduce that $\gamma(\mathcal{H}) = 0$, and hence that $\mathcal{H}$ is a van der Corput set.

COROLLARY 9. *Let $P(z) \in \mathbb{Z}[z]$ and suppose that $P(z) \longrightarrow +\infty$ as $z \longrightarrow +\infty$. Then $\mathcal{H} = \{P(n) > 0 : n > 0\}$ is a van der Corput set if and only if for every positive integer q the congruence $P(z) \equiv 0 \pmod{q}$ has a root.*

In particular, the set of positive perfect squares is a van der Corput set.

PROOF. If q is chosen so that the congruence $P(z) \equiv 0 \pmod{q}$ has no solution, then $\delta(\mathcal{H}) \ge 1/q$ by Corollary 2, and hence $\mathcal{H}$ is not a van der Corput set.

Suppose that the congruence $P(z) \equiv 0 \pmod{q}$ has a solution for every positive integer q, and let x be irrational. Let $r_1, r_2, \ldots, r_K$ be the solutions of the congruence $\pmod{q!}$; here $K = K(q!) > 0$. The leading coefficient of the polynomial $P(q!z+r_k)x$ is irrational, so by Weyl's theorem the numbers $P(q!n+r_k)x$ are uniformly distributed $\pmod 1$. A finite union of uniformly distributed sequences is also uniformly distributed; hence the sequence $\mathcal{H}_q x$ is uniformly distributed. Hence by Theorem 7, $\mathcal{H}$ is a van der Corput set.

COROLLARY 10. *Let a be a fixed integer, and put $\mathcal{H} = \{p + a : p > -a\}$. Then $\mathcal{H}$ is a van der Corput set if and only if $a = \pm 1$.*

PROOF. Suppose that q is a prime that divides a. Then the set $\mathcal{H}$ contains at most finitely many multiples of q, and hence by Corollaries 2 and 3 we see that $\mathcal{H}$ is not a van der Corput set, except possibly when $a = \pm 1$.

Suppose now that $a = \pm 1$, and let x be an irrational number. A classical theorem of Vinogradov (see §25 of Davenport [7]) asserts that $\sum_{p \le x} e(px) = o(\pi(x))$. If k is a non-zero integer then this also holds with x replaced by kx. Hence by Weyl's criterion it follows that the numbers px are uniformly distributed $\pmod 1$.

This argument extends to primes in arithmetic progressions, as follows. Since

$$\frac{1}{q}\sum_{h=1}^{q} e\Big(\frac{(n-b)h}{q}\Big) = \begin{cases} 1 & \text{if } n \equiv b \pmod{q}, \\ 0 & \text{otherwise,} \end{cases}$$

it follows that

$$\sum_{\substack{p\leq x \\ p\equiv b \pmod q}} e(pkx) = \frac{1}{q}\sum_{p\leq x} e(pkx)\sum_{h=1}^{q} e\Big(\frac{(p-b)h}{q}\Big)$$

$$= \frac{1}{q}\sum_{h=1}^{q} e\Big(\frac{-bh}{q}\Big)\sum_{p\leq x} e(p(kx+r/q)).$$

Since $kx + r/q$ is irrational, the inner sum on the right is $o(\pi(x))$ as $x \longrightarrow \infty$, and hence the left hand side is also $o(\pi(x))$. It follows by Weyl's criterion that if $(b,q) = 1$ then the numbers $\{px\}_{p\equiv b \pmod q}$ are uniformly distributed (mod 1). In the notation of Theorem 7, the set $\mathcal{H}_q x$ is uniformly distributed (mod 1), and hence $\mathcal{H}$ is a van der Corput set.

6. Intersective sets. We now relate the van der Corput sets to a second class of sets, called *intersective sets*. First we introduce some notation. Let $\mathcal{A}$ denote an arbitrary set of positive integers, and let $A(N)$ denote its counting function,

$$A(N) = \sum_{\substack{a\in\mathcal{A} \\ a\leq N}} 1.$$

Let $\overline{d}(\mathcal{A})$ denote the upper asymptotic density of $\mathcal{A}$,

$$\overline{d}(\mathcal{A}) = \limsup_{N\to\infty} \frac{A(N)}{N}.$$

We let $\mathcal{A} - \mathcal{A}$ denote the difference set of $\mathcal{A}$, that is, $\mathcal{A} - \mathcal{A} = \{a - a' : a \in \mathcal{A}, a' \in \mathcal{A}\}$. We call a set $\mathcal{H}$ *intersective* if $\mathcal{H} \cap (\mathcal{A} - \mathcal{A}) = \emptyset$ implies that $\overline{d}(\mathcal{A}) = 0$.

As with van der Corput sets, we define a measure of how close $\mathcal{H}$ is to being intersective. Put

(24) $\iota = \sup_{\substack{\mathcal{A} \\ \mathcal{H}\cap(\mathcal{A}-\mathcal{A})=\emptyset}} \overline{d}(\mathcal{A}).$

We establish an inequality between ι and the quantities already considered.

THEOREM 8. *Let $\mathcal{H}$ be a set of positive integers. Let δ be defined as in (5), and let ι be defined as above. Then $\iota \leq \delta$.*

It follows that any van der Corput set is also intersective. J. Bourgain [5] has proved that the converse is false: There exist intersective sets that are not van der Corput.

PROOF. Let $\mathcal{A}$ be a set of positive integers such that $\mathcal{H} \cap (\mathcal{A} - \mathcal{A}) = \emptyset$. If $\overline{d}(\mathcal{A}) = 0$ then there is nothing to prove. Suppose that $\overline{d}(\mathcal{A}) > 0$, and put

$$y_n = \begin{cases} \overline{d}(\mathcal{A})^{-1/2} & \text{if } n \in \mathcal{A}, \\ 0 & \text{otherwise.} \end{cases}$$

If $h \in \mathcal{H}$ then $y_{n+h}\overline{y_n} = 0$, so (12) holds. As (11) obviously holds as well, we see that $\{y_n\} \in \mathcal{Y}_2$. As

$$\limsup_{N \to \infty} \frac{1}{N} \left| \sum_{n=1}^{N} y_n \right| = \overline{d}(\mathcal{A})^{1/2},$$

we deduce from (13) that $\beta_2 \geq \overline{d}(\mathcal{A})^{1/2}$. From (24) we conclude that $\beta_2 \geq \iota^{1/2}$, and the proof is complete.

7. Heilbronn sets. Dirichlet's theorem, in its sharpest form, asserts that for every positive integer N and every real number θ there is an integer n, $1 \leq n \leq N$, such that

$$(25) \qquad \|n\theta\| \leq \frac{1}{N+1}.$$

This is best possible, as we see by taking $\theta = 1/(N+1)$. Heilbronn [8] proved an analogue of this in which the integers n are required to be perfect squares. Precisely, if $\epsilon > 0$ and $N > N_0(\epsilon)$ then for any real number θ there is an integer n, $1 \leq n \leq N$, such that

$$(26) \qquad \|n^2\theta\| < N^{-\frac{1}{2}+\epsilon}.$$

It would be interesting to understand what other sets of positive integers might take the place of the perfect squares, in a theorem of this sort. We call a set $\mathcal{H}$ of positive integers a *Heilbronn set* if for every real number θ and every $\epsilon > 0$ there is an $h \in \mathcal{H}$ such that $\|h\theta\| < \epsilon$. As with the sets already considered, we may measure how close a set is to being a Heilbronn set, by letting

$$(27) \qquad \eta = \sup_{\theta} \inf_{h \in \mathcal{H}} \|h\theta\|.$$

Thus $\mathcal{H}$ is a Heilbronn set if and only if $\eta = 0$. The form of our definition does not refer to an initial segment of $\mathcal{H}$, as in Heilbronn's theorem, but the difference is immaterial. To see this, let $\mathcal{H}_N = \{h \in \mathcal{H} : h \leq N\}$. Then by a simple compactness argument one finds that

$$(28) \qquad \lim_{N \to \infty} \eta(\mathcal{H}_N) = \eta(\mathcal{H}).$$

Since the sharp form (25) of Dirichlet's theorem can be proved using Fejér's kernel (see p. 99)), it is reasonable to apply cosine polynomials to estimate η.

THEOREM 9. *Let $\mathcal{H}$ be a set of positive integers, let $\delta(\mathcal{H})$ be defined as in (5), and let $\eta(\mathcal{H})$ be defined as above. Then $\eta \leq \delta$. Hence if $\mathcal{H}$ is a van der Corput set then it is a Heilbronn set.*

PROOF. Let $T \in \mathcal{T}(\mathcal{H})$, with T written as in (3). Suppose that $0 < \epsilon \leq 1/2$, and put $f(x) = \max(0, 1 - \|x\|/\epsilon)$. We consider the expression

$$
(29) \qquad\qquad a_0 + \sum_h a_h f(h\theta)
$$

where θ is some real number. The function $f(x)$ is continuous and of bounded variation. Hence its Fourier series is absolutely convergent, and converges to $f(x)$. On inserting this formula for $f(x)$, we see that the above is

$$
= a_0 + \sum_h a_h \sum_k \widehat{f}(k) e(kh\theta).
$$

Since $f(x)$ is an even function, its Fourier coefficients $\widehat{f}(k)$ are real. Moreover, the expression (29) is real, so we may take real parts without affecting the value of the expression. Hence the above is

$$
= a_0 + \sum_h a_h \sum_k \widehat{f}(k) \cos 2\pi kh\theta.
$$

On inverting the order of summation, we see that this is

$$
= \sum_k \widehat{f}(k) T(k\theta).
$$

But $\widehat{f}(k) = \frac{1}{\epsilon}\left(\frac{\sin \pi k\epsilon}{\pi k}\right)^2 \geq 0$ and $T(k\theta) \geq 0$ for all k. Hence the sum above is at least as large as the contribution of the term $k = 0$. But $\widehat{f}(0) = \epsilon$ and $T(0) = 1$, so the above is

$$
\geq \epsilon.
$$

Suppose that $\epsilon > a_0$. Then there must be at least one h in the sum in (29) for which $a_h > 0$ and $f(h\theta) > 0$. For such an h we see that $h \in \mathcal{H}$ and $\|h\theta\| < \epsilon$. Since this holds for every $\epsilon > a_0$, it follows that $\inf_{h \in \mathcal{H}} \|h\theta\| \leq a_0$. Since this holds for every $T \in \mathcal{T}(\mathcal{H})$, it follows that $\inf_{h \in \mathcal{H}} \|h\theta\| \leq \delta$. Finally, since this holds for every real number θ, it follows that $\eta \leq \delta$, and the proof is complete.

To dismiss any possibility of a converse, we construct a set that is Heilbronn but not intersective (and hence not van der Corput).

EXAMPLE 3. Let

$$
\mathcal{H} = \{h \in \mathbb{Z}^+ : \|h\sqrt{2}\| > \frac{1}{10} \text{ or } \|h\sqrt{3}\| > \frac{1}{10}\}.
$$

We show first that $\mathcal{H}$ is a Heilbronn set. Suppose that θ is rational, say $\theta = a/q$. The number $q\sqrt{2}$ is irrational, and hence the sequence $\{nq\sqrt{2}\}_{n=1}^{\infty}$ is dense in

$\mathbb{T}$. In particular, there is an $n > 0$ such that $\|nq\sqrt{2}\| > 1/10$. Put $h = nq$. Then $h \in \mathcal{H}$ and $\|h\theta\| = 0$. Next suppose that $\theta \notin \mathbb{Q}$ but $\theta \in \mathbb{Q}(\sqrt{2})$. Then the numbers $1, \theta, \sqrt{3}$ are linearly independent over $\mathbb{Q}$, and hence by Kronecker's theorem the points $(h\theta, h\sqrt{3})$ are dense in $\mathbb{T}^2$. Consequently for any $\epsilon > 0$ there is an $h > 0$ such that $\|h\theta\| < \epsilon$ and $\|h\sqrt{3}\| > 1/10$ (and hence $h \in \mathcal{H}$). Finally, suppose that $\theta \notin \mathbb{Q}(\sqrt{2})$. Then $1, \theta, \sqrt{2}$ are linearly independent over $\mathbb{Q}$, and we proceed as in the preceding case but with $\sqrt{3}$ replaced by $\sqrt{2}$. This exhausts all cases, so we conclude that $\mathcal{H}$ is a Heilbronn set.

We now show that $\mathcal{H}$ is not intersective. Take

$$\mathcal{A} = \{a \in \mathbb{Z}^+ : \|a\sqrt{2}\| < \frac{1}{20}, \ \|a\sqrt{3}\| < \frac{1}{20}\}.$$

Since $1, \sqrt{2}, \sqrt{3}$ are linearly independent over $\mathbb{Q}$, we know by the stronger form of Kronecker's theorem that the points $(n\sqrt{2}, n\sqrt{3})$ are uniformly distributed in $\mathbb{T}^2$. Hence $\mathcal{A}$ has asymptotic density $d(\mathcal{A}) = 1/100$. Moreover, if $a \in \mathcal{A}$ and $a' \in \mathcal{A}$ then $\|(a - a')\sqrt{2}\| < 1/10$ and $\|(a - a')\sqrt{3}\| < 1/10$, so that $\mathcal{H} \cap (\mathcal{A} - \mathcal{A}) = \emptyset$. Hence $\iota(\mathcal{H}) \geq 1/100$, and we see that $\mathcal{H}$ is not intersective.

8. Notes. It seems that the first known example of a van der Corput set, other than the positive integers, was given by Delange (see Bertrandias [3]), who showed that for any integer $q > 0$, the multiples of q form a van der Corput set. This is a trivial consequence of our Corollary 1. Theorem 1 is due to Kamae and Mendes-France [9]; this has been extended by Peres [11]. Theorems 3–6 are due to Ruzsa [14]. Theorems 7 and 8 are due to Kamae and Mendes-France [9]. Ruzsa (private communication) suggests the following alternative formulation of Theorem 7: If for every q there is an $\mathcal{L} \subseteq \mathcal{H}_q$ such that $\mathcal{L}x$ is uniformly distributed (mod 1) for every irrational real number x, then $\mathcal{H}$ is a van der Corput set. Alon and Peres [1] have given a simpler proof of Bourgain's result that an intersective set need not be van der Corput. Bertrand-Mathis [4] has shown that a set is intersective if and only if it is Poincaré recurrent. Theorem 9 is a previously-unpublished result of the author. The exponent in (26) has recently been improved: A. Zaharescu (to appear) has shown that $N^{-1/2+\epsilon}$ may be replaced by $N^{-4/7+\epsilon}$. One might conjecture that (26) holds with the right hand side replaced by $N^{-1+\epsilon}$. For further discussion surrounding Heilbronn's theorem, see Baker [2] and Schmidt [19]. Kříž [10] has shown that there exist Heilbronn sets that are not intersective, and hence not van der Corput.

References

1. N. Alon and Y. Peres, *Euclidean Ramsey theory and a construction of Bourgain* (to appear).

2. R. C. Baker, *Diophantine Inequalities*, Oxford University Press, New York, 1986.

3. J.-P. Bertrandias, *Suites pseudo-altéatoires et critères d'équiré-partition modulo un*, Compositio Math. **16** (1964), 23–28.

4. A. Bertrand-Mathis, *Ensembles intersectifs et recurrence de Poincaré*, Israel J. Math. **55** (1986), 184–198.

5. J. Bourgain, *Ruzsa's problem on sets of recurrence*, Israel J. Math. **59** (1987), 150–166.

6. J. G. van der Corput, *Diophantische Ungleichungen I. Zur Gleichverteilung modulo Eins*, Acta Math. **56** (1931), 373–456.

7. H. Davenport, *Multiplicative Number Theory*, Second Edition, Springer-Verlag, New York, 1980.

8. H. Heilbronn, *On the distribution of the sequence θn^2 (mod 1)*, Quart. J. Math. (2) **19** (1948), 249–256.

9. T. Kamae and M. Mendes-France, *van der Corput's difference theorem*, Israel J. Math. **31** (1978), 335–342.

10. I. Kříž, *Large independent sets in shift-invariant graphs: solution of Bergelson's problem*, Graphs Combin. **3** (1987), 145–158.

11. Y. Peres, *Applications of Banach limits to the study of sets of integers*, Israel J. Math. **62** (1988), 17–31.

12. I. Ruzsa, *On difference sets*, Studia Sci. Math. Hungar. **13** (1978), 319–326.

13. _____, *Uniform distribution, positive trigonometric polynomials and difference sets*, Seminar on Number Theory 1981/1982, No. 18, Univ. Bordeaux I, Talence, 1982, 18 pp.

14. _____, *Connections between the uniform distribution of a sequence and its differences*, Topics in Classical Number Theory (Budapest, 1981), North-Holland, Amsterdam, 1984, pp. 1419–1443.

15. _____, *Sets of sums and differences*, Seminar on number theory, Paris 1982–83, Birkhäuser, Boston, 1984, pp. 267–273.

16. _____, *On measures of intersectivity*, Acta Math. Hungar. **43** (1984), 335–340.

17. _____, *Difference sets without squares*, Period. Math. Hungar. **15** (1984), 205–209.

18. H. H. Schaefer, *Topological Vector Spaces*, Springer-Verlag, New York, 1971.

19. W. M. Schmidt, *Small fractional parts of polynomials*, Regional Conference Series No. 32, Amer. Math. Soc., Providence, 1977.

20. A. Zygmund, *Trigonometric Series, Vol. II*, Second Edition, Cambridge University Press, Cambridge, 1968.

Chapter 3. Exponential sums I: The Methods of Weyl and van der Corput

1. Introduction. Several methods have been devised for estimating exponential sums, although most of the resulting bounds fall far short of what we believe to be the truth. In this section we outline the primary techniques, discuss the conjectures that lie beyond, and consider instructive examples. In §2 we consider sums of the form

$$(1) \qquad S = \sum_{n=1}^{N} e\big(P(n)\big)$$

where $P(x)$ is a polynomial with real coefficients. Such a sum is called a *Weyl sum*, and we derive Weyl's estimate for these sums. In §3 we treat sums of the form $\sum e(f(n))$ where f is a suitably smooth function of a real variable. Following van der Corput, we construct two ways of transforming such sums. One involves van der Corput's Lemma (Chapter 2, §1), the other the Poisson summation formula. For an important class of functions f these transformations may be applied systematically, to form the *method of exponent pairs*, which we discuss in §4.

2. Weyl's method. Let S denote the Weyl sum (1), and suppose that the polynomial $P(x)$ has degree k. We first consider $k = 1$. Since

$$\sum_{n=1}^{N} e(n\alpha) = \frac{e((N+1)\alpha) - e(\alpha)}{e(\alpha) - 1}$$

$$= e\big((N+1)\alpha/2\big) \frac{e(N\alpha/2) - e(-N\alpha/2)}{e(\alpha/2) - e(-\alpha/2)}$$

$$= e\big((N+1)\alpha/2\big) \frac{\sin \pi N\alpha}{\sin \pi\alpha},$$

we see that if $P(x) = \alpha x + \beta$ then

$$|S| \le \frac{1}{|\sin \pi\alpha|} \le \frac{1}{2\|\alpha\|}$$

where $\|\alpha\|$ denotes the distance from α to the nearest integer. If $\|\alpha\| \leq 1/(2N)$ then the above bound is worse than the trivial bound $|S| \leq N$. In either case we find that

$$(2) \qquad \left| \sum_{n=1}^{N} e(\alpha n + \beta) \right| \leq \min\left(N, \frac{1}{2\|\alpha\|}\right).$$

To treat quadratic polynomials we employ Weyl differencing (recall (1) in Chapter 2), by which we see that

$$(3) \qquad |S|^2 \ll N + \sum_{h=1}^{N-1} \left| \sum_{n=1}^{N-h} e\big(P(n+h) - P(n)\big) \right|.$$

If $P(x) = \alpha x^2 + \beta x + \gamma$ then $P(x+h) - P(x) = 2\alpha h x + \alpha h^2 + \beta h$, so by (2) we deduce that

$$(4) \qquad |S|^2 \ll N + \sum_{h=1}^{2N} \min\left(N, \frac{1}{\|h\alpha\|}\right).$$

If $\alpha = 0$ then this gives $|S|^2 \ll N^2$, which is trivial, even though the sum may be much smaller (depending on the value of β). Similarly, if α is a rational number with small denominator, or is very near to such a number, then the upper bound above is large. Thus we see that the bound above depends on the nature of the rational approximations to α. This is somewhat the true nature of things, if we are to bound $|S|$ in terms of α alone, without regard to the value of β.

We now address the problem of estimating the sum on the right hand side of (4). We begin with the special case $\alpha = a/q$ where $(a, q) = 1$. We note that

$$\sum_{h=1}^{q} \min\left(N, \frac{1}{\|ha/q\|}\right) \leq N + \sum_{h=1}^{q-1} \frac{1}{\|ha/q\|}.$$

Here the numbers ha run over all non-zero residues modulo q, so the above is

$$\ll N + \sum_{m=1}^{q-1} \frac{q}{m}$$

$$(5) \qquad \ll N + q \log q.$$

By applying this to $\leq 2N/q + 1$ blocks each of length $\leq q$, we deduce that

$$\sum_{h=1}^{2N} \min\left(N, \frac{1}{\|ha/q\|}\right) \ll \left(\frac{N}{q} + 1\right)\left(N + q\log q\right)$$

$$\ll \frac{N^2}{q} + N\log q + q\log q.$$

Since the sum in (4) is a continuous function of α, it follows that this same upper bound applies to the sum provided that α is sufficiently close to a/q. We now show that it is enough to have

$$(6) \qquad \left| \alpha - \frac{a}{q} \right| \leq \frac{1}{q^2}.$$

Suppose that α satisfies this constraint, and that $(a, q) = 1$. Let M be a fixed integer, let u be a fixed real number, and let $N(u)$ denote the number of integers n, $M < n \leq M + q$, such that $\|n\alpha - u\| \leq 1/(2q)$. Then

$$(7) \qquad \sum_{n=M+1}^{M+q} \min\left(N, \frac{1}{\|n\alpha\|}\right) \ll N + q \sum_{m=1}^{q/2} \frac{N(m/q) + N((q-m)/q)}{m}.$$

We show that

$$(8) \qquad N(u) \leq 3$$

for any u. To this end we write $\alpha = a/q + \delta$, so that $|\delta| \leq 1/q^2$. We also write $n = M + m$, $u = v + M\alpha$, so that the assertion $\|n\alpha - u\| \leq 1/(2q)$ is equivalent to $\|m\alpha - v\| \leq 1/(2q)$. Since $\|m\delta\| < q\delta \leq 1/q$, it follows by the triangle inequality that $\|ma/q - v\| < 3/(2q)$. There are at most 3 numbers of the form r/q in the interval $(v - \frac{3}{2q}, v + \frac{3}{2q})$. The number ma/q must coincide (mod 1) with one of these numbers. Thus m must fall in one of at most three residue classes (mod q). Since $0 \leq m < q$, it follows that there are at most 3 admissible values of m, and we have (8).

By inserting (8) in (7), we see that the estimate (5) still applies. By considering $\leq (H/q + 1)$ blocks of length $\leq q$, we deduce that

$$(9) \qquad \sum_{h=1}^{H} \min\left(N, \frac{1}{\|h\alpha\|}\right) \ll \frac{HN}{q} + H \log q + N + q \log q$$

provided that α satisfies (6).

By applying (9) to (4), we obtain the following fundamental result.

THEOREM 1. (Weyl) *Suppose that $P(x) = \alpha x^2 + \beta x + \gamma$ where α satisfies* (6) *for some relatively prime integers a and q. Then*

$$(10) \qquad \sum_{n=1}^{N} e\big(P(n)\big) \ll \frac{N}{\sqrt{q}} + \sqrt{N \log q} + \sqrt{q \log q}.$$

By elaborating on this method we extend this to Weyl sums of higher degree.

THEOREM 2. *Suppose that $P(x) = \sum_{j=0}^{k} \alpha_j x^j$, that $|\alpha - a/q| \leq 1/q^2$, and that $(a, q) = 1$. Then*

$$\sum_{n=1}^{N} e\big(P(n)\big) \ll_k N^{1+\epsilon} \left(\frac{1}{q} + \frac{1}{N} + \frac{q}{N^k} \right)^{\delta}$$

where $\delta = 2^{1-k}$.

Here, and similarly on subsequent occasions, the symbol $\ll_k$ is used to indicate that the implicit constant may depend on the parameter k.

PROOF. We apply the Weyl shift $k - 1$ times, after which the polynomial remaining is linear. More precisely, we square both sides of (3), and apply Cauchy's inequality to see that

$$|S|^4 \ll N^2 + N \sum_{h=1}^{N-1} \left| \sum_{n=1}^{N-h} e\big(P_h(x)\big) \right|^2$$

where $P_h(x) = P(x + h) - P(x)$. Here we have a sum over h in which the summand is the square of a Weyl sum. Thus by (3) again, the above is

$$\ll N^2 + N \sum_{h_1=1}^{N-1} \left(N + \sum_{h_2=1}^{N-h_1-1} \left| \sum_{n=1}^{N-h_1-h_2} e\big(P_{h_1}(x + h_2) - P_{h_1}(x)\big) \right| \right)$$

$$\ll N^3 + N \sum_{h_1,h_2} \left| \sum_n e\big(P_{h_1,h_2}(x)\big) \right|,$$

say. Continuing inductively, we find that

$$|S|^{2^r} \ll_r N^{2^r-1} + N^{2^r-r-1} \sum_{h_1,\ldots,h_r} \left| \sum_n e(P_{h_1,\ldots,h_r}(n)) \right|.$$

We take $r = k - 1$, and observe that $P_{h_1,\ldots,h_{k-1}}(x)$ is a linear polynomial with leading coefficient $k! h_1 h_2 \cdots h_{k-1} \alpha_k$. Thus by (2) we deduce that

$$|S|^{2^{k-1}} \ll_k N^{2^{k-1}-1} + N^{2^{k-1}-k} \sum_{h_1,\ldots,h_{k-1}} \min\left(N, \frac{1}{\|k! h_1 h_2 \cdots h_{k-1} \alpha_k\|} \right).$$

We note that the numbers $k! h_1 h_2 \cdots h_{k-1}$ lie in the interval $[1, k! N^{k-1}]$, and that the number of solutions of the equation $k! h_1 h_2 \cdots h_{k-1} = h$ is $\leq d_{k-1}(h) \ll_k h^\epsilon$. Hence the expression above is

$$\ll_k N^{2^{k-1}-1} + N^{2^{k-1}-k+\epsilon} \sum_{h=1}^{k! N^{k-1}} \min\left(N, \frac{1}{\|h \alpha_k\|} \right),$$

and by (9) this is

$$\ll_k N^{2^{k-1}-1} + N^{2^{k-1}+\epsilon} q^{-1} + N^{2^{k-1}-1+\epsilon} \log q + N^{2^{k-1}-k+\epsilon} q \log q.$$

We may suppose that $q \leq N^k$, for otherwise the proposed bound is weaker than the trivial bound $|S| \leq N$. Hence $\log q \ll_k N^\epsilon$, and we have the stated result.

To put our bounds in perspective, we now construct examples of Weyl sums that are moderately large.

THEOREM 3. *Let P be a polynomial with integral coefficients. For any positive integers N, q there exists an integer h such that*

$$\left| \sum_{n=1}^{N} e\left(\frac{P(n) + hn}{q} \right) \right| \geq \frac{N}{\sqrt{q}}.$$

PROOF. Let $c(r)$ denote the number of integers n, $1 \leq n \leq N$, such that $n \equiv r \pmod{q}$. Thus

$$\sum_{h=1}^{q} \left| \sum_{n=1}^{N} e\left(\frac{P(n) + hn}{q} \right) \right|^2 = \sum_{h=1}^{q} \left| \sum_{r=1}^{q} c(r) e\left(\frac{P(r) + hr}{q} \right) \right|^2.$$

By the orthogonality relations among the additive characters (mod q) we see that this is

$$= q \sum_{r=1}^{q} |c(r)|^2.$$

By Cauchy's inequality this is

$$\geq \left(\sum_{r=1}^{q} c(r) \right)^2 = N^2.$$

This gives the stated result.

From Theorem 3 we see that the first term in the bound (10) of Theorem 1 can not be reduced. For Weyl sums of degree $k > 2$ we now exhibit a better lower bound, but only for certain special values of q.

THEOREM 4. *Let N, k, p, a be given, with $p > k \geq 2$, $(a, q) = 1$, and p prime. Then there exists a polynomial $P \in \mathbb{R}[x]$ of degree k and leading coefficient a/p^k such that*

$$\left| \sum_{n=1}^{N} e\big(P(n)\big) \right| \geq N/p.$$

If we put $q = p^k$, then the leading coefficient is a/q, and the Weyl sum is larger than $Nq^{-1/k}$.

PROOF. We first show that

(11)
$$\sum_{n=1}^{p^k} e\left(\frac{an^k}{p^k} \right) = p^{k-1}.$$

To see this, write $n = mp^{k-1} + r$. Then $an^k \equiv akmp^{k-1}r^{k-1} + ar^k \pmod{p^k}$, so the sum is

$$\sum_{r=1}^{p^{k-1}} e\left(\frac{ar^k}{p^k} \right) \sum_{m=1}^{p} e\left(\frac{akmr^{k-1}}{p^k} \right).$$

The inner sum vanishes unless $p|r^{k-1}$, in which case $p|r$ and the inner sum is p. Thus the above is

$$p \sum_{\substack{r=1 \\ p|r}}^{p^{k-1}} e\left(\frac{ar^k}{p^k}\right) = p \cdot p^{k-2} = p^{k-1}.$$

The relation (11) gives the desired result if $N = p^k$. As for general N, we note that

$$\sum_{m=1}^{p^k} \left| \sum_{n=1}^{N} e\left(\frac{a(m+n)^k}{p^k}\right) \right| \geq \sum_{m=1}^{p^k} \Re \sum_{n=1}^{N} e\left(\frac{a(m+n)^k}{p^k}\right)$$

$$= \Re \sum_{n=1}^{N} \sum_{m=1}^{p^k} e\left(\frac{a(m+n)^k}{p^k}\right).$$

By (11) this is

$$\Re \sum_{n=1}^{N} p^{k-1} = Np^{k-1}.$$

Thus

$$\left| \sum_{n=1}^{N} e\left(\frac{a(m+n)^k}{p^k}\right) \right| \geq N/p$$

for at least one of the p^k values of m.

If the Weyl sum of a particular polynomial $P(x)$ is large, then the sum of a second polynomial $Q(x)$ may be expected to be large if its coefficients are sufficiently close to those of P. In this direction the following result is instructive.

THEOREM 5. *Suppose that* $P_{\boldsymbol{\alpha}}(x) = \sum_{j=1}^{k} \alpha_j x^j$ *is a polynomial with real coefficients. Put*

$$M(\alpha_2, \dots, \alpha_k) = \max_{\alpha_1} \left| \sum_{n=1}^{N} e\big(P_{\boldsymbol{\alpha}}(n)\big) \right|.$$

If $Q(x) = \sum_{j=1}^{k} \beta_j x^j$ *and* $\|\alpha_j - \beta_j\| \leq 1/(2N)^j$ *for* $1 \leq j \leq k$, *then*

$$M(\alpha_2, \dots, \alpha_k) \approx M(\beta_2, \dots, \beta_k).$$

PROOF. By adding suitable integers to the β_j, we may suppose that $|\alpha_j - \beta_j| \leq 1/(2N)^j$ for all j. Let f be the function with period 1 such that

$$f(x) = \begin{cases} e\big(P(2Nx) - Q(2Nx)\big) & \text{if } 0 \leq x \leq 1/2, \\ 2e\big(P(N) - Q(N)\big)(1 - x) & \text{if } 1/2 \leq x \leq 1. \end{cases}$$

Let $\widehat{f}(m)$ be the Fourier coefficient of f. Since Var $f' \ll 1$, we know that $\widehat{f}(m) \ll m^{-2}$, and hence the Fourier expansion of f converges to f, $f(x) =$

$\sum_m \widehat{f}(m)e(mx)$. Choose α so that $\left|\sum e(P(n) + \alpha n)\right| = M(\alpha_2, \ldots, \alpha_k)$. Then

$$\sum_{n=1}^{N} e(P(n) + \alpha n) = \sum_{n=1}^{N} f\left(\frac{n}{2N}\right) e(Q(n) + \alpha n)$$

$$= \sum_{n=1}^{N} e(Q(n) + \alpha n) \sum_m \widehat{f}(m) e\left(\frac{mn}{2N}\right)$$

$$= \sum_m \widehat{f}(m) \sum_{n=1}^{N} e\left(Q(n) + (\alpha + \frac{m}{2N})n\right).$$

This has absolute value

$$\leq M(\beta_2, \ldots, \beta_k) \sum_m |\widehat{f}(m)| \ll M(\beta_2, \ldots, \beta_k).$$

Thus $M(\alpha_2, \ldots, \alpha_k) \ll M(\beta_2, \ldots, \beta_k)$, and the opposite inequality follows by reversing the roles of P and Q.

The estimates of Theorems 3 & 4 are most effective when q is small, say $1 \leq q \leq N^{k/2}$. By using Theorem 5 we may construct examples of large Weyl sums with $N^{k/2} < q < N^k$.

THEOREM 6. *There is a constant $c_k > 0$ such that if $k \geq 2$ and if*

$$N^{k/2} \leq q \leq \left(\frac{N}{k \log N}\right)^k$$

then there is an integer a, $(a,q) = 1$, and a polynomial $P(x)$ of degree k with leading coefficient a/q, such that

$$\left|\sum_{n=1}^{N} e(P(n))\right| > c_k q^{1/k}.$$

PROOF. Let $\mathcal{I} = [2Nq^{-1/k}, 4Nq^{-1/k}]$. By an estimate of Chebyshev the product of all primes $p \in \mathcal{I}$ is $> \exp\left(Nq^{-1/k}\right)$, which is $\geq N^k$ since $q \leq \left(\frac{N}{k \log N}\right)^k$. Hence there is a prime $p \in \mathcal{I}$ that does not divide q. Let p be such a prime, and choose integers a and b so that $ap^k - bq = 1$. Then $(a,q) = (b,p) = 1$ and

$$\left|\frac{a}{q} - \frac{b}{p^k}\right| = \frac{1}{qp^k} \leq \frac{1}{(2N)^k}.$$

Let $Q(x)$ be a polynomial as in Theorem 4 with degree k and leading coefficient b/p^k such that $\left|\sum_n e(Q(n))\right| > N/p$. Let $P(x)$ have the same coefficients as those of $Q(x)$ except that the leading coefficient b/p^k is replaced by a/q, and the coefficient of the linear term is suitably altered. The stated result follows by Theorem 5.

In the absence of unanticipated phenomena, we might hazard a guess as to the best possible estimate of a Weyl sum.

CONJECTURE 1. *Let k be fixed, $k \geq 2$, and let ϵ be fixed, $\epsilon > 0$. If $P(x) = \sum_{j=1}^{k} \alpha_j x^j$, if $\left|\alpha_k - a/q\right| \leq 1/q^2$, and if $(a, q) = 1$, then*

$$\sum_{n=1}^{N} e\bigl(P(n)\bigr) \ll N^{1+\epsilon} \left(\frac{1}{q} + \frac{q}{N^k}\right)^{1/k}.$$

We see that when $k = 2$, the bound of Theorem 1 is best possible, apart possibly from the logarithmic factors. When $k = 3$, the bound of Theorem 2 is still not so far from the lower bounds of Theorems 3, 4, and 6. However, when k is large the bound of Theorem 2 makes very little progress toward the above Conjecture. In the next Chapter we discuss a method, originated by I. M. Vinogradov, that gives much better bounds than Theorem 2 when k is large, though it still falls considerably short of the Conjecture.

3. van der Corput's method. We consider now exponential sums

$$\sum_{n=a}^{b} e\bigl(f(n)\bigr)$$

in which f is smooth in an appropriate sense, but not necessarily a polynomial. van der Corput proposed two processes by which the problem of estimating a given exponential sum is reduced to that of estimating some other sum or family of sums. Process A proceeds by an application of van der Corput's Lemma; here the simpler Weyl shift does not suffice.

THEOREM 7. *(Process A) Let $f_h(x) = f(x + h) - f(x)$ where $f(x)$ is a real-valued function on $[a, b]$. Let H be an integer, $H \leq b - a$, such that*

$$(12) \qquad \sum_{h=1}^{H} \left| \sum_{n=a}^{b-h} e\bigl(f_h(n)\bigr) \right| \leq b - a.$$

Then

$$(13) \qquad \sum_{n=a}^{b} e\bigl(f(n)\bigr) \ll \frac{b-a}{H^{1/2}}.$$

PROOF. By van der Corput's Lemma, as found in Chapter 2, §1, we see that

$$\sum_{a}^{b} e\bigl(f(n)\bigr) \ll (b-a)H^{-1/2} + \left(\frac{b-a}{H} \sum_{h=1}^{H} \left| \sum_{n=a}^{b-h} e\bigl(f_h(n)\bigr) \right| \right)^{1/2}.$$

This gives the stated result.

As Process B is more involved, we first sketch the approach. Let $r(x) = e\bigl(f(x)\bigr)$ for $a \leq x \leq b$, $r(x) = 0$ otherwise, where a and b are integers, $a \leq b$. Then by the Poisson summation formula,

$$\sum_{a}^{b} e\bigl(f(x)\bigr) = \sum_{n} r(n) = \sum_{\nu} \widehat{r}(\nu).$$

Suppose that f' is monotonically increasing, and put $\alpha = f'(a)$, $\beta = f'(b)$. If ν lies well outside the interval $[\alpha, \beta]$ then $\widehat{r}(\nu)$ is small, but if $\nu \in [\alpha, \beta]$ then there is a point $x_\nu \in [\alpha, \beta]$ such that $f'(x_\nu) = \nu$. Hence the integral

$$\widehat{r}(\nu) = \int_a^b e(f(x) - \nu x)\, dx$$

has a stationary phase at $x = x_\nu$, and we find that

$$\widehat{r}(\nu) = \frac{e(f(x_\nu) - \nu x_\nu + 1/8)}{\sqrt{f''(x_\nu)}} + \text{error terms.}$$

For $y \in [\alpha, \beta]$, put $g(y) = f(f'^{-1}(y)) - y f'^{-1}(y)$. Then

$$\sum_a^b e(f(n)) = e(1/8) \sum_\alpha^\beta \frac{e(g(\nu))}{\sqrt{f''(x_\nu)}} + \text{error terms.}$$

Suppose that $0 < \lambda_2 \leq f''(x) \leq A\lambda_2$ for $a \leq x \leq b$. Then by partial summation, the sum above is

$$\ll \frac{1}{\sqrt{\lambda_2}} \max_{\alpha \leq \gamma \leq \beta} \left| \sum_\alpha^\gamma e(g(\nu)) \right|.$$

As the error terms are generally small enough to be ignored, we find that an estimate for the sum $\sum e(g(\nu))$ yields an estimate for the original sum $\sum e(f(n))$.

If we apply Process B to the new sum $\sum e(g(\nu))$ then we are taken back to $\sum e(f(n))$. Thus there is no point in applying this process twice in succession. Also, any bound for $\sum e(f(n))$ is equivalent to a corresponding bound for $\sum e(g(\nu))$. For example, we have the trivial bound

$$(14) \qquad \sum_\nu e(g(\nu)) \ll \beta - \alpha + 1.$$

Since $\beta - \alpha = f'(b) - f'(a) = (b-a)f''(\xi) \leq (b-a)A\lambda_2$, we deduce that

$$\sum_n e(f(n)) \ll \lambda_2^{-1/2}(A\lambda_2(b-a) + 1) \ll_A \lambda_2^{1/2}(b-a) + \lambda_2^{-1/2}.$$

This estimate may also be derived by relatively elementary reasoning. The advantage of the more elaborate analytic approach outlined above is that it offers the possibility of deriving a better estimate, if we can replace the trivial bound (14) by something smaller.

The main ingredients of Process B are contained in Theorems 8 and 9; in Theorem 10 we combine them to form Process B. To prepare for the proofs of these results we first establish two useful estimates.

LEMMA 1. *Let $r(x)$ and $\theta(x)$ be real-valued functions on $[a, b]$ such that $r(x)$ and $\theta'(x)$ are continuous. Suppose that $\theta'(x)/r(x)$ is positive and monotonically increasing on this interval. If $0 < \lambda_1 \leq \theta'(a)/r(a)$ then*

$$(15) \qquad \left| \int_a^b r(x)e(\theta(x))\, dx \right| \leq \frac{1}{\pi\lambda_1}.$$

PROOF. Let $g(x) = r(x)/\theta'(x)$. We may express the integral above as a Riemann-Stieltjes integral,

$$\frac{1}{2\pi i}\int_a^b g(x)\, de\big(\theta(x)\big).$$

On integrating by parts, we see that this is

$$= \left[\frac{g(x)e\big(\theta(x)\big)}{2\pi i}\right]_a^b - \frac{1}{2\pi i}\int_a^b e\big(\theta(x)\big)\, dg(x).$$

Hence by the triangle inequality we see that

$$\left|\int_a^b r(x)e\big(\theta(x)\big)\, dx\right| \le \frac{g(a)+g(b)}{2\pi} + \frac{1}{2\pi}\int_a^b |dg(x)|.$$

Since $g(x)$ is monotonically decreasing, this last integral has value $g(a) - g(b)$. On inserting this in the above, we obtain the stated bound.

It is instructive to view the inequality (15) and its proof geometrically. For $a \le t \le b$ let $Z(t) = \int_a^t r(x)e\big(\theta(x)\big)\, dx$. This is a curve in the complex plane, whose radius of curvature at time t is $g(t)/(2\pi)$. Since these radii are monotonically decreasing, the osculating circles are nested. Thus the initial osculating circle, of radius $g(a)/(2\pi)$, contains the entire curve. Since the point $Z(a) = 0$ lies on this initial circle, and since the distance from $Z(a)$ to $Z(b)$ is at most the diameter of this circle, we deduce that $|Z(b)| \le g(a)/\pi$.

LEMMA 2. *Let $f(x)$ be a real-valued function on $[a,b]$, and suppose that $0 < \lambda_2 \le f''(x)$ throughout this interval. Then*

$$\left|\int_a^b e\big(f(x)\big)\, dx\right| \le \frac{4}{\sqrt{\pi\lambda_2}}.$$

In Theorem 9 we see that a more precise estimate can be given for an integral of this kind, if additional hypotheses are introduced. The prototypical integral of this kind arises when $f(x) = x^2$. In Figure 1 we see that the curve $Z(t) = \int_{-\infty}^t e\big(x^2\big)\, dx$ spirals tightly, except near the inflection point at $t = 0$.

PROOF. Let $\delta > 0$ be a parameter to be determined later, and let $\mathfrak{I}$ be that portion of the interval $[a,b]$ for which $|f'(x)| \le \delta$. Thus $\mathfrak{I}$ is an interval whose length is $\le 2\delta/\lambda_2$. We estimate the contribution of this interval trivially:

$$\left|\int_{\mathfrak{I}} e\big(f(x)\big)\, dx\right| \le 2\delta/\lambda_2.$$

The complementary portion $[a,b]\setminus\mathfrak{I}$ of the interval consists of at most two intervals, to each of which we may apply Lemma 1 with $\lambda_1 = \delta$. On adding these estimates we deduce that

$$\left|\int_a^b e\big(f(x)\big)\, dx\right| \le \frac{2\delta}{\lambda_2} + \frac{2}{\pi\delta}.$$

This is minimized by taking $\delta = (\lambda_2/\pi)^{1/2}$, and we obtain the stated estimate.

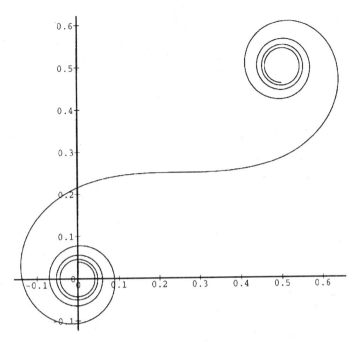

FIGURE 1.   Fresnel's Integral $Z(t) = \int_{-\infty}^{t} e(x^2)\, dx$, for $-2 \leq t \leq 2$.

THEOREM 8. (Truncated Poisson) *Let f be a real-valued function, and suppose that f' is continuous and increasing on $[a,b]$. Put $\alpha = f'(a)$, $\beta = f'(b)$. Then*

$$(16) \qquad \sum_{a \leq n \leq b} e(f(n)) = \sum_{\alpha - 1 \leq \nu \leq \beta + 1} \int_{a}^{b} e(f(x) - \nu x)\, dx + O(\log(2 + \beta - \alpha)).$$

PROOF. Let N be an integer such that $|N - (\alpha + \beta)/2| \leq 1/2$. If we replace $f(x)$ by $f(x) - Nx$ then the terms in the sum on the left are unchanged, $f'(x)$ is still continuous and increasing, and the sum on the right is unchanged, although the indexing of the terms has been translated, as α has been replaced by $\alpha' = \alpha - N$, and β has been replaced by $\beta' = \beta - N$. We note that $\alpha' + \beta' = \alpha + \beta - 2N$, so that $|\alpha' + \beta'| \leq 1$. Thus by making a change of variables of this sort, we may suppose that $|\alpha + \beta| \leq 1$.

Let $r(x) = e(f(x))$ for $a \leq x \leq b$, and put $r(x) = 0$ otherwise. Then $r \in L^1(\mathbb{R})$, and r has bounded variation on $\mathbb{R}$, so by the Poisson Summation Formula (see p. 68 of Zygmund [52]),

$$\sum_{n} \frac{r(n^+) + r(n^-)}{2} = \lim_{K \to \infty} \sum_{-K}^{K} \widehat{r}(k).$$

Since $r(x)$ is continuous apart from the possible jump discontinuities at a or b, the left hand side here is within $O(1)$ of the left hand side in (16). The integral on the right in (16) is simply $\widehat{r}(\nu)$, so to complete the proof it suffices to show that

(17)
$$\sum_{\substack{k\notin[\alpha-1,\beta+1]\\|k|\leq K}} \widehat{r}(k) \ll \log(2+\beta-\alpha)$$

for all sufficiently large K. By integrating by parts, we find that

$$\widehat{r}(k) = \frac{e\big(f(a)-ka\big)}{2\pi ik} - \frac{e\big(f(b)-kb\big)}{2\pi ik} + \frac{1}{k}\int_a^b f'(x)e\big(f(x)-kx\big)\,dx.$$

If $k > \beta$ then $(f'-k)/f'$ is increasing, so by Lemma 1 this integral is $\ll \beta/(k-\beta)$. Hence the sum of the contributions made by these integrals is

$$\ll \sum_{k>\beta+1} \frac{\beta}{k(k-\beta)} \ll \log(2+\beta).$$

We treat $k < \alpha$ similarly, and deduce that the left hand side of (17) is

$$\frac{e\big(f(a)\big)}{2\pi i} \sum_{\substack{k\notin[\alpha-1,\beta+1]\\0<|k|\leq K}} \frac{e(ka)}{k} - \frac{e\big(f(b)\big)}{2\pi i} \sum_{\substack{k\notin[\alpha-1,\beta+1]\\0<|k|\leq K}} \frac{e(kb)}{k} + O\big(\log(2+\beta-\alpha)\big).$$

Since $|\alpha+\beta| \leq 1$, we may pair each k in these sums with $-k$, except for at most one k, whose contribution is bounded. Hence the above is

$$e\big(f(b)\big) \sum_{\beta+1<k\leq K} \frac{\sin 2\pi kb}{\pi k} - e\big(f(a)\big) \sum_{\beta+1<k\leq K} \frac{\sin 2\pi ka}{\pi k} + O\big(\log(2+\beta-\alpha)\big).$$

By using partial summation we know that the Fourier series $\sum \frac{1}{k}\sin 2\pi kx$ is boundedly convergent. Thus the sums above are uniformly $O(1)$. Hence we have (17), and the proof is complete.

We now address the problem of refining the estimate given by Lemma 2. Suppose that $g(x)$ is a real-valued function, that $g'(x_0) = 0$ for some $x_0 \in [a,b]$, and that

(18)
$$0 < \lambda_2 \leq g''(x)$$

throughout this interval. Let $q(x)$ be the quadratic Taylor approximation to $g(x)$ at x_0,

$$q(x) = g(x_0) + \frac{1}{2}g''(x_0)(x-x_0)^2.$$

We expect that $q(x)$ gives a good approximation to $g(x)$, at least when x is near x_0. Consider the idealized situation in which $g(x)$ is exactly $q(x)$. By an easy calculation we see that

$$\int_{-\infty}^{\infty} e\big(q(x)\big)\,dx = \frac{e\big(g(x_0)+1/8\big)}{\sqrt{g''(x_0)}}.$$

As $q'(x)$ is increasing, we see by Lemma 1 with $\lambda_1 = \lambda_2(b - x_0)$ that

$$\int_b^\infty e\big(q(x)\big)\,dx \ll \frac{1}{\lambda_2(b - x_0)}.$$

If x_0 is near b then this estimate is weak, and we use Lemma 2 instead to see that

$$\int_b^\infty e\big(q(x)\big)\,dx \ll \frac{1}{\sqrt{\lambda_2}}.$$

We may treat $\int_{-\infty}^a \cdots$ similarly, and thus we find that

$$(19) \qquad \int_a^b e\big(q(x)\big)\,dx = \frac{e\big(g(x_0) + 1/8\big)}{\sqrt{g''(x_0)}} + O(R_1)$$

where

$$(20) \qquad R_1 = \min\left(\frac{1}{\lambda_2(x_0 - a)}, \frac{1}{\sqrt{\lambda_2}}\right) + \min\left(\frac{1}{\lambda_2(b - x_0)}, \frac{1}{\sqrt{\lambda_2}}\right).$$

In the general situation, $g(x)$ is not a quadratic polynomial, but if the higher derivatives of g are not too large then the expression above provides a good approximation to the integral in question.

THEOREM 9. (Stationary Phase) *Let $g(x)$ be a real-valued function on $[a,b]$, and suppose that $g'(x_0) = 0$ for some $x_0 \in [a,b]$. We suppose that (18) holds throughout this interval, and in addition that $|g^{(3)}(x)| \le \lambda_3$ and that $|g^{(4)}(x)| \le \lambda_4$ for all $x \in [a,b]$. Then*

$$(21) \qquad \int_a^b e\big(g(x)\big)\,dx = \frac{e\big(g(x_0) + 1/8\big)}{\sqrt{g''(x_0)}} + O(R_1) + O(R_2)$$

where R_1 is given by (20) and

$$(22) \qquad R_2 = (b - a)\lambda_2^{-2}\lambda_4 + (b - a)\lambda_2^{-3}\lambda_3^2.$$

If instead of (18) we have

$$(23) \qquad g''(x) \le -\lambda_2 < 0$$

then we apply Theorem 9 to $-g(x)$, and take complex conjugates in (21). This gives a similar results, but the main term must be replaced by

$$(24) \qquad \frac{e\big(g(x_0) - 1/8\big)}{\sqrt{|g''(x_0)|}}.$$

If $(b-a)\sqrt{\lambda_2} < 1$ then Theorem 9 offers no improvement on Lemma 2. Suppose that

$$(25) \qquad (b - a)\sqrt{\lambda_2} \ge 1.$$

In most applications,

$$(26) \qquad \lambda_3 \ll \lambda_2(b - a)^{-1}, \qquad \lambda_4 \ll \lambda_2(b - a)^{-2}.$$

From these inequalities and (25) it follows that $R_2 \ll R_1$.

PROOF. We multiply both sides of (21) by $e\big(-g(x_0)\big)$ to reduced to the case $g(x_0) = 0$. Similarly, we may translate coordinates so that $x_0 = 0$. We write $g(x) = q(x) + r(x)$. From Taylor's formula with the remainder expressed as an integral we see that

(27)
$$r(x) = \frac{1}{2}x^3 \int_0^1 (1-u)^2 g^{(3)}(xu)\, du.$$

Similarly, $r'(x)$ is the linear Taylor approximation to $g'(x)$, and hence

(28)
$$r'(x) = x^2 \int_0^1 (1-u) g^{(3)}(xu)\, du.$$

In view of (19), it suffices to show that

(29)
$$\int_a^b e\big(q(x)\big)\Big(e\big(r(x)\big) - 1\Big)\, dx \ll R_1 + R_2.$$

By integrating by parts we find that this integral is

(30)
$$\left[\frac{e\big(q(x)\big)\Big(e\big(r(x)\big) - 1\Big)}{2\pi i g''(0)x} \right]_a^b$$
$$- \frac{1}{g''(0)} \int_a^b e\big(q(x)\big) \left[\frac{e\big(r(x)\big)r'(x)}{x} - \frac{e\big(r(x)\big) - 1}{2\pi i x^2} \right] dx.$$

Here the upper endpoint contributes an amount

$$\ll \frac{1}{g''(0)b} \ll R_1,$$

and the lower endpoint is treated similarly. We now write the integral in (30) as $T_1 - T_2$, where T_1 arises from the first term in the brackets, and T_2 from the second.

To treat T_1 we let $h(x) = r'(x)/x^2$, $j(x) = g'(x)/x$, and note that

$$T_1 = \int_a^b \frac{h(x)}{j(x)} e\big(g(x)\big) g'(x)\, dx$$

On integrating by parts, we see that this is

$$= \left[\frac{h(x)e\big(g(x)\big)}{j(x)2\pi i} \right]_a^b - \int_a^b \frac{d}{dx}\left(\frac{h(x)}{j(x)} \right) \frac{e\big(g(x)\big)}{2\pi i}\, dx.$$

Since $h(x)$ is the integral in (28), we see that $h(x) \ll \lambda_3$. By differentiating this integral with respect to x, we also see that $h'(x) \ll \lambda_4$. Similarly, $j(x) = \int_0^1 g''(xu)\, du \geq \lambda_2$ by (18), and $j'(x) = \int_0^1 u g^{(3)}(xu)\, du \ll \lambda_3$. Hence

$$\frac{d}{dx}\left(\frac{h}{j} \right) = \frac{h'}{j} - \frac{hj'}{j^2} \ll \lambda_4 \lambda_2^{-1} + \lambda_3^2 \lambda_2^{-2},$$

so that

$$T_1 \ll \lambda_2^{-1}\lambda_3 + \lambda_4\lambda_2^{-1}(b-a) + \lambda_3^2\lambda_2^{-2}(b-a).$$

To bound T_2, let $\mathfrak{I} = [c,d]$ denote that portion of the interval $[a,b]$ for which $|x| \le \delta$, where δ is a parameter to be determined later, and let $\mathfrak{J}$ be the complement, $\mathfrak{J} = [a,b] \setminus \mathfrak{I}$. Put $k(x) = r(x)/x^3$. From (27) we see that $k(x) \ll \lambda_3$, and that $k'(x) \ll \lambda_4$. Set $m(x) = \big(e(x)-1\big)/x$. Then $m(x) \ll 1$, and $m'(x) \ll 1$. The contribution of $\mathfrak{I}$ to T_2 is

$$\int_c^d \Big(e\big(q(x)\big)x\Big)\Big(m\big(r(x)\big)k(x)\Big)\,dx.$$

By integrating by parts we see that this is

$$= \left[\frac{e\big(q(x)\big)}{2\pi i g''(0)} m\big(r(x)\big)k(x) \right]_c^d$$

$$- \frac{1}{2\pi i g''(0)} \int_c^d e\big(q(x)\big)\Big(m'\big(r(x)\big)r'(x)k(x) + m\big(r(x)\big)k'(x)\Big)\,dx$$

$$\ll \lambda_2^{-1}\lambda_3 + \lambda_2^{-1}\int_c^d \lambda_3^2 x^2 + \lambda_4 \,dx$$

$$\ll \lambda_2^{-1}\lambda_3 + \lambda_2^{-1}\lambda_3^2(d^3 - c^3) + \lambda_2^{-1}\lambda_4(d-c)$$

$$\ll \lambda_2^{-1}\lambda_3 + \lambda_2^{-1}\lambda_3^2\delta^3 + \lambda_2^{-1}\lambda_4(b-a).$$

As for the contribution of $\mathfrak{J}$, we note that $\mathfrak{J}$ consists of at most two intervals. We consider separately the integrals $\int_{\mathfrak{J}} e(g(x))/x^2 \,dx$, $\int_{\mathfrak{J}} e(q(x))/x^2 \,dx$. To apply Lemma 1 to the first of these integrals we must consider the quantity $g'(x)x^2$. The absolute value of this is bounded below by $\lambda_2\delta^3$, and the quantity is increasing since its derivative is $g''(x)x^2 + 2g'(x)x > 0$. Hence by Lemma 1, the first of these integrals is $\ll \lambda_2^{-1}\delta^{-3}$. We similarly apply Lemma 1 to the second of these integral, which gives rise to the expression $q'(x)x^2 = g''(0)x^3$. This is monotonically increasing, and has modulus bounded below by $\lambda_2\delta^3$. Hence by Lemma 1, the second of these integrals is also $\ll \lambda_2^{-1}\delta^{-3}$. On combining these estimates, we conclude that

$$T_2 \ll \lambda_2^{-1}\lambda_3 + \lambda_2^{-1}\lambda_3^2\delta^3 + \lambda_2^{-1}\lambda_4(b-a) + \lambda_2^{-1}\delta^{-3}.$$

To optimize this estimate we take $\delta = \lambda_3^{-1/3}$. We combine this with our estimate of T_1 to see that the integral (29) is

$$\ll R_1 + \lambda_2^{-1}(T_1 + T_2)$$

$$\ll R_1 + \lambda_2^{-2}\lambda_3 + \lambda_2^{-2}\lambda_4(b-a) + \lambda_2^{-3}\lambda_3^2(b-a).$$

Put $U = \lambda_2^{-1}(b-a)^{-1}$. We may suppose that $U \ll R_1$, for otherwise $R_1 \approx \lambda_2^{-1/2}$ and the stated estimate is immediate from Lemma 2. We observe that the second term above is the geometric mean of U and the fourth term above. Hence it is majorized by the maximum of the first term and the fourth term, and therefore may be omitted. This completes the proof.

By taking $g(x) = f(x) - \nu x$, and summing over ν, we achieve our goal.

THEOREM 10. (Process B) *Let A be a positive absolute constant. Suppose that $f(x)$ is a real-valued function such that $0 < \lambda_2 \leq f''(x) \leq A\lambda_2$ for all $x \in [a, b]$, and suppose that $|f^{(3)}(x)| \leq A\lambda_2(b - a)^{-1}$ and that $|f^{(4)}(x)| \leq A\lambda_2(b - a)^{-2}$ throughout this interval. Put $f'(a) = \alpha$, $f'(b) = \beta$. For integers $\nu \in [\alpha, \beta]$ let x_ν be the root of the equation $f'(x) = \nu$. Then*

(31)
$$\sum_{a \leq n \leq b} e\big(f(n)\big) = e(1/8) \sum_{\alpha \leq \nu \leq \beta} \frac{e\big(f(x_\nu) - \nu x_\nu\big)}{\sqrt{f''(x_\nu)}} + O\big(\log(2 + \beta - \alpha)\big) + O(\lambda_2^{-1/2}).$$

Here the second error term is the same size as that of any particular term in the sum on the right, while the first error term is only slightly larger than the size of the terms in the sum on the left.

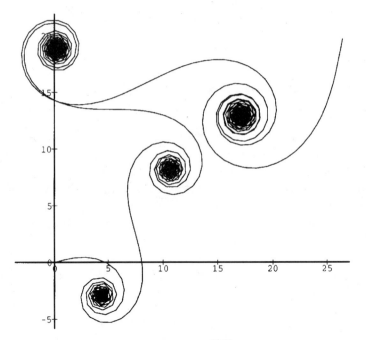

FIGURE 2. Partial sums of $\sum_{n=1001}^{2000} e(8000 \log n)$.

The geometric significance of Process B is particularly apparent when $\beta - \alpha$ is large, but much smaller than $b - a$. In Figure 2, the sum $\sum_{n=1001}^{2000} e(8000 \log n)$ is depicted as a chain of unit vectors in the complex plane. When f' is near an integer, two consecutive terms are nearly equal, and several consecutive vectors will pull in the same direction. For $f(x) = 8000 \log x$, this happens when n is near 1000, near 1143, near 1333, near 1500, and near 2000. On the other hand, if f' is approximately $\nu + 1/2$ for some integer ν, then each term is approximately the negative of the preceding one, and there is tremendous cancellation. This occurs when n is near 1067, near 1231, near 1455, and near 1778. Indeed, in each of the ranges $1067 \leq n \leq 1231$, $1231 \leq n \leq 1455$, $1455 \leq n \leq 1778$ the partial sums resemble a scaled and rotated copy of the graph of Fresnel's integral (recall Figure 1). In Theorem 10 we see that such a way of thinking can be made rigorous.

In general, the fractional parts of the numbers $f(x_\nu) - \nu x_\nu$ are widely dispersed, so that the right hand side of (31) involves an exponential sum in which the degree of cancellation remains to be determined. However, we can contrive examples to the contrary. If $f(x) = (x/3)^{3/2}$ then $f(x_\nu) - \nu x_\nu = -4\nu^3 \in \mathbb{Z}$, and there is no cancellation on the right hand side in (31). By applying Theorem 10, one may show that

$$\sum_{n=1}^{N} e((n/3)^{3/2}) = 2^{1/4} 3^{-3/2} N^{3/4} + O(N^{1/4}).$$

Partial sums of this series are depicted below.

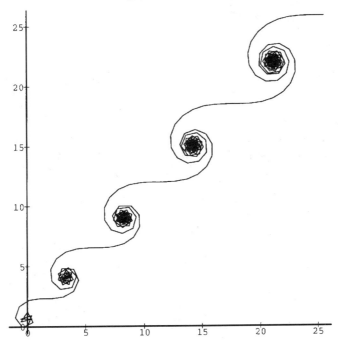

FIGURE 3. The sum $\sum_{n=1}^{300} e((n/3)^{3/2})$.

At the opposite extreme, if we take $f(x) = (2x/3)^{3/2}$, then $f(x_\nu) - \nu x_\nu = -\nu^3/2$, so that $e(f(x_\nu) - \nu x_\nu) = (-1)^\nu$, and hence

$$\sum_{n=1}^{N} e((2n/3)^{3/2}) \ll N^{1/4}.$$

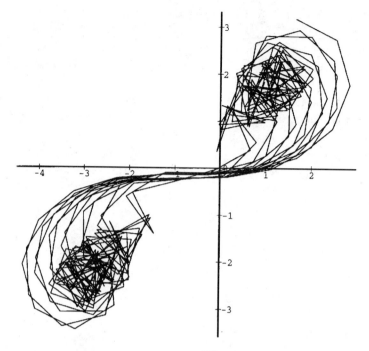

FIGURE 4. The sum $\sum_{n=1}^{300} e\big((2n/3)^{3/2}\big)$.

4. Exponent pairs. Among the sums to which van der Corput's processes might be applied, in connection with the Riemann zeta function we would like to bound sums of the form $\sum e(c \log n)$. The 'Dirichlet divisor problem' asks for an estimate of the error term $\Delta(x)$ in the asymptotic relation

$$(32) \qquad \sum_{n \leq x} d(n) = x \log x + (2\gamma - 1)x + \Delta(x).$$

Since

$$\Delta(x) = -2 \sum_{n \leq \sqrt{x}} ((x/n)) + O(1)$$

where

$$((u)) = \{u\} - \frac{1}{2} = -\sum_{k \neq 0} \frac{e(ku)}{2\pi i k},$$

this leads us to seek bounds for sums of the form $\sum e(c/n)$. Similarly, in connection with the distribution of squarefree numbers we wish to bound $\sum e(c/n^2)$. In all these cases the function f that arises has the property that $f'(x) = T/x^\sigma$ for some $T > 0$, $\sigma > 0$. (This last inequality is critical, as it eliminates from consideration the bizarre situations displayed in Figures 3 and 4.) If we put $f_h(x) = f(x + h) - f(x)$ then f_h is no longer of this form, though it is approximately of this form. We now describe the class of functions that we are willing to consider.

DEFINITION 1. *Let N and R be positive integers, and let σ, T, δ be positive real numbers. We let $\mathcal{F}(N, \sigma, T; R, \delta)$ denote the family of those functions $f(x)$ with domain $[a, b] \subseteq [N, 2N]$, with R continuous derivatives on $[a, b]$, and such that if $0 \leq r < R$ then*

$$(33) \quad \left| f^{(r+1)}(x) - (-1)^r \sigma(\sigma+1) \cdots (\sigma+r) T x^{-\sigma-r} \right| \leq \delta \sigma(\sigma+1) \cdots (\sigma+r) T x^{-\sigma-r}$$

uniformly for $a \leq x \leq b$.

After a little experimentation with van der Corput's processes, one finds that for functions of the type described above the bound obtained always takes the shape

$$(34) \qquad \sum_a^b e\big(f(n)\big) \ll \big(\max |f'|\big)^k N^l,$$

at least when $\max |f'| \gg 1$. The pairs (k, l) for which such an estimate is established all lie in the square

$$(35) \qquad 0 \leq k \leq \frac{1}{2} \leq l \leq 1.$$

We formalize this as follows.

DEFINITION 2. *The pair (k, l) lying in the square (35) is called an* exponent pair *if for each $\sigma > 0$ there is a $\delta = \delta(k, l, \sigma)$ and a positive integer $R = R(k, l, \sigma)$ such that if $N \geq 1$, $T \geq N^\sigma$ then*

$$\sum_a^b e\big(f(n)\big) \ll \left(\frac{T}{N^\sigma}\right)^k N^l$$

uniformly for all $f \in \mathcal{F}(N, \sigma, T; R, \delta)$. (The implicit constant may depend only on k, l, σ.)

By using Process A we discover that if (k, l) is an exponent pair then so also is $\left(\frac{k}{2k+2}, \frac{k+l+1}{2k+2}\right)$. By applying Process B we find that if (k, l) is an exponent pair then so also is $(l - 1/2, k + 1/2)$. In view of the trivial bound $\left| \sum_{a \leq n \leq b} e\big(f(n)\big) \right| \leq N$, we see that $(0, 1)$ is an exponent pair. Hence by Process B, $(1/2, 1/2)$ is an exponent pair. By applying Process A to this pair we obtain the exponent pair $(1/6, 2/3)$. Some further exponent pairs are exhibited in Table 1.

Suppose that (k, l) is an exponent pair. If $k \leq k' \leq 1/2$ and $l \leq l' \leq 1/2$ then (k', l') is clearly an exponent pair, because the associated estimate is weaker. Suppose that (k_1, l_1) and (k_2, l_2) are exponent pairs, and choose $t \in [0, 1]$. Then

$$\left| \sum e\big(f(n)\big) \right| = \left| \sum e\big(f(n)\big) \right|^t \left| \sum e\big(f(n)\big) \right|^{1-t}$$

$$\ll \left(\left(\frac{T}{N^\sigma}\right)^{k_1} N^{l_1} \right)^t \left(\left(\frac{T}{N^\sigma}\right)^{k_2} N^{l_2} \right)^{1-t}$$

$$= \left(\frac{T}{N^\sigma}\right)^{tk_1 + (1-t)k_2} N^{tl_1 + (1-t)l_2}.$$

TABLE 1. Some Exponent Pairs.

k	l	OPERATION
0/1	1/1	
1/254	247/254	$AAAAAAB$
1/126	20/21	$AAAAAB$
1/86	161/172	$AAAABAAB$
1/62	57/62	$AAAAB$
1/50	181/200	$AAABABAAB$
1/42	25/28	$AAABAAB$
2/53	181/212	$AABABAAAB$
1/24	27/32	$AABABAAB$
1/22	101/121	$AABABABAAB$
1/20	33/40	$AABAAB$
13/238	97/119	$AABAABAAB$
11/186	25/31	$AABAAAB$
4/49	75/98	$ABABAAAB$
11/128	97/128	$ABABAABAAB$
1/11	3/4	$ABABAAB$
1/10	81/110	$ABABABAAB$
13/106	75/106	$ABAABAAB$
11/86	181/258	$ABAABABAAB$
11/78	161/234	$ABAAABAAB$
22/117	25/39	$BABAAABAAB$
26/129	27/43	$BABAABABAAB$
11/53	33/53	$BABAABAAB$
13/55	3/5	$BABABABAAB$
1/4	13/22	$BABABAAB$
33/128	75/128	$BABABAABAAB$
13/49	57/98	$BABABAAAB$
19/62	52/93	$BAABAAAB$
75/238	66/119	$BAABAABAAB$
13/40	11/20	$BAABAAB$
81/242	6/11	$BAABABABAAB$
11/32	13/24	$BAABABAAB$
75/212	57/106	$BAABABAAAB$
11/28	11/21	$BAAABAAB$
81/200	13/25	$BAAABABAAB$
13/31	16/31	$BAAAAB$
75/172	22/43	$BAAAABAAB$
19/42	32/63	$BAAAAAB$
60/127	64/127	$BAAAAAAB$
1/2	1/2	B

Thus $(tk_1 + (1-t)k_2, tl_1, (1-t)l_2)$ is an exponent pair, we see that the set of exponent pairs is a convex set. In the negative direction, it is not difficult to show that $(0, l)$ is not an exponent pair if $l < 1$, and that $(k, 1/2)$ is not an exponent pair if $k < 1/2$. Otherwise we expect that all points in the square (35) to be exponent pairs. This is equivalent to

CONJECTURE 2. *For every $\epsilon > 0$, $(\epsilon, 1/2 + \epsilon)$ is an exponent pair.*

From the theory of the Riemann zeta function it is known that if (k, l) is an exponent pair then

$$\zeta(\frac{1}{2} + it) \ll t^\theta \log t$$

for $t \geq 2$, where $\theta = (k + l - 1/2)/2$. Moreover, the log factor can be omitted if $l > k$. The pair $(1/6, 2/3)$ gives $\theta = 1/6$, and the exponent pair $(11/82, 57/82)$ gives $\theta = 27/164$. Conjecture 2 implies the Lindelöf Hypothesis, which asserts that we may take θ arbitrarily small. Conjecture 2 also yields the best possible exponent in the divisor problem (32), namely $\Delta(x) \ll x^{1/4+\epsilon}$.

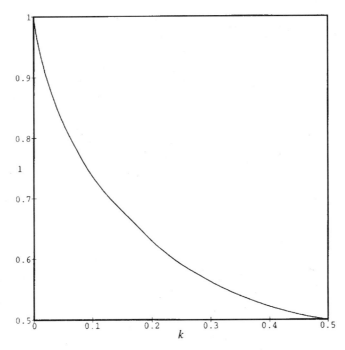

FIGURE 5. Boundary of the set of Exponent Pairs obtainable by van der Corput's processes.

The exponent pairs (k, l) that can be established by using Processes A and B form a proper subset of the square (35); the boundary of this region is depicted in Figure 5. For many years these were the only known exponent pairs, but recently a small advance has been achieved. Bombieri and Iwaniec [2] introduced a new idea that allowed them to show that

$$\zeta(\frac{1}{2} + it) \ll t^{9/56+\epsilon}.$$

Huxley and Watt [27] used this idea to show, more generally, that $(9/56 + \epsilon, 37/56 + \epsilon)$ is an exponent pair. This pair cannot be attained using only Processes A and B, but by starting with this pair one can generate further new pairs, using these processes. In Figure 6 the boundary of the new larger region of exponent pairs is drawn, next to the old boundary. The improvement is slight, but we do see that there are exponent pairs beyond those generated by Processes A and B.

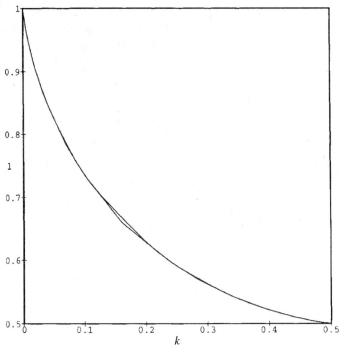

FIGURE 6. Boundary of the set of Exponent Pairs derived from the pair $(9/56 + \epsilon, 37/56 + \epsilon)$.

5. Notes. §2. Weyl's method is found in the original papers of Weyl [50, 51]. For further discussion on this topic, see Heath-Brown [16], Loxton [31], Loxton and Vaughan [32], and Vaughan [45, 46].

§3. van der Corput developed his method in a series of papers; see van der Corput [3–8] and van der Corput and Koksma [9]. Other early accounts are found in Nieland [37], Walfisz [47]. It was Titchmarsh [40] who gave the two processes their names. Titchmarsh [41–43] also extended the method to deal with two-dimensional sums. A full account of van der Corput's method has been given by Graham and Kolesnik [14]. The truncated form of the Poisson summation formula (Theorem 8) was derived by van der Corput [3], and is familiar as Lemma 4.7 of Titchmarsh [**44**]. In estimating the integral with a stationary phase (as we have done in Theorem 9), van der Corput [**4**] made no use of the fourth derivative, and obtained the larger error term $O(\lambda_2^{-4/5}\lambda_3^{1/5})$ in place of our R_2. Heath-Brown (see pp. 90–91 of Titchmarsh [**44**]) has noted that an alternative argument gives an error term $O(\lambda_2^{-1}\lambda_3^{1/3})$. The advantage of Theorem 9 is that it yields the good error terms in Theorem 10 that had been obtained previously only under additional assumptions involving analyticity, as in Heath-Brown [**15**]. A stronger version of Theorem 9 is found in an obscure monograph of S. H. Min, and also in a forthcoming monograph on exponential sums by M. N. Huxley. Deshouillers [**12**] has discussed curves similar to those in Figures 3 and 4. For further consideration of the geometric aspects of the partial sums of a series see Berry and Goldberg [**1**], Coutsias and Kazarinoff [**10**], Dekking and Mendes-France [**11**], Mendes-France [**33–35**], and Moore and van der Poorten [**36**].

§4. Exponent pairs were invented by van der Corput; the approach was refined by Phillips [**38**]. Rankin [**39**] considered the problem of finding the optimal sequence of operations when the object is to minimize $k + l$, and Graham [**13**] has developed tools for dealing with such issues. For further developments arising from the initiative of Bombieri and Iwaniec, see Heath-Brown and Huxley [**18**], Huxley [**19–25**], Huxley and Kolesnik [**26**], Huxley and Watt [**28**, **29**], Iwaniec and Mozzochi [**30**], and Watt [**49**].

References

1. M. V. Berry and J. Goldberg, *Renormalization of curlicues*, Nonlinearity **1** (1988), 1–26.

2. E. Bombieri and H. Iwaniec, *On the order of* $\zeta(\frac{1}{2} + it)$, Ann. Scuola Norm. Sup. Pisa Cl. Sci. (4) **13** (1986), 449–472.

3. J. G. van der Corput, *Zahlentheoretische Abschätzungen*, Math. Ann. **84** (1921), 53–79.

4. _____, *Verschärfung der Abschätzung beim Teilerproblem*, Math. Ann. **87** (1922), 39–65.

5. _____, *Neue zahlentheoretische Abschätzungen, erste Mitteilung*, Math. Ann. **89** (1923), 215–254.

6. _____, *Zum Teilerproblem*, Math. Ann. **98** (1928), 697–716.

7. _____, *Zahlentheoretische Abschätzungen, mit Anwendung auf Gitterpunkt-probleme*, Math. Zeit. **28** (1928), 301–310.

8. _____, *Neue zahlentheoretische Abschätzungen, zweite Mitteilung*, Math. Zeit. **29** (1929), 397–426.

9. J. G. van der Corput and J. F. Koksma, *Sur l'ordre de grandeur de la fonction* $\zeta(s)$ *de Riemann dans la bande critique*, Annales de Toulouse (3) **22** (1930), 1–39.

10. E. A. Coutsias and N. D. Kazarinoff, *Disorder, Renormalizability, Theta functions, and Cornu Spirals*, Physica D **26D** (1987), 295–310.

11. F. M. Dekking and M. Mendes-France, *Uniform distribution modulo one: a geometrical viewpoint*, J. Reine Angew. Math. **329** (1981), 143–153.

12. J.-M. Deshouillers, *Geometric aspect of Weyl sums*, Elementary and Analytic Theory of Numbers, Banach Center Pub. 17, PWN Polish Sci. Pub., Warsaw, 1985, pp. 75–82.

13. S. W. Graham, *An algorithm for computing optimal exponent pairs*, J. London Math. Soc. (2) **33** (1986), 203–218.

14. S. W. Graham and G. Kolesnik, *van der Corput's method of exponential sums*, Cambridge University Press, Cambridge, 1991.

15. D. R. Heath-Brown, *The Pjateckiĭ-Šapiro prime number theorem*, J. Number Theory **16** (1983), 242–266.

16. _____, *Weyl's inequality, Hua's inequality, and Waring's problem*, J. London Math. Soc. (2) **38** (1988), 216–230.

17. _____, *The fractional part of αn^k*, Mathematika **35** (1988), 28–37.

18. D. R. Heath-Brown and M. N. Huxley, *Exponential sums with a difference*, Proc. London Math. Soc. (3) **61** (1990), 227–250.

19. M. N. Huxley, *Exponential sums and the Riemann zeta function*, Theorie des nombres (Quebec, 1987), de Gruyter, Berlin, 1989, pp. 417–423.

20. _____, *The fractional parts of a smooth sequence*, Mathematika **35** (1988), 292–296.

21. _____, *Modular functions and trigonometric sums*, Automorphic functions and their applications (Khabarovsk, 1988), Acad. Sci. USSR, Inst. Appl. Math. Khabarovsk, 1990, pp. 186–194.

22. _____, *Exponential sums and lattice points*, Proc. London Math. Soc. (3) **60** (1990), 471–502; *Corrigenda* **66** (1993), 70; *II* (3) **66** (1993), 279–301.

23. _____, *Exponential sums after Bombieri and Iwaniec*, Journées Arithmétiques (Luminy, 1989), Astérisque (1991), No. 198–200, 165–175.

24. _____, *Exponential sums and rounding error*, J. London Math. Soc. (2) **43** (1991), 367–384.

25. _____, *Exponential sums and the Riemann zeta function IV*, Proc. London Math. Soc. (3) **66** (1993), 1–40.

26. M. N. Huxley and G. Kolesnik, *Exponential sums and the Riemann zeta function III*, Proc. London Math. Soc. (3) **62** (1991), 449–468; *Corrigenda* **66** (1993), 302.

27. M. N. Huxley and N. Watt, *Exponential sums and the Riemann zeta function*, Proc. London Math. Soc. (3) **57** (1988), 1–24.

28. _____, *Exponential sums with a parameter*, Proc. London Math. Soc. (3) **59** (1989), 233–252.

29. _____, *The Hardy-Littlewood method for exponential sums*, Number Theory, Vol. I (Budapest, 1987), North-Holland, Amsterdam, 1990, pp. 173–191.

30. H. Iwaniec and C. J. Mozzochi, *On the divisor and circle problems*, J. Number Theory **29** (1988), 60–93.

31. J. H. Loxton, *The distribution of exponential sums*, Mathematika **32** (1985), 16–25.

32. J. H. Loxton and R. C. Vaughan, *The estimation of complete exponential sums*, Canadian Math. Bull. **28** (1985), 440–454.

33. M. Mendes-France, *Entropy of curves and uniform distribution*, Topics in Classical Number Theory (Budapest, 1981), North-Holland, Amsterdam, 1984, pp. 1051–1067.

34. _____, *Entropie, dimension et thermodynamique des courbes planes*, Séminar de Théorie du Nombres (Paris, 1981–1982), Séminar Delange-Pisot-Poitou, Birkhäuser Verlag, Boston, 1983, pp. 153–177.

35. _____, *Folding paper and thermodynamics*, Phys. Rep. **103** (1984), 161–172.

36. R. R. Moore and A. J. van der Poorten, *On the Thermodynamics of curves and other curlicues*, Miniconference on Geometry and Physics (Canberra, 1989), Proc. Center Math. Anal. Australian Nat. Univ. 22, 1989, pp. 82–109.

37. L. W. Nieland, *Zum Kreisproblem*, Math. Ann. **98** (1928), 717–736.

38. E. Phillips, *The zeta-function of Riemann; further developments of van der Corput's method*, Quart. J. Math. **4** (1933), 209–225.

39. R. A. Rankin, *van der Corput's method and the method of exponent pairs*, Quart. J. Math. (2) **6** (1955), 147–153.

40. E. C. Titchmarsh, *On van der Corput's method and the zeta-function of Riemann, II*, Quart. J. Math. **2** (1931), 313-320.

41. _____, *On Epstein's zeta-function*, Proc. London Math. Soc. (2) **36** (1934), 485–500.

42. _____, *The lattice-points in a circle*, Proc. London Math. Soc. (2) **38** (1935), 96–115; *Corrigendum*, 555.

43. _____, *On the order of $\zeta(\frac{1}{2} + it)$*, Quart. J. Math. **13** (1942), 11–17.

44. _____, *The Theory of the Riemann Zeta-Function, Second Edition* (D. R. Heath-Brown, ed.), Oxford University Press, Oxford, 1986.

45. R. C. Vaughan, *The Hardy-Littlewood Method*, Cambridge Tract 80, Cambridge University Press, Cambridge, 1981.

46. _____, *Some remarks on Weyl sums*, Topics in classical number theory (Budapest, 1981), North-Holland, Amsterdam, 1984, pp. 1585–1602.

47. A. Walfisz, *Zur Abschätzung von $\zeta(\frac{1}{2} + it)$*, Nachr. Akad. Wiss. Göttingen (1924), 155–158.

48. _____, *Weylsche Exponentialsummen in der neueren Zahlentheorie*, Deutcher Verlag Wiss., Berlin, 1963.

49. N. Watt, *Exponential sums and the Riemann zeta-function II*, J. London Math. Soc. (2) **39** (1989), 385–404.

50. H. Weyl, *Über ein Problem aus dem Gebiete der diophantischen Approximationen*, Nachr. Ges. Wiss. Göttingen, Math.-phys. Kl. (1914), 234–244;

Gesammelte Abhandlungen, Band I, Springer-Verlag, Berlin-Heidelberg-New York, 1968, pp. 487–497.

51. _____, *Über die Gleichverteilung von Zahlen mod. Eins*, Math. Ann. **77** (1916), 313–352; Gesammelte Abhandlungen, Band I, Springer-Verlag, Berlin-Heidelberg-New York, 1968, pp. 563–599; Selecta Hermann Weyl, Birkhäuser Verlag, Basel-Stuttgart, 1956, pp. 111–147.

52. A. Zygmund, *Trigonometric Series, Vol. I*, Second Edition, Cambridge University Press, Cambridge, 1968.

Chapter 4. Exponential sums II: Vinogradov's Method

1. Introduction. We now develop a method invented by I. M. Vinogradov for estimating the Weyl sums $\sum_{n=1}^{N} e(P(n))$. Vinogradov's method provides estimates superior to those of Weyl when $\deg P$ is large (say > 10 or so). Vinogradov took his motivation from the following argument of Mordell.

THEOREM 1. (Mordell) *Let* $P(x) = \sum_{j=1}^{k} c_j x^j$ *be a polynomial with integral coefficients. If* p *is prime,* $p > k \geq 2$, $p \nmid c_k$, *then*

$$\sum_{n=1}^{p} e\left(\frac{P(n)}{p}\right) \ll \sqrt{k}\, p^{1-1/k}.$$

The polynomial $P(x)$ considered above has constant term 0. This occasions no loss of generality, since a non-zero constant term would merely multiply the exponential sum by a unimodular constant.

PROOF. Write $\mathbf{a} = (a_1, \ldots, a_k)$, put $P(x, \mathbf{a}) = \sum_{j=1}^{k} a_j x^j$, and set

$$S(\mathbf{a}) = \sum_{n=1}^{p} e\left(P(n, \mathbf{a})/p\right).$$

We first show that

(1) $$\sum_{\mathbf{a}} |S(\mathbf{a})|^{2k} \leq k!\, p^{2k}$$

where the sum is over all k-tuples $\mathbf{a}$ for which $1 \leq a_j \leq p$ for $1 \leq j \leq k$. Put $s_j(\mathbf{m}) = m_1^j + \cdots + m_k^j$. On multiplying out the power and inverting the order of summation, we find that the left hand side is

(2) $$\sum_{m_1=1}^{p} \cdots \sum_{m_k=1}^{p} \sum_{n_1=1}^{p} \cdots \sum_{n_k=1}^{p} \prod_{j=1}^{k} \left(\sum_{a_j=1}^{p} e\left(\frac{(s_j(\mathbf{m}) - s_j(\mathbf{n}))a_j}{p}\right) \right).$$

The sum over a_j vanishes unless $s_j(\mathbf{m}) \equiv s_j(\mathbf{n}) \pmod{p}$. Thus the above is

(3) $$p^k \sum_{\substack{\mathbf{m},\mathbf{n} \\ s_j(\mathbf{m}) \equiv s_j(\mathbf{n})\,(p) \\ (1 \leq j \leq k)}} 1.$$

For $1 \leq j \leq k$ let $\sigma_j(\mathbf{m})$ denote the j-th elementary symmetric function of the m_i. The s_j and the σ_j are linked by the Newton-Girard identities,

$$\sum_{i=0}^{j-1}(-1)^i \sigma_i s_{j-i} \equiv (-1)^{j-1} j \sigma_j \quad (\bmod\ p)$$

for $1 \leq j \leq k$. (For convenience we set $\sigma_0 = 1$.) Since $p > k$, these identities allow us to show, by induction on j, that if $s_j(\mathbf{m}) \equiv s_j(\mathbf{n})$ (mod p) for $1 \leq j \leq k$ then $\sigma_j(\mathbf{m}) \equiv \sigma_j(\mathbf{n})$ (mod p) for $1 \leq j \leq k$. But then the two polynomials $\prod(x - m_i)$, $\prod(x - n_i)$ are identically the same (mod p), so that the m_i and the n_i are the same, up to permutations. Hence for any choice of $\mathbf{m}$ there are at most $k!$ choices of the $\mathbf{n}$ for which $s_j(\mathbf{m}) \equiv s_j(\mathbf{n})$ (mod p) for $1 \leq j \leq k$. As there are p^k choices of $\mathbf{m}$ in (3), we have (1). Since $S(0) = p$, it is clear that the sum in (1) is at least as large as p^{2k}.

Suppose that r, s are integers with $p \nmid r$. Put $P_{r,s}(x) = P(rx + s) - P(s)$. Since the map $x \mapsto rx + s$ merely permutes the residue classes (mod p), we see that

$$(4) \qquad \sum_{n=1}^{p} e\left(\frac{P_{r,s}(n)}{p}\right) = e\left(-P(s)/p\right) \sum_{n=1}^{p} e\left(P(n)/p\right).$$

Let K denote the number of distinct polynomials (mod p) among the $P_{r,s}(x)$. Then there are K terms on the left hand side of (1) that contribute $|S(\mathbf{c})|^{2k}$ where $\mathbf{c} = (c_1, \ldots, c_k)$, so that

$$(5) \qquad |S(\mathbf{c})|^{2k} \leq \frac{k!}{K} p^{2k}.$$

We prove that K is large by bounding the multiplicity to which a given polynomial may occur among the $P_{r,s}(x)$. Consider those r, s for which the coefficients of x^k and x^{k-1} in $P_{r,s}(x)$ have prescribed values, say

$$c_k r^k \equiv b_k \quad (\bmod\ p)$$
$$c_k k r^{k-1} s + c_{k-1} r^{k-1} \equiv b_{k-1} \quad (\bmod\ p).$$

Here the first congruence has at most k solutions in the unknown r, and if r is assigned to one of these values then the second congruence is linear in s (with the coefficient of s not divisible by p), so there is precisely one value of s for which the second congruence holds. Hence of the $p(p-1)$ polynomials $P_{r,s}(x)$ with $r \not\equiv 0$ (mod p), no one occurs more than k times, and thus $K \geq p(p-1)/k$. We insert this in (5), and take $2k$-th roots to obtain the the stated result.

With Mordell's argument as a guide, we put $\boldsymbol{\alpha} = (\alpha_1, \ldots, \alpha_k) \in \mathbb{T}^k$, we set

$$(6) \qquad P(x, \boldsymbol{\alpha}) = \sum_{j=1}^{k} \alpha_j x^j,$$

and let

$$(7) \qquad S(\boldsymbol{\alpha}) = \sum_{n=1}^{N} e\big(P(n,\boldsymbol{\alpha})\big).$$

Our first task is to bound the integral

$$(8) \qquad J_k(N;b) = \int_{\mathbb{T}^k} |S(\boldsymbol{\alpha})|^{2b}\, d\boldsymbol{\alpha}.$$

In §2 we shall prove

THEOREM 2. (Vinogradov's Mean Value Theorem) *Let k and b be arbitrary positive integers. In the notation* (6)–(8) *above, we have*

$$(9) \qquad J_k(N;b) \ll_{k,b} N^{2b-(1-\delta)k(k+1)/2}$$

where $\delta = e^{-b/k^2}$.

If we expand the power in (8) and exchange the order of summation and integration, we find that

$$(10) \qquad J_k(N;b) = \sum_{\mathbf{m},\mathbf{n}} \prod_{j=1}^{k} \left(\int_{\mathbb{T}} e\big((s_j(\mathbf{m}) - s_j(\mathbf{n}))\alpha_j\big)\, d\alpha_j \right)$$

where $s_j(\mathbf{m}) = m_1^j + \cdots + m_b^j$ and $\mathbf{m}$ and $\mathbf{n}$ run independently over $\{1,\dots,N\}^b$. This corresponds to Mordell's (2). The integral vanishes unless $s_j(\mathbf{m}) = s_j(\mathbf{n})$, and hence $J_k(N;b)$ is the number of solutions of the simultaneous equations

$$(11) \qquad s_j(\mathbf{m}) = s_j(\mathbf{n}) \qquad (1 \le j \le k)$$

with variables $\mathbf{m}, \mathbf{n} \in \{1,\dots,N\}^b$. For each of the N^b possible values of $\mathbf{m}$ we may obtain a solution of (11) by taking $\mathbf{n} = \mathbf{m}$. Thus

$$(12) \qquad J_k(N;b) \ge N^b.$$

A further lower bound for $J_k(N;b)$ can be derived by considering the contribution to (8) made by $\boldsymbol{\alpha}$ near $\mathbf{0}$. Put

$$\Omega = \big\{\boldsymbol{\alpha} \in \mathbb{T}^k : \|\alpha_j\| \le \tfrac{1}{8kN^j}\big\}.$$

If $\boldsymbol{\alpha} \in \Omega$ and $1 \le n \le N$ then $|\alpha_j n^j| \le \frac{1}{8k}$, and hence $|P(n,\boldsymbol{\alpha})| \le 1/8$, so that $\Re\big(P(n,\boldsymbol{\alpha})\big) \ge 1/\sqrt{2}$. Consequently $|S(\boldsymbol{\alpha})| \ge \Re S(\boldsymbol{\alpha}) \ge N/\sqrt{2}$ for $\boldsymbol{\alpha} \in \Omega$. As $\operatorname{meas}\Omega = (4k)^{-k}N^{-k(k+1)/2}$, we deduce that

$$(13) \qquad J_k(N;b) \gg_{k,b} N^{2b-k(k+1)/2}.$$

In addition to the peak in the integrand near $\boldsymbol{\alpha} = \mathbf{0}$, we anticipate the existence of other peaks near points $\boldsymbol{\alpha}$ whose coordinates are rational numbers with small denominators. However, we may hope that when b is large, say $b \gg k^2$, the sum of such contributions converges. This leads us to formulate

CONJECTURE 1. *For any positive integers k and b,*

$$J_k(N;b) \ll_{k,b} N^{b+\epsilon} + N^{2b-k(k+1)/2+\epsilon}.$$

We see that Theorem 2 falls short of this conjecture because of the term involving δ in (9). When b is small compared with k^2, the bound of Theorem 2 is so weak as to be useless, but when $b \approx k^2$, the bound is already quite useful. If b is a little larger still, say $b \geq 4k^2 \log k$, then δ is quite small, and the bound of (9) is virtually as powerful as the Conjecture.

If $|S(\boldsymbol{\alpha})|$ is large then $|S(\boldsymbol{\beta})|$ is large for all $\boldsymbol{\beta}$ in a certain neighborhood $\Omega(\boldsymbol{\alpha})$ of $\boldsymbol{\alpha}$. However, this neighborhood is rather small, roughly meas $\Omega(\boldsymbol{\alpha}) \approx N^{-k(k+1)/2}$, which forces us to use large values of b. By mimicking Mordell's argument, we can show that $J_k(N;k) \ll k!N^k$ (see Lemma 2(a) below), but this is of little help, as we require a good bound for $J_k(N;b)$ when $b \gg k^2$.

Let $P(x) = P(x, \boldsymbol{\alpha})$ be a given polynomial, and put $P_l(x) = P(x+l) - P(l)$. Corresponding to Mordell's (4), we see that

$$\sum_{n=1}^{N} e\big(P_l(n)\big) = e\big(-P(l)\big) \sum_{n=1}^{N} e\big(P(n)\big) \quad + 2\theta|l|$$

where $|\theta| \leq 1$. Let $\boldsymbol{\alpha}(l)$ denote the sequence of coefficients of $P_l(x)$. If $|S(\boldsymbol{\alpha})|$ is large then $|S(\boldsymbol{\alpha}(l))|$ is large, and hence $|S(\boldsymbol{\beta})|$ is large for all $\boldsymbol{\beta}$ in a suitable neighborhood Ω_l of $\boldsymbol{\alpha}(l)$. If α_k is near a rational number a/q whose denominator is neither too large nor too small, then we obtain a large number of disjoint neighborhoods Ω_l. By proceeding in this way, in §3 we prove

THEOREM 3. *Suppose that $P(x)$ is a polynomial of degree k with real coefficients whose leading coefficient α_k satisfies the inequality*

$$\left|\alpha_k - \frac{a}{q}\right| \leq \frac{1}{q^2}$$

with $(a, q) = 1$ and $N \leq q \leq N^{k-1}$. Then

$$\sum_{n=1}^{N} e\big(P(n)\big) \ll_k N^{1 - \frac{1}{11k^2 \log k}}.$$

Our approach allows us to treat q outside this range, but the upper bound becomes weaker. Many different techniques have been devised for deriving bounds for Weyl sums from Vinogradov's Mean Value Theorem. The method outlined above is conceptually simple, and follows the model of Mordell's argument. In §4 we give a new and relatively elementary argument of this sort, which gives the following inequality.

THEOREM 4. *Suppose that $P(x)$ is a polynomial of degree k with real coefficients whose leading coefficient α_k satisfies the inequality*

$$\left|\alpha_k - \frac{a}{q}\right| \leq \frac{1}{q^2}$$

with $(a,q) = 1$. Then

$$\sum_{n=1}^{N} e\big(P(n)\big) \ll (b^k k)^{\frac{1}{2b}} N \left(\frac{J_{k-1}(3N; 2b)}{N^{2b-k(k-1)/2}} \right)^{\frac{1}{2b}} \left(\frac{1}{q} + \frac{\log q}{N} + \frac{q \log q}{N^k} \right)^{\frac{1}{2b}}.$$

Used in conjunction with the Vinogradov Mean Value Theorem, this gives a second proof of Theorem 3. If we had Conjecture 1, then by taking $b = k(k-1)/2$ we could prove the stronger estimate

$$\sum_{n=1}^{N} e\big(P(n)\big) \ll_k N^{1+\epsilon} \left(\frac{1}{q} + \frac{\log q}{N} + \frac{q \log q}{N^k} \right)^{\frac{1}{k(k-1)}},$$

which improves on Weyl's estimate for $k \geq 6$.

2. Vinogradov's Mean Value Theorem. We begin by noting that the sum $S(\boldsymbol{\alpha})$ defined in (7) is an exponential polynomial in k variables. That is, it is of the general form

$$T(\boldsymbol{\alpha}) = \sum_{\boldsymbol{\lambda}} r(\boldsymbol{\lambda}) e(\boldsymbol{\lambda} \cdot \boldsymbol{\alpha})$$

where $\boldsymbol{\lambda}$ runs over a finite subset of $\mathbb{Z}^k$. Given such a $T(\boldsymbol{\alpha})$, we can recover its coefficients $r(\boldsymbol{\lambda})$ by means of the Fourier coefficient formula

$$r(\boldsymbol{\lambda}) = \int_{\mathbb{T}^k} T(\boldsymbol{\alpha}) e(-\boldsymbol{\lambda} \cdot \boldsymbol{\alpha}) \, d\boldsymbol{\alpha}.$$

Hence if $T_i(\boldsymbol{\alpha}) = \sum_{\boldsymbol{\lambda}} r_i(\boldsymbol{\lambda}) e(\boldsymbol{\lambda} \cdot \boldsymbol{\alpha})$ for $i = 1, 2$ then

$$(14) \qquad \int_{\mathbb{T}^k} T_1(\boldsymbol{\alpha}) \overline{T_2(\boldsymbol{\alpha})} e(-\boldsymbol{\mu} \cdot \boldsymbol{\alpha}) \, d\boldsymbol{\alpha} = \sum_{\boldsymbol{\lambda}} r_1(\boldsymbol{\lambda}) \overline{r_2}(\boldsymbol{\lambda} - \boldsymbol{\mu}).$$

Since $S(\boldsymbol{\alpha})$ is an exponential polynomial in the α_j, so also is $S(\boldsymbol{\alpha})^b$, say $S(\boldsymbol{\alpha})^b = \sum_{\boldsymbol{\lambda}} r(\boldsymbol{\lambda}) e(\boldsymbol{\lambda} \cdot \boldsymbol{\alpha})$. Here $r(\boldsymbol{\lambda})$ is the number of solutions of the system

$$(15) \qquad n_1^h + \cdots + n_b^h = \lambda_h \qquad (1 \leq h \leq k)$$

in integers n_j, $1 \leq n_j \leq N$. Thus by (14) with $\boldsymbol{\mu} = \mathbf{0}$, we see that

$$J_k(N; b) = \int_{\mathbb{T}^k} |S(\boldsymbol{\alpha})|^{2b} \, d\boldsymbol{\alpha} = \sum_{\boldsymbol{\lambda}} r(\boldsymbol{\lambda})^2,$$

and we see that this is the number of solutions of the system

$$(16) \qquad m_1^h + \cdots + m_b^h = n_1^h + \cdots + n_b^h \qquad (1 \leq h \leq k)$$

where $1 \leq m_j, n_j \leq N$. As we proceed, we repeatedly relate an integral to the number of solutions of a corresponding system of equations, as above. To facilitate this, we let $N(\mathcal{S}_1, \mathcal{S}_2; \boldsymbol{\mu})$ denote the number of solutions of the system

$$(17) \qquad \sum_{j=1}^{b} m_j^h = \mu_h + \sum_{j=1}^{b} n_j^h \qquad (1 \leq h \leq k)$$

with $\mathbf{m} \in \mathcal{S}_1$ and $\mathbf{n} \in \mathcal{S}_2$. If $\mathcal{S}_1 = \mathcal{S}_2$ then for brevity we write $N(\mathcal{S}; \boldsymbol{\mu})$, and if in addition $\boldsymbol{\mu} = \mathbf{0}$ then we write $N(\mathcal{S})$. Thus $J_k(N; b) = N(\mathcal{S})$ where $\mathcal{S} = \{1, 2, \dots, N\}^b$. We first note some elementary properties of these quantities.

LEMMA 1. *In the above notation,*
(a) *If $\mathcal{S}_1 \subseteq \mathcal{S}_2$ then $N(\mathcal{S}_1) \leq N(\mathcal{S}_2)$.*
(b) *If $\mathcal{S} = \bigcup_{m=1}^{M} \mathcal{S}_m$ then $N(\mathcal{S}) \leq M \sum_{m=1}^{M} N(\mathcal{S}_m)$.*
(c) *$N(\mathcal{S}; \boldsymbol{\mu}) \leq N(\mathcal{S})$.*
(d) *If $\mathbf{d} = (d, d, \dots, d)$ then $N(\mathcal{S}_1 + \mathbf{d}, \mathcal{S}_2 + \mathbf{d}) = N(\mathcal{S}_1, \mathcal{S}_2)$.*

PROOF. (a) Obvious.

(b) Let $r(\boldsymbol{\lambda})$ denote the number of solutions of the system (15) with $\mathbf{n} \in \mathcal{S}$, and for $1 \leq \mu \leq M$ let $r_\mu(\boldsymbol{\lambda})$ denote the number of solutions of this system with $\mathbf{n} \in \mathcal{S}_\mu$. Clearly $r(\boldsymbol{\lambda}) \leq r_1(\boldsymbol{\lambda}) + \cdots + r_M(\boldsymbol{\lambda})$, and hence by Cauchy's inequality

$$N(\mathcal{S}) = \sum_{\boldsymbol{\lambda}} r(\boldsymbol{\lambda})^2$$

$$\leq \sum_{\boldsymbol{\lambda}} \left(\sum_{\mu=1}^{M} r_\mu(\boldsymbol{\lambda}) \right)^2$$

$$\leq \sum_{\boldsymbol{\lambda}} M \sum_{\mu=1}^{M} r_\mu(\boldsymbol{\lambda})^2$$

$$= M \sum_{\mu=1}^{M} N(\mathcal{S}_\mu).$$

(c) It is instructive to consider two proofs. Firstly,

$$N(\mathcal{S}; \boldsymbol{\mu}) = \sum_{\boldsymbol{\lambda}} r(\boldsymbol{\lambda}) r(\boldsymbol{\lambda} - \boldsymbol{\mu})$$

which by Cauchy's inequality is

$$\leq \left(\sum_{\boldsymbol{\lambda}} r(\boldsymbol{\lambda})^2 \right)^{1/2} \left(\sum_{\boldsymbol{\lambda}} r(\boldsymbol{\lambda} - \boldsymbol{\mu})^2 \right)^{1/2}$$

$$= \sum_{\boldsymbol{\lambda}} r(\boldsymbol{\lambda})^2 = N(\mathcal{S}).$$

Secondly, by (14) we see that

$$N(\mathcal{S}; \boldsymbol{\mu}) = \int_{\mathbb{T}^k} |T(\boldsymbol{\alpha})|^2 e(-\boldsymbol{\mu} \cdot \boldsymbol{\alpha}) \, d\boldsymbol{\alpha},$$

which by the triangle inequality is

$$\leq \int_{\mathbb{T}^k} |T(\boldsymbol{\alpha})|^2 \, d\boldsymbol{\alpha} = N(\mathcal{S}).$$

(d) We observe that $(\mathbf{m} + \mathbf{d}, \mathbf{n} + \mathbf{d})$ is a solution of the system

$$\sum_{j=1}^{b} m_j^h = \sum_{j=1}^{b} n_j^h \qquad (1 \le h \le k)$$

if and only if $(\mathbf{m}, \mathbf{n})$ is a solution.

With these observations in hand, we establish the simplest estimates for the mean value $J_k(N; b)$.

LEMMA 2. *Let* $J_k(N; b)$ *be defined as in* (8). *Then*
(a) $J_k(N; b) \le k! N^{2b-k}$ *for* $b \ge k$.
(b) $J_k(N; b) \le b! N^b$ *for* $b \le k$.
(c) $J_k(N; b) \ge N^b$.
(d) $J_k(N; b) \ge (2b+1)^{-k} N^{2b-k(k+1)/2}$.

PROOF. (a) In counting the number of solutions of the system (16), we assign values to all the variables except for $m_1, \ldots, m_k$. Then $m_1, \ldots, m_k$ must satisfy a system of equations of the form $\sum_{j=1}^{k} m_j^h = \lambda_h$ for $1 \le h \le k$. By the Newton-Girard identities, this determines the elementary symmetric functions of the m_j, and hence the m_j are uniquely determined, apart from their order. Thus there are $\le k!$ possible choices of $m_1, \ldots, m_k$. Since we have N^{2b-k} possible choices for the other variables, this gives the result.

(b) Express $N_b(N; b)$ as the number of solutions of the system (16). If we restrict the variables by setting $m_j = n_j = 1$ for $k < j \le b$ then the number of solutions is $N_k(N; b)$. Hence $N_k(N; b) \le N_b(N; b)$ if $k \le b$. The stated bound now follows by applying part (a) with $k = b$.

(c) As already noted, we obtain N^b solutions of the system (16) by setting $m_j = n_j$ for all j. Alternatively, $J_k(N; b) \ge N_k(N; 1)^b$ by Hölder's inequality, and from (16) we see that $J_k(N; 1) = N$.

(d) Let $\mathcal{S} = \{1, 2, \ldots, N\}^b$. Then

$$\sum_{\boldsymbol{\mu}} N(\mathcal{S}; \boldsymbol{\mu}) = N^{2b}.$$

Since we may suppose that $|\mu_h| \le bN^h$, we see by Lemma 1(c) that the above sum is

$$\le N(\mathcal{S}) \sum_{\boldsymbol{\mu}} 1 = N(\mathcal{S})(2b+1)^k N^{k(k+1)/2}.$$

Since $N(\mathcal{S}) = J_k(N; , b)$, this gives the desired lower bound.

We now come to the main lemma in our argument, one that is still reminiscent of Mordell's reasoning.

LEMMA 3. (Linnik's Lemma) *Suppose that* $p > k$, *and let* $M(\boldsymbol{\lambda})$ *denote the number of solutions of the system of congruences*

$$m_1^h + \cdots + m_k^h \equiv \lambda_h \pmod{p^h} \qquad (1 \le h \le k)$$

where the m_j are distinct (mod p) and $1 \leq m_j \leq p^k$. Then for any $\boldsymbol{\lambda}$,

$$M(\boldsymbol{\lambda}) \leq k! p^{k(k-1)/2}.$$

PROOF. Choose residue classes μ_h (mod p^k) so that $\mu_h \equiv \lambda_h$ (mod p^h). There are $p^{k(k-1)/2}$ such $\boldsymbol{\mu}$. Thus it remains to show that there are at most $k!$ choices of the $\mathbf{m}$ so that the m_j are distinct (mod p), $1 \leq m_j \leq p^k$, and

$$\sum_{j=1}^{k} m_j^h \equiv \mu_h \quad (\text{mod } p^k) \qquad\qquad (1 \leq h \leq k).$$

Since $(k!, p) = 1$, we see by the Newton-Girard identities that if

$$\sum_{j=1}^{k} m_j^h \equiv \sum_{j=1}^{k} n_j^h \quad (\text{mod } p^k) \qquad\qquad (1 \leq h \leq k)$$

then the respective elementary symmetric functions of the m_j and the n_j are congruent (mod p^k), and hence the two polynomials $P(x) = \prod_j (x - m_j)$, $Q(x) = \prod_j (x - n_j)$ are identically congruent (mod p^k). Since $P(m_1) = 0$, we deduce that $Q(m_1) \equiv 0$ (mod p^k). But if the n_j are distinct (mod p) then it follows that $n_j \equiv m_1$ (mod p^k) for some j. In this way we see that the n_j are a permutation of the m_j. Hence the μ_h determine the m_j uniquely (mod p^k), up to permutations. This completes the proof.

We now establish an inductive step in which $J_k(N; b)$ is bounded in terms of $J_k(N', b - k)$. We argue so as to make Linnik's Lemma applicable.

LEMMA 4. *Suppose that $b \geq 2k$, $k \geq 2$, and that $N \geq (c_1 k)^{4k}$. Then*

$$J_k(N; b) \ll_{k,b} N^b + N^{\frac{3}{2}k - \frac{5}{2} + \frac{2b}{k}} J_k\big([N^{1-1/k}]; b - k\big).$$

PROOF. Let $\mathcal{S} = \{1, 2, \ldots, N\}^b$, and write $\mathcal{S} = \mathcal{T} \cup \mathcal{U}$ where $\mathcal{T}$ consists of those members of $\mathcal{S}$ for which the coordinates $m_1, m_2, \ldots, m_b$ take at least k distinct values, and where $\mathcal{U}$ consists of those members of $\mathcal{S}$ for which the coordinates take at most $k - 1$ distinct values. Then

(18) $J_k(N; b) = N(\mathcal{S}) \leq 2N(\mathcal{T}) + 2N(\mathcal{U}).$

Since $N(\mathcal{U})$ counts members of $\mathcal{U} \times \mathcal{U}$, it is clear that $N(\mathcal{U}) \leq (\text{card}\,\mathcal{U})^2$. For $1 \leq j \leq k - 1$ choose an integer v_j, $1 \leq v_j \leq N$. There are at most $(k-1)^b$ members of $\mathcal{U}$ whose coordinates are taken from the set $\{v_1, v_2, \ldots, v_{k-1}\}$. Also, there are N^{k-1} ways of choosing the v_j. Hence card $\mathcal{U} \leq (k-1)^b N^{k-1}$, and thus

(19) $N(\mathcal{U}) \leq (k-1)^{2b} N^{2k-2} \ll_{k,b} N^b.$

Let $\mathcal{T}^*$ consist of those members of $\mathcal{T}$ for which the first k coordinates $m_1, \ldots, m_k$ are distinct. To each point $\mathbf{m} \in \mathcal{T}$ we associate a point $\mathbf{m}^* \in T^*$ by moving the first k distinct coordinates of $\mathbf{m}$ into the first k positions. The equations (16) are invariant under such permutations of coordinates, so the pair $(\mathbf{m}, \mathbf{n})$ is counted by $N(\mathcal{T})$ if and only if $(\mathbf{m}^*, \mathbf{n}^*)$ is counted by $N(\mathcal{T}^*)$. Since each member of $\mathcal{T}^*$ corresponds to at most $\binom{b}{k}$ members of $\mathcal{T}$, it follows that

$$(20) \qquad N(\mathcal{T}) \leq \binom{b}{k}^2 N(\mathcal{T}^*).$$

Now let $\mathcal{P}$ be a set of k^3 primes in the interval $(2N^{1/k}, 4N^{1/k}]$, and let $\mathcal{T}^*(p)$ consist of those members of $\mathcal{T}$ for which the first k coordinates $m_1, m_2, \ldots, m_k$ are distinct (mod p). We show that

$$(21) \qquad \bigcup_{p \in \mathcal{P}} \mathcal{T}^*(p) = \mathcal{T}^*.$$

To see this, note that if $m_1, m_2, \ldots, m_k$ are distinct then

$$0 < \left| \prod_{i<j} (m_i - m_j) \right| < N^{k(k-1)/2}.$$

On the other hand, if there is no prime $p \in \mathcal{P}$ such that the numbers $m_1, \ldots, m_k$ are distinct (mod p), then

$$(22) \qquad \prod_{p \in \mathcal{P}} p \, \Big| \, \prod_{i<j} (m_i - m_j).$$

But

$$\prod_{p \in \mathcal{P}} p > \left(2N^{1/k}\right)^{k^3} > N^{k(k-1)/2}.$$

Since this is inconsistent with (22), we deduce that there is a $p \in \mathcal{P}$ for which the first k coordinates $m_1, m_2, \ldots m_k$ are distinct (mod p). Hence we have (21). By Lemma 1(b) it follows that

$$(23) \qquad N(\mathcal{T}^*) \leq k^3 \sum_{p \in \mathcal{P}} N(\mathcal{T}^*(p)).$$

Now let $\mathcal{T}^*(p, l)$ denote the set of those members of $\mathcal{T}^*(p)$ for which $m_{k+1} \equiv m_{k+2} \equiv \cdots \equiv m_b \equiv l$ (mod p). The next step of our proof is to establish that

$$(24) \qquad N(\mathcal{T}^*(p)) \leq p^{2b-2k} \max_l N(\mathcal{T}^*(p, l)).$$

To this end, let

$$T(\boldsymbol{\alpha}) = \sum_{\mathbf{m} \in \mathcal{M}(p)} e\big(P(m_1, \boldsymbol{\alpha}) + \cdots + P(m_k, \boldsymbol{\alpha})\big)$$

where $\mathcal{M}(p) = \{(m_1, m_2 \ldots, m_k) : m_i \text{ distinct (mod } p), 1 \leq m_i \leq N\}$. Writing

$$T(\boldsymbol{\alpha}) S(\boldsymbol{\alpha})^{b-k} = \sum_{\boldsymbol{\lambda}} r(\boldsymbol{\lambda}) e(\boldsymbol{\lambda} \cdot \boldsymbol{\alpha}),$$

we that $r(\boldsymbol{\lambda})$ is the number of solutions of (15) with $\mathbf{m} \in \mathcal{T}^*(p)$. Thus by (14),

$$N(\mathcal{T}^*(p)) = \int_{\mathbb{T}^k} |T(\boldsymbol{\alpha})|^2 |S(\boldsymbol{\alpha})|^{2b-2k} \, d\boldsymbol{\alpha}.$$

We now group the terms in $S(\alpha)$ according to residue classes (mod p):

$$S(\alpha) = \sum_{l=0}^{p-1} \sum_{\substack{n=1 \\ n \equiv l \, (p)}}^{N} e(P(n,\alpha)) = \sum_{l=0}^{p-1} S_l(\alpha),$$

say. Then by Hölder's inequality

$$|S(\alpha)|^{2b-2k} = \left| \sum_{l=0}^{p-1} S_l(\alpha) \right|^{2b-2k} \leq p^{2b-2k-1} \sum_{l=0}^{p-1} |S_l(\alpha)|^{2b-2k},$$

so that

$$N(\mathcal{T}^*(p)) \leq p^{2b-2k-1} \sum_{l=0}^{p-1} \int_{\mathbb{T}^k} |T(\alpha)|^2 |S_l(\alpha)|^{2b-2k} \, d\alpha$$

$$\leq p^{2b-2k} \max_l \int_{\mathbb{T}^k} |T(\alpha)|^2 |S_l(\alpha)|^{2b-2k} \, d\alpha.$$

Since this last integral is $N(\mathcal{T}^*(p,l))$, we have (24).

The preliminary reductions made thus far allow us to apply Linnik's Lemma. By Lemma 1(d) we see that if $\mathbf{l} = (l, l, \ldots, l)$ then $N(\mathcal{T}^*(p,l)) = N(\mathcal{T}^*(p,l) - \mathbf{l})$. This latter quantity is, by definition, the number of solutions of the system

$$m_1^h + \cdots + m_k^h = n_1^h + \cdots + n_k^h$$
(25)
$$+ p^h(\xi_1^h + \cdots + \xi_{b-k}^h - \eta_1^h - \cdots - \eta_{b-k}^h) \qquad (1 \leq h \leq k).$$

where the m_j are distinct (mod p), $1-l \leq m_j \leq N-l$, the n_j are distinct (mod p), $1-l \leq n_j \leq N-l$, and the ξ_j, η_j are integers in the interval $[(1-l)/p, (N-l)/p]$. To estimate the number of solutions of the system (25), suppose that the n_j have been chosen; there are $\leq N^k$ possibilities. Put $\mu_h = n_1^h + \cdots + n_k^h$. For there to be a solution of (25), the m_j must satisfy the congruences

$$m_1^h + \cdots + m_k^h \equiv \mu_h \pmod{p^k}.$$

By Linnik's Lemma the number of solutions of this (mod p^k) is $\leq k! p^{k(k-1)/2}$. But $p^k > N$ for all $p \in \mathcal{P}$, and thus each m_j is uniquely determined by its residue class (mod p^k). With the n_j and m_j determined, to obtain a solution of (25) the ξ_j and η_j must satisfy a system of the form

(26) $\xi_1^h + \cdots + \xi_{b-k}^h = \nu_h + \eta_1^h + \cdots + \eta_{b-k}^h \qquad (1 \leq h \leq k).$

By Lemma 1(c) we see that the number of solutions of this system is largest when $\boldsymbol{\nu} = \mathbf{0}$; thus we assume that this is the case. Choose d_l so that $0 < (1-l)/p + d_l \leq 1$. Then by Lemma 1(d) the number of solutions is unchanged if we replace the interval $[(1-l)/p, (N-l)/p]$ by $[1, (N-l)/p + d_l]$. But for $p \in \mathcal{P}$,

$$\frac{N-l}{p} + d_l \leq \frac{N}{p} + 1 \leq \frac{N^{1-1/k}}{2} + 1 \leq [N^{1-1/k}].$$

Hence by Lemma 1(a) it suffices to consider variables in the interval $[1, [N^{1-1/k}]]$. Thus the number of solutions of the system (26) is $\leq J_k([N^{1-1/k}]; b-k)$, and hence

$$N(\mathcal{T}^*(p, l)) \leq k! p^{k(k-1)/2} N^k J_k([N^{1/1/k}]; b-k).$$

On combining this with (18), (19), (20), (23), and (24), we obtain the desired estimate, and the proof of Lemma 4 is complete.

PROOF OF THEOREM 2. If $k = 1$ then

$$|S(\boldsymbol{\alpha})| \leq \min\left(N, \frac{1}{\|\boldsymbol{\alpha}\|}\right),$$

so that

$$J_1(N; b) \leq \int_0^1 \min\left(N^{2b}, \|\boldsymbol{\alpha}\|^{-2b}\right) d\boldsymbol{\alpha} \leq 4N^{2b-1},$$

which suffices. Assume now that $k \geq 2$. Suppose first that $1 \leq b \leq k$. Then $J_k(N; b) \leq b! N^b$ by Lemma 2(b). This suffices, since the inequality $e^x \geq 1 + x$ gives

$$(1 - \delta)k(k+1)/2 \leq b(1 + 1/k)/2 \leq b.$$

Assume next that $k \leq b \leq 2k - 1$. Then $J_k(N; b) \leq k! N^{2b-k}$ by Lemma 2(a). To show that this suffices, we demonstrate that

(27)
$$(1 - \delta)k(k+1)/2 < k$$

in this range. Here the left hand side is an increasing function of b, so we may suppose that $b = 2k - 1$. Now

$$\log\left(1 - \frac{2}{k+1}\right)^{-1} = \sum_{r=1}^{\infty} \frac{1}{r}\left(\frac{2}{k+1}\right)^r > \frac{2}{k+1} + \frac{2}{(k+1)^2} > \frac{2k-1}{k^2},$$

so that

$$e^{-(2k-1)/k^2} > 1 - \frac{2}{k+1},$$

which gives (27).

It remains to consider the situation $b \geq 2k$, $k \geq 2$. We may also assume that $N > (c_1 k)^{4k}$, for otherwise

$$J_k(N; b) \leq N^{2b} \ll_{k,b} 1.$$

We induct on b. By the inductive hypothesis,

$$J_k([N^{1-1/k}]; b-k) \ll_{k,b} N^{(2(b-k)-(1-\delta_{b-k})k(k+1)/2)(1-1/k)}.$$

This with Lemma 4 gives

$$J_k(N; b) \ll_{k,b} N^b + N^{2b-(1-(1-1/k)\delta_{b-k})k(k+1)/2}.$$

Now $(1 - 1/k)\delta_{b-k} < e^{-1/k}\delta_{b-k} = \delta_b$. Also $1 - \delta_b \geq 1 - b/k^2$, so that $(1 - \delta_b)k(k+1)/2 \leq b(k+1)/(2k) \leq b$. Hence

$$J_k(N; b) \ll_{k,b} N^{2b-(1-\delta_b)k(k+1)/2},$$

and the proof is complete.

3. A bound for Weyl sums. To relate $S(\boldsymbol{\alpha})$ to $S(\boldsymbol{\beta})$ when $\boldsymbol{\beta}$ is near $\boldsymbol{\alpha}$, we let

$$S^*(\boldsymbol{\alpha}) = \max_{M \leq N} \left| \sum_{1 \leq n \leq M} e\big(P(n, \boldsymbol{\alpha})\big) \right|,$$

and we prove the following result.

LEMMA 5. *If* $|\alpha_j - \beta_j| \leq \frac{1}{2kN^j}$ *for* $1 \leq j \leq k$ *then*

$$\frac{1}{1 + \pi} S^*(\boldsymbol{\alpha}) < S^*(\boldsymbol{\beta}) < (1 + \pi)S^*(\boldsymbol{\alpha}).$$

PROOF. By symmetry it suffices to establish the second of these inequalities. Let $f(u) = \sum_{1 \leq n \leq u} e\big(P(n, \boldsymbol{\alpha})\big)$. Then

$$\sum_{n=1}^{M} e\big(P(n, \boldsymbol{\beta})\big) = \int_{1^-}^{M} e\big(P(u, \boldsymbol{\beta}) - P(u, \boldsymbol{\alpha})\big) \, df(u),$$

which by integration by parts is

$$= e\big(P(M, \boldsymbol{\beta}) - P(M, \boldsymbol{\alpha})\big) f(M)$$

$$- 2\pi i \int_{1}^{M} f(u) \big(P'(u, \boldsymbol{\beta}) - P'(u, \boldsymbol{\alpha})\big) e\big(P(u, \boldsymbol{\beta}) - P(u, \boldsymbol{\alpha})\big) \, du.$$

Here the first term has absolute value not exceeding $S^*(\boldsymbol{\alpha})$. To estimate the integral we first use the triangle inequality to see that

$$\big|P'(u, \boldsymbol{\beta}) - P'(u, \boldsymbol{\alpha})\big| \leq \sum_{j=1}^{k} |\beta_j - \alpha_j| j u^{j-1} \leq \frac{1}{2k} \sum_{j=1}^{k} j u^{j-1}/N^j$$

for $u \geq 0$. Hence by a second application of the triangle inequality, the integral has absolute value not exceeding

$$\frac{S^*(\boldsymbol{\alpha})}{2k} \int_{0}^{N} \sum_{j=1}^{k} j u^{j-1}/N^j \, du = \frac{1}{2} S^*(\boldsymbol{\alpha}).$$

This gives the stated inequality.

Having introduced S^*, we must now relate moments of S^* to those of S.

LEMMA 6. *For positive integers* N, b, k,

$$\int_{\mathbb{T}^k} S^*(\boldsymbol{\alpha})^{2b} \, d\boldsymbol{\alpha} < (\log eN)^{2b} \int_{\mathbb{T}^k} |S(\boldsymbol{\alpha})|^{2b} \, d\boldsymbol{\alpha}.$$

PROOF. Let $K(\alpha) = \max\big(N, 1/(2\|\alpha\|)\big)$. We begin by showing that

$$(28) \qquad \max_{1 \leq M \leq N} \left| \sum_{1 \leq n \leq M} c_n \right|^{2b} \leq (\log eN)^{2b-1} \int_{\mathbb{T}} \left| \sum_{n=1}^{N} c_n e(n\alpha) \right|^{2b} K(\alpha) \, d\alpha$$

for arbitrary complex numbers $c_1, \ldots c_N$. To see this we first note that

$$\sum_{n=1}^{M} c_n = \int_{\mathbb{T}} \left(\sum_{n=1}^{N} c_n e(n\alpha) \right) \left(\sum_{n=1}^{M} e(-n\alpha) \right) d\alpha.$$

Here the second factor in the integrand has absolute value not exceeding $K(\alpha)$ (recall (2) in Chapter 3). Since

$$(29) \qquad \int_{\mathbb{T}} K(\alpha) \, d\alpha = \log eN,$$

we obtain (28) by Hölder's inequality.

We now take $c_n = e\big(P(n, \boldsymbol{\alpha})\big)$ in (28), and integrate both sides over $\boldsymbol{\alpha} \in \mathbb{T}^k$. A second appeal to (29) then gives the stated inequality.

With these lemmas in place, we are now in a position to derive an estimate for a Weyl sum from Vinogradov's Mean Value Theorem, in a manner that emulates Mordell's argument.

PROOF OF THEOREM 3. Consider the polynomial

$$P(x + l, \boldsymbol{\alpha}) - P(l, \boldsymbol{\alpha})$$

where l is some integer. This is a member of $\mathbb{T}[x]$ that vanishes at $x = 0$, and hence this polynomial is $P(x, \boldsymbol{\alpha}(l))$ for some unique point $\boldsymbol{\alpha}(l) \in \mathbb{T}^k$. Indeed, by the binomial theorem we may calculate the coefficients $\alpha_j(l)$ of $P(x, \boldsymbol{\alpha}(l))$ explicitly in terms of the coefficients α_j of $P(x, \boldsymbol{\alpha})$, and we find that

$$(30) \qquad \alpha_j(l) = \sum_{j \leq i \leq k} \alpha_i \binom{i}{j} l^{i-j}$$

for $1 \leq j \leq k$. Although the coefficient vectors $\boldsymbol{\alpha}$, $\boldsymbol{\alpha}(l)$ are quite different, the associated Weyl sums are closely related, at least when $|l|$ is not too large. To see this, note that

$$S(\boldsymbol{\alpha}(l)) = \sum_{n=1}^{N} e\big(P(n, \boldsymbol{\alpha}(l))\big) = e\big(-P(l, \boldsymbol{\alpha})\big) \sum_{j=l+1}^{N+l} e\big(P(n, \boldsymbol{\alpha})\big).$$

Since the sum on the right differs from $S(\boldsymbol{\alpha})$ in only $2|l|$ terms, we deduce that

$$(31) \qquad |S(\boldsymbol{\alpha}(l))| \geq |S(\boldsymbol{\alpha})| - 2|l|.$$

In particular, if $|S(\boldsymbol{\alpha})|$ is large then $|S(\boldsymbol{\alpha}(l))|$ is also large, provided that $|l| \leq |S(\boldsymbol{\alpha})|/4$. From Lemma 5 we see that if $|S(\boldsymbol{\alpha})|$ is large, then S^* is large throughout the neighborhood

$$(32) \qquad \Omega(\boldsymbol{\alpha}) = \left\{ \boldsymbol{\beta} \in \mathbb{T}^k : |\beta_j - \alpha_j| \leq \frac{1}{2kN^j} \qquad (1 \leq j \leq k) \right\}$$

of $\boldsymbol{\alpha}$. A single neighborhood of this kind is perfectly consistent with Vinogradov's Mean Value Theorem. After all, $|S(\boldsymbol{\alpha})|$ *is* large when $\boldsymbol{\alpha} = \mathbf{0}$. Indeed, $S(\mathbf{0}) = N$. However, if the neighborhoods $\Omega(\boldsymbol{\alpha}(l))$ are disjoint, and if we have a large number of them, then their total effect, combined with Vinogradov's Mean Value Theorem, allows us to derive a non-trivial upper bound for $|S(\boldsymbol{\alpha})|$.

In order to show that a large number of the neighborhoods $\Omega(\boldsymbol{\alpha}(l))$ are disjoint, we use our hypothesis concerning the rational approximation to the leading coefficient α_k. From the definition (32) of these neighborhoods we see that if $\Omega(\boldsymbol{\alpha}(l_1))$ and $\Omega(\boldsymbol{\alpha}(l_2))$ have non-empty intersection then

$$\|\alpha_{k-1}(l_1) - \alpha_{k-1}(l_2)\| \le \frac{1}{kN^{k-1}}.$$

By taking $j = k - 1$ in (30) we see that $\alpha_{k-1}(l) = \alpha_{k-1} + k\alpha_k l$. Thus the inequality displayed above asserts that

$$\|(l_1 - l_2)k\alpha_k\| \le \frac{1}{kN^{k-1}}.$$

By the triangle inequality, the left hand side above is

$$\ge \left\|\frac{(l_1 - l_2)ka}{q}\right\| - \frac{|l_1 - l_2|k}{q^2}.$$

Suppose we take $L = [N^{23/24}] + 1$, and restrict l to the range $1 \le l \le L$. If $1 \le l_1 < l_2 \le L$ then $|l_1 - l_2| \le N^{23/24}$. Hence $(l_1 - l_2)k \not\equiv 0 \pmod q$, since $q \ge N$ and we may assume that $N > (2k)^{24}$. Thus the above is

$$\ge \frac{1}{q} - \frac{N^{23/24}k}{q^2}.$$

Since $q \ge N > 2kN^{23/24}$, the above is

$$> \frac{1}{q} - \frac{1}{2q} = \frac{1}{2q}.$$

Finally, since $q \le N^{k-1}$, the above is

$$\ge \frac{1}{2N^{k-1}}.$$

We may assume that $k \ge 3$, since otherwise a stronger estimate is given by Theorem 2 of Chapter 3. Hence we see that the last term in the chain of inequalities displayed above is larger than the first. This gives a contradiction, so we conclude that the neighborhoods $\Omega(\boldsymbol{\alpha}(l))$ are disjoint for $1 \le l \le L$.

We may assume that $|S(\boldsymbol{\alpha})| \ge 4L$, for otherwise we are done. From (31) we deduce that $|S(\boldsymbol{\alpha}(l))| \ge \frac{1}{2}|S(\boldsymbol{\alpha})|$ for $1 \le l \le L$. By Lemma 5 it follows that $S^*(\boldsymbol{\beta}) \ge \frac{1}{2(1+\pi)}|S(\boldsymbol{\alpha})| \ge |S(\boldsymbol{\alpha})|/9$ uniformly for $\boldsymbol{\beta} \in \Omega(\boldsymbol{\alpha}(l))$, $1 \le l \le L$. Since meas $\Omega(\boldsymbol{\alpha}(l)) = k^{-k}N^{-k(k+1)/2}$, we deduce that

$$\frac{L|S(\boldsymbol{\alpha})|^{2b}}{k^k 9^{2b} N^{k(k+1)/2}} \le \int_{\mathbb{T}^k} S^*(\boldsymbol{\beta})^{2b} \, d\boldsymbol{\beta}.$$

By Lemma 6 and Theorem 2, this is

$$\ll_{k,b} (\log eN)^{2b} N^{2b-(1-\delta)k(k+1)/2}.$$

Hence

$$S(\boldsymbol{\alpha}) \ll_{k,b} N^{1-\frac{23}{48b}+\delta k(k+1)/(4b)} \log eN.$$

We take $b = [3k^2 \log k]$. Then

$$\delta k(k+1) \le e^{1/k^2} k^{-2}(k+1) < 1/2$$

for $k \ge 3$, and hence the exponent of N is $< 1 - 1/(11k^2 \log k)$. This gives the stated result.

4. An alternative derivation. In this section we prove Theorem 4. Let $c_1, \ldots, c_N$ be arbitrary complex numbers, and put $S = \sum_{n=1}^{N} c_n$. Thus

$$(33) \qquad S^b = \sum_{\mathbf{n}} c_{n_1} c_{n_2} \cdots c_{n_b}$$

where $\mathbf{n}$ runs over $\{1, 2, \ldots, N\}^b$. Let $s_j(\mathbf{n}) = n_1^j + \cdots + n_b^j$. We classify the $\mathbf{n}$ according to the value of $\mathbf{s} = (s_1(\mathbf{n}), s_2(\mathbf{n}), \ldots, s_{k-2}(\mathbf{n}))$. Let

$$\mathcal{S} = \{1, 2, \ldots, bN\} \times \{1, 2, \ldots, bN^2\} \times \cdots \times \{1, 2, \ldots, bN^{k-2}\}.$$

Since $1 \le n_i^j \le N^j$, we may restrict our attention to points $\mathbf{s} \in \mathcal{S}$. For $\mathbf{s} \in \mathcal{S}$ put

$$\mathcal{N}(\mathbf{s}) = \{\mathbf{n} \in \{1, \ldots, N\}^b : s_j(\mathbf{n}) = s_j \quad (1 \le j \le k-2)\}.$$

Then the sum in (33) can be partitioned into subsums,

$$S^b = \sum_{\mathbf{s} \in \mathcal{S}} \sum_{\mathbf{n} \in \mathcal{N}(\mathbf{s})} c_{n_1} c_{n_2} \cdots c_{n_b}.$$

Since card $\mathcal{S} = b^{k-2} N^{(k-1)(k-2)/2}$, by Cauchy's inequality we see that

$$(34) \qquad |S|^{2b} \le b^{k-2} N^{(k-1)(k-2)/2} \sum_{\mathbf{s} \in \mathcal{S}} \left| \sum_{\mathbf{n} \in \mathcal{N}(\mathbf{s})} c_{n_1} c_{n_2} \cdots c_{n_b} \right|^2.$$

On squaring out we obtain a triple sum that may be written

$$(35) \qquad \sum_{\substack{\mathbf{m}, \mathbf{n} \\ s_j(\mathbf{m})=s_j(\mathbf{n}) \\ 1 \le j \le k-2}} c_{m_1} \cdots c_{m_b} \overline{c_{n_1}} \cdots \overline{c_{n_b}}.$$

Now take $c_n = e(P(n))$ where $P(x) = \sum_{j=1}^{k} \alpha_j x^j$. For b-tuples $\mathbf{m}$, $\mathbf{n}$ that satisfy the above constraints the summand is

$$e\big((s_k(\mathbf{m}) - s_k(\mathbf{n}))\alpha_k + (s_{k-1}(\mathbf{m}) - s_{k-1}(\mathbf{n}))\alpha_{k-1}\big).$$

Now put $m = m_1$, $m_i = m + u_i$ for $2 \le i \le b$, and $n_i = m + v_i$ for $1 \le i \le b$. Then

$$(36) \qquad s_j(\mathbf{u}) = \sum_{i=1}^{b}(m_i - m)^j = \sum_{r=0}^{j} \binom{j}{r} s_r(\mathbf{m})(-m)^{j-r},$$

and similarly

$$(37) \qquad s_j(\mathbf{v}) = \sum_{i=1}^{b}(n_i - m)^j = \sum_{r=0}^{j}\binom{j}{r}s_r(\mathbf{n})(-m)^{j-r}.$$

Hence the relations $s_j(\mathbf{m}) = s_j(\mathbf{n})$ for $1 \leq j \leq k - 2$ imply that $s_j(\mathbf{u}) = s_j(\mathbf{v})$ for $1 \leq j \leq k - 2$. In addition, we observe from (36) and (37) that

$$s_{k-1}(\mathbf{u}) - s_{k-1}(\mathbf{v}) = s_{k-1}(\mathbf{m}) - s_{k-1}(\mathbf{n}),$$

and that

$$s_k(\mathbf{u}) - s_k(\mathbf{v}) = s_k(\mathbf{m}) - s_k(\mathbf{n}) - km(s_{k-1}(\mathbf{m}) - s_{k-1}(\mathbf{n})).$$

For brevity we put $d_j = d_j(\mathbf{u}, \mathbf{v}) = s_j(\mathbf{u}) - s_j(\mathbf{v})$. Then the sum in (34) may be written as

$$(38) \qquad \sum_{\substack{\mathbf{u},\mathbf{v} \\ d_j=0 \\ 1\leq j\leq k-2}} e(d_k\alpha_k + d_{k-1}\alpha_{k-1}) \sum_m e(kd_{k-1}m\alpha_k).$$

Here the u_i and v_i lie in the set $\{-N, \ldots, N\}$, and m is subject to the constraints

$$1 \leq m \leq N,$$
$$1 - u_i \leq m \leq N - u_i \qquad (2 \leq i \leq b),$$
$$1 - v_i \leq m \leq N - v_i \qquad (1 \leq i \leq b).$$

In any case, m runs over an interval of length $\leq N$, so the inner sum above is

$$\ll \min\left(N, \frac{1}{\|kd_{k-1}\alpha_k\|}\right)$$

by (2) of Chapter 3. Let $R_1(h)$ denote the number of solutions of the system of equations

$$u_2^j + \cdots + u_b^j = v_1^j + \cdots + v_b^j \qquad (1 \leq j \leq k - 2),$$
$$u_2^{k-1} + \cdots + u_b^{k-1} = h + v_1^{k-1} + \cdots + v_b^{k-1}$$

in integral variables for which $|u_i| \leq N$, $|v_i| \leq N$. Then the expression (38) is

$$(39) \qquad \ll \sum_h R_1(h) \min\left(N, \frac{1}{\|kh\alpha_k\|}\right).$$

Now let m be an arbitrary integer such that $N + 1 \leq m \leq 2N$. Put $m_1 = m$, set $m_i = m + u_i$ for $2 \leq i \leq b$, and put $n_i = m + v_i$ for $1 \leq i \leq b$. Then $R_1(h)$ is the number of solutions of the system

$$(40) \qquad \begin{aligned} s_j(\mathbf{m}) &= s_j(\mathbf{n}) \qquad (1 \leq j \leq k - 2), \\ s_{k-1}(\mathbf{m}) &= h + s_{k-1}(\mathbf{n}) \end{aligned}$$

in integral variables for which

$$m_1 = m,$$

(41)
$$m - N \leq m_i \leq m + N \qquad (2 \leq i \leq b),$$
$$m - N \leq n_i \leq m + N \qquad (1 \leq i \leq b).$$

Let $R_2(h)$ denote the number of solutions of (40) subject to the weaker constraints

$$1 \leq m_i \leq 3N \qquad (1 \leq i \leq b),$$
$$1 \leq n_i \leq 3N \qquad (1 \leq i \leq b).$$

Since for each $m_1 \in [N+1, 2N]$ the solutions above include the $R_1(h)$ solutions of (40) subject to (41), it is evident that $R_2(h) \geq N R_1(h)$. Clearly

$$R_2(h) = \int_{\mathbb{T}^{k-1}} \left| \sum_{n=1}^{3N} e\big(P(n,\boldsymbol{\alpha})\big) \right|^{2b} e(-h\alpha_{k-1})\, d\boldsymbol{\alpha}$$

where $P(x, \boldsymbol{\alpha}) = \sum_{j=1}^{k-1} \alpha_j x^j$ is a polynomial of degree $k-1$. By taking absolute values in the integral we see that $R_2(h) \leq R_2(0)$ for all h. (Alternatively, appeal to Lemma 1(c).) But $R_2(0) = J_{k-1}(3N; b)$, so the sum (39) is

$$\ll \frac{1}{N} J_{k-1}(3N; b) \left(N + \sum_{h=1}^{2bkN^{k-1}} \min\left(N, \frac{1}{\|h\alpha_k\|} \right) \right),$$

and by (9) of Chapter 3 this is

$$\ll bk N^{k-1} J_{k-1}(3N; b) \left(\frac{1}{q} + \frac{\log q}{N} + \frac{q \log q}{N^k} \right).$$

The desired estimate now follows by inserting this in (34).

If $k = 3$ and $b = 2$ then $R_1(0) \ll N$ and $R_1(h) \ll N^\epsilon$ for $h \neq 0$, and the argument above gives

$$S \ll N^{1+\epsilon} \left(\frac{1}{q} + \frac{1}{N} + \frac{q \log q}{N^3} \right)^{1/4},$$

the same as Weyl's method.

5. Notes. §1. Expositions of Vinogradov's method are found in Chapter 6 of Vinogradov [23], Chapter 6 of Titchmarsh [16], Hua [7], Walfisz [25], Chapter 4 of Chandrasekharan [4], Chapter 10 of Ellison and Mendes-France [5], Chapter 5 of Vaughan [18], Chapter 4 of Baker [2], and Chapter 6 of Karatsuba [10]. Our presentation is influenced primarily by the lectures that A. E. Ingham gave on this subject at Cambridge University (they are accurately recounted by Ellison and Mendes-France), and by the approach of Bombieri [3]. For the first investigations on this topic, see Vinogradov [19, 20, 21]. The method has been further refined and explored by Linnik [12, 13], Hua [6], Vinogradov [22, 24],

Korobov [11], Karatsuba [8, 9], Stechkin [15], Arkhipov and Karatsuba [1], Tyrina [17], Bombieri [3], and Wooley [26–30].

Theorem 1 is found in Mordell [14]. By keeping track of the constants, one may show that the implicit constant in Theorem 2 is $< (Ck)^{4b^2/k+8bk}$. When used in connection with Waring's problem, k is fixed and b is chosen in terms of k, so this dependence is immaterial. However, when used to estimate the Riemann zeta function one allows k to tend to infinity, in which case this dependence is of critical importance. However, a method of Korobov [11] (see §3 of Bombieri [3]) allows one to avoid the effect of these constants in such applications.

§2. For the introduction of Linnik's Lemma into this subject, see Linnik [12, 13].

§3. Lemma 5 is based on Lemma 1 of Bombieri [3], but our method of proof is simpler and yields better constants (Bombieri would have e^π where we have $1 + \pi$). Bombieri has noted that by using Hunt's theorem one can replace the factor $(\log eN)^{2b}$ in Lemma 6 by $(Cb)^{4b}$ where C is an absolute constant.

§4. The argument here was discovered by the author in the course of an attempt to derive improved bounds for Weyl sums. As it stands, it leads only to the same estimate that is obtained by the classical approach recounted in §3. It remains to be seen whether the line of reasoning here can be modified so as to obtain a sharper estimate. Wooley has noted that when $k = 3$ and $b = 2$ the expression (38) is precisely the second order Weyl difference equation for cubes.

References

1. G. I. Arkhipov and A. A. Karatsuba, *A new estimate of an integral of I. M. Vinogradov*, Izv. Akad. Nauk SSSR Ser. Mat. **42** (1978), 751–762.

2. R. C. Baker, *Diophantine Inequalities*, LMS Monographs New Series 1, Oxford University Press, Oxford, 1986.

3. E. Bombieri, *On Vinogradov's mean value theorem and Weyl sums*, Automorphic forms and analytic number theory, Univ. Montréal, Montréal, 1990, pp. 7–24.

4. K. Chandrasekharan, *Arithmetical Functions*, Grundl. Math. Wiss. 167, Springer-Verlag, New York, 1970.

5. W. J. Ellison and M. Mendes-France, *Les nombres premiers*, Hermann, Paris, 1975.

6. L. K. Hua, *An improvement of Vinogradov's mean value theorem and several applications*, Quart. J. Math. Oxford **20** (1949).

7. _____, *Additive Primzahltheorie*, Leipzig, 1959.

8. A. A. Karatsuba, *Estimates of trigonometric sums by Vinogradov's method, and some applications*, Proc. Steklov. Inst. Math. **119** (1971), 241–255.

9. _____, *The mean value of the modulus of a trigonometric sum*, Izv. Akad. Nauk SSSR **37** (1973), 1203–1227.

10. _____, *Basic Analytic Number Theory*, Springer-Verlag, Berlin, 1993.

11. N. M. Korobov, *Weyl's estimates of sums and the distribution of primes*, Dokl. Akad. Nauk SSSR **123** (1958), 28–31.

12. Ju. V. Linnik, *On Weyl's sums*, Dokl. Akad. Nauk SSSR **34** (1942), 184–186.

13. _____, *On Weyl's sums*, Mat. Sbornik N.S. **12(54)** (1943), 28–39.

14. L. J. Mordell, *On a sum analogous to a Gauss's sum*, Quart. J. Math. **3** (1932), 161–167.

15. S. B. Stechkin, *On mean values of the modulus of a trigonometric sum*, Trudy Mat. Inst. Steklov. **134** (1975), 283–309.

16. E. C. Titchmarsh, *The Theory of the Riemann Zeta-Function, Second Edition* (D. R. Heath-Brown, ed.), Oxford University Press, Oxford, 1986.

17. O. V. Tyrina, *A new estimate for a trigonometric integral of I. M. Vinogradov*, Izv. Akad. Nauk SSSR Ser. Mat. **51** (1987), 363–378, 447; Math. USSR Izvestia **30** (1988), 337–351.

18. R. C. Vaughan, *The Hardy-Littlewood Method*, Cambridge Tract 80, Cambridge University Press, Cambridge, 1981.

19. I. M. Vinogradov, *On Weyl's sums*, Mat. Sbornik **42** (1935), 521–530.

20. _____, *A new method of resolving of certain general questions in the theory of numbers*, Mat. Sbornik **43** (1936), 9–19.

21. _____, *A new method of estimation of trigonometrical sums*, Mat. Sbornik **43** (1936), 175–188.

22. _____, *General theorems on the upper bound of the modulus of a trigonometric sum*, Izv. Akad. Nauk SSSR Ser. Mat. **15** (1951), 109-130.

23. _____, *The Method of Trigonometrical Sums in the Theory of Numbers*; translated by K. F. Roth, Anne Davenport, Interscience, London, 1954.

24. _____, *A new estimate for $\zeta(1 + it)$*, Izv. Akad. Nauk SSSR **22** (1958), 161–164.

25. A. Walfisz, *Weylsche Exponentialsummen in derj neueren Zahlentheorie*, Deutcher Verlag Wiss., Berlin, 1963.

26. T. D. Wooley, *On Vinogradov's mean value theorem*, Mathematika **39** (1992), 379–399.

27. _____, *On Vinogradov's mean value theorem, II*, Michigan Math. J. **40** (1993), 175–180.

28. _____, *Quasi-diagonal behaviour in certain mean value theorems of additive number theory*, J. Amer. Math. Soc. (to appear).

29. _____, *New estimates for Weyl sums*, Quart. J. Math. Oxford (to appear).

30. _____, *New estimates for smooth Weyl sums*, J. London Math. Soc. (to appear).

Chapter 5. An Introduction to Turán's Method

1. Introduction. In the two preceding chapters we have given upper bounds for the size of exponential sums. However, for some purposes it is useful to have estimates in the opposite direction. For example, let s_ν denote the power sum

$$(1) \qquad s_\nu = \sum_{n=1}^{N} b_n z_n^\nu.$$

Here the b_n and z_n are complex numbers, and ν is a non-negative integer. We seek assertions to the effect that not all the s_ν are small, when ν runs over some range. It is important that this range not be too short, for if $\mathcal{N}$ is a set of fewer than N non-negative integers then for any choice of the z_n one may find a choice of the b_n, not all of them 0, so that $s_\nu = 0$ for all $\nu \in \mathcal{N}$. (The system is linear and homogeneous in the unknown b_n, with more variables than equations.) At the opposite extreme, if we allow an extremely long range then we may expect a very good lower bound. For example, by Dirichlet's theorem we know that there is a ν, $1 \le \nu \le 8^N$ such that $\|\nu \arg z_n\| \le 1/8$ for all n. If $b_n \ge 0$ for all n then we deduce that

$$(2) \qquad |s_\nu| \ge \frac{1}{\sqrt{2}} \sum_{n=1}^{N} b_n |z_n|^\nu$$

for such a ν. Alternatively, if the numbers $\arg z_n$ are linearly independent over $\mathbb{Q}$ then by Kronecker's theorem there exist arbitrarily large positive integers ν such that

$$|s_\nu| \ge (1 - \epsilon) \sum_{n=1}^{N} |b_n| |z_n|^\nu.$$

Here the b_n are arbitrary, but the result is a little unsatisfactory, since we do not know how large we must take ν, as a function of ϵ. (Any quantitative result in this direction must depend on a measure of the linear independence of the numbers $\arg z_n$.)

As our problem is very broadly defined, we narrow the focus somewhat. In the first instance we seek a lower bound for $\max |s_\nu|$ where ν runs over an interval of the type $M + 1 \le \nu \le M + N$. Here $M \ge 0$. The lower bound is to be expressed in terms of $|s_0|$ and $\min |z_n|$. (After normalization, this is equivalent to assuming that $|z_n| \ge 1$ for all n.) Each aspect of this is subject to some variation: We might substitute $\Re s_\nu$ for $|s_\nu|$, we might replace the maximum by an ℓ^p norm, we might consider a longer range, $M + 1 \leq \nu \leq M + H$ where $H \geq N$, and finally we might seek results that depend instead on $\max |z_n|$. In all these situations no hypothesis is made concerning the nature of the b_n, but we find that stronger conclusions may be drawn if we assume that $b_n \geq 0$ for all n, or if $b_n = 1$ for all n.

Rather than attempt to survey all known results in this area, we are content to exhibit examples of the main results of the primary types. In §2 we derive "Turán's First Main Theorem," in which $|z_n| \geq 1$ for all n. In §3 we apply the First Main Theorem to give a natural proof of the Fabry gap theorem. In §4 we consider a variant of the First Main Theorem in which ν is allowed to run over a longer range. In §5 we consider "Turán's Second Main Theorem," in which $\max |z_n| = 1$. Finally in §6 we treat non-negative b_n. In the next chapter we shall apply some of these last results to give lower bounds for various kinds of discrepancies in the theory of uniform distribution.

2. Turán's First Main Theorem. We now address the simplest situation described above.

THEOREM 1. (Turán's First Main Theorem) *Let s_ν be defined by* (1), *and suppose that $|z_n| \geq 1$ for all n. Then for any non-negative integer M there is an index ν in the interval $M + 1 \leq \nu \leq M + N$ such that*

$$(3) \qquad\qquad |s_\nu| \geq c(M, N)|s_0|$$

where

$$(4) \qquad\qquad c(M, N) = \left(\sum_{k=0}^{N-1} \binom{M + k}{k} 2^k \right)^{-1}.$$

The constant here is best possible, but because of its complicated structure in practice it is usually replaced by the slightly smaller quantity

$$(5) \qquad\qquad \left(\frac{N}{2e(M + N)} \right)^{N-1}.$$

To see that this number is indeed smaller, note that

$$\sum_{k=0}^{N-1} \binom{M + k}{k} 2^k \leq 2^{N-1} \sum_{k=0}^{N-1} \binom{M + k}{k}$$
$$= 2^{N-1} \binom{M + N}{N - 1}$$
$$\leq 2^{N-1} \frac{(M + N)^{N-1}}{(N - 1)!}.$$

Since $(N-1)! \geq (N/e)^{N-1}$, the above is

$$\leq \left(\frac{2e(M+N)}{N}\right)^{N-1}.$$

PROOF. We may assume that the z_n are distinct, for otherwise we could combine terms and replace N by a smaller number. Let $a_0, \ldots, a_{N-1}$ be complex numbers to be chosen later. Clearly

$$(6) \qquad \left|\sum_{\nu=0}^{N-1} a_\nu s_{M+1+\nu}\right| \leq \left(\sum_{\nu=0}^{N-1} |a_\nu|\right) \max_{M+1 \leq \nu \leq M+N} |s_\nu|.$$

The sum on the left is

$$\sum_{n=1}^{N} b_n z_n^{M+1} \sum_{\nu=0}^{N-1} a_\nu z_n^\nu = \sum_{n=1}^{N} b_n z_n^{M+1} p(z_n)$$

where $p(z) = \sum_{\nu=0}^{N-1} a_\nu z^\nu$. We choose the a_ν so that

$$(7) \qquad p(z_n) = z_n^{-M-1}$$

for $1 \leq n \leq N$. This is a non-singular linear system of N equations in N unknowns, so these equations determine the a_ν uniquely. To complete the proof it suffices to show that

$$(8) \qquad \sum_{\nu=0}^{N-1} |a_\nu| \leq \sum_{k=0}^{N-1} \binom{M+k}{k} 2^k.$$

To this end we express the polynomial $p(z)$ in the form

$$p(z) = \sum_{k=0}^{N-1} c_k \prod_{n=1}^{k} (z - z_n).$$

By the calculus of residues we may verify that

$$c_k = \frac{1}{2\pi i} \oint_{|z|=R} \frac{p(z)}{\prod_{n=1}^{k+1}(z - z_n)} dz$$

where R is chosen so that $R > |z_k|$ for all k. We observe that for any non-negative integer M,

$$\frac{1}{2\pi i} \oint_{|z|=R} \frac{z^{-M-1}}{\prod_{n=1}^{k+1}(z - z_n)} dz = 0$$

since the integrand is regular and $\ll R^{-2}$. Subtracting this from the former integral, we deduce that

$$c_k = \frac{1}{2\pi i} \oint_{|z|=R} \frac{p(z) - z^{-M-1}}{\prod_{n=1}^{k+1}(z - z_n)} dz.$$

In view of (7), the integrand is regular at each of the points z_n. Thus the only singularity in the integrand is the pole of order $M+1$ at $z = 0$. By Cauchy's

Theorem we may replace the contour of integration by a circle $|z| = r$ with $r < 1$. Since $p(z)/\prod_{n=1}^{k+1}(z - z_n)$ is regular on and within this new contour, we conclude that

$$c_k = \frac{-1}{2\pi i} \oint_{|z|=r} \frac{z^{-M-1}}{\prod_{n=1}^{k+1}(z - z_n)}\, dz$$

$$= \frac{(-1)^k}{z_1 \cdots z_{k+1} 2\pi i} \oint_{|z|=r} \prod_{n=1}^{k+1}\left(1 - \frac{z}{z_n}\right)^{-1} z^{-M-1}\, dz$$

$$= \frac{(-1)^k}{z_1 \cdots z_{k+1}} C_{M,k}$$

where

$$\prod_{n=1}^{k+1}\left(1 - \frac{z}{z_n}\right)^{-1} = \sum_{m=0}^{\infty} C_{M,k} z^m$$

for $|z| < 1$. Since the power series

$$\frac{1}{1 - z/z_n} = \sum_{m=0}^{\infty} z_n^{-m} z^m$$

has coefficients of modulus ≤ 1, and since

$$\left(\sum_{m=0}^{\infty} z^m\right)^{k+1} = (1 - z)^{-k-1} = \sum_{m=0}^{\infty} \binom{k+m}{k} z^m,$$

we deduce that $|C_{M,k}| \leq \binom{M+k}{k}$, and hence that

$$|c_k| \leq \frac{\binom{M+k}{k}}{|z_1 \cdots z_{k+1}|}.$$

On one hand we have

$$p(z) = \sum_{k=0}^{N-1} c_k \prod_{n=1}^{k}(z - z_n) = \sum_{\nu=0}^{N-1} a_\nu z^\nu.$$

Correspondingly, we put

$$P(z) = \sum_{k=0}^{N-1}\binom{M+k}{k}(z+1)^k = \sum_{\nu=0}^{N-1} A_\nu z^\nu.$$

On comparing coefficients we find that $|a_\nu| \leq A_\nu$, and hence that

$$\sum_{\nu=0}^{N-1}|a_\nu| \leq \sum_{\nu=0}^{N-1} A_\nu = P(1) = \sum_{k=0}^{N-1}\binom{M+k}{k}2^k,$$

This is (8), so the proof is complete.

   To see that the constant is best possible, observe that if all the z_n are very close to -1 then $C_{m,k}$ is approximately $(-1)^m\binom{k+m}{k}$, and hence c_k is approximately $(-1)^{m+1}\binom{m+k}{k}$. Consequently the respective coefficients of $(-1)^{M+1}p(z)$ and of $P(z)$ are approximately equal, and hence $\sum|a_\nu|$ is approximately $P(1)$. Finally, choose the b_n so that $s_\nu = 1$ for all ν in the range $M + 1 \leq \nu \leq M + N$. This system has a unique solution. With the b_n chosen in this way, we see that the two sides of (6) are nearly equal. Thus we may come as close as we like to achieving equality in (3).

In examples of the above sort it is not necessary that all the z_n be close to -1; it is sufficient for all the z_n to be close to some common value. On examining the above proof, one finds that in inequality in (3) is strict when $N > 1$, except when $s_0 = 0$. Thus the constant, though best possible, is not attained.

3. Fabry's Gap Theorem. As a representative application of the First Main Theorem, we prove the following useful result.

LEMMA 1. *Suppose that $T(x)$ is an exponential polynomial of N terms and period 1, say*

$$T(x) = \sum_{n=1}^{N} b_n e(\lambda_n x)$$

where the λ_n are integers. Let I be a closed arc of $\mathbb{T}$, and let L denote the length of I. Then

$$\max_I |T(x)| \geq \left(\frac{L}{2e}\right)^{N-1} \max_{\mathbb{T}} |T(x)|.$$

The striking feature of this bound is that it does not depend on the size of the λ_n. The constant on the right hand side is not best possible, but by considering the case $T(x) = \left(1 - e(x)\right)^{N-1}$, $I = [-L/2, L/2]$ we see that the inequality would be false if the factor were replaced by $\left(\frac{\pi}{2} L\right)^{N-1}$.

PROOF. By translating we may assume that $T(x)$ takes its maximum modulus at $x = 0$. If $0 \in I$ then the result is trivial, so we may assume that $I = [\alpha, \beta]$ with $0 < \alpha < \beta < 1$. Put $\delta = (\beta - \alpha)/N$, $M = [\alpha/\delta]$. Then $\nu\delta \in I$ for $M + 1 \leq \nu \leq M + N$. Take $z_n = e(\lambda_n \delta)$. With s_ν defined by (1), we see that $s_\nu = T(\nu\delta)$. Thus by the First Main Theorem with the smaller factor (5) it follows that

$$\max_I |T(x)| \geq \max_{M+1\leq\nu\leq M+N} |s_\nu| \geq \left(\frac{N}{2e(M+N)}\right)^{N-1} |T(0)|.$$

But

$$M \leq \frac{\alpha}{\delta} = \frac{\alpha N}{\beta - \alpha}$$

so that

$$M + N \leq \frac{\beta}{\beta - \alpha},$$

and hence

$$\frac{N}{M+N} \geq \frac{\beta - \alpha}{\beta} \geq \beta - \alpha = L.$$

Thus we have the stated result.

Suppose that $f(z)$ is a power series expressed in the form

(9)
$$f(z) = \sum_{n=1}^{\infty} a_n z^{\lambda_n}$$

where $0 \leq \lambda_1 < \lambda_2 < \cdots$. The Fabry gap theorem asserts ·that the circle of convergence of f is its natural boundary, if $\lambda_n/n \longrightarrow \infty$ as $n \longrightarrow \infty$. To prove this, we shall apply Lemma 1 to the power series expansion of $f^{(k)}(z)$. However, this latter expansion has infinitely many terms, whereas Lemma 1 applies only to finite sums. Consequently we must first truncate the expansion, so as to make Lemma 1 applicable. We accomplish this as follows.

LEMMA 2. *If f is regular for $|z| < 1$, and if $0 < r < 1$, then there is a positive number $C = C(r)$ such that*

$$\sum_{n>Ck} \binom{n}{k} \left| \frac{f^{(n)}(0)}{n!} \right| r^{n-k} < 1$$

for all sufficiently large k, say $k > k_0(f, r)$.

PROOF. Clearly $\binom{n}{k} < n^k/k! < (en/k)^k$. By the Cauchy inequalities we also see that $\left| f^{(n)}(0)/n! \right| < r^{-n/2}$ for all $n > n_0(f, r)$. Thus the sum above is majorized by

$$\sum_{n>Ck} \left(\frac{en}{k} \right)^k r^{(n-2k)/2}.$$

The ratio between consecutive terms is $\left(\frac{n+1}{n} \right)^k r^{1/2} < e^{k/n} r^{1/2}$, which is $< r^{-1/3}$ if $n > Ck$ and $C > 6/\log \frac{1}{r}$. Hence the sum is

$$\ll_r \left(eCr^{(C-2)/2} \right)^k.$$

By choosing C large as a function of r we may make the base of the exponential $< 1/2$. For such a C, the original sum is < 1 if $k > k_0(f, r)$.

THEOREM 2. (Fabry) *Suppose that the power series (9) has radius of convergence 1, where $0 \leq \lambda_1 < \lambda_2 < \cdots$. If $\lim_{n\to\infty} \lambda_n/n = \infty$ then the circle of convergence $|z| = 1$ is a natural boundary of f.*

PROOF. Suppose that f is regular at some point on the unit circle $|z| = 1$. Without loss of generality we may suppose that f is regular at $z = 1$. Thus f is regular for $|z - 1| \leq 3\pi\delta$, if δ is sufficiently small. Let r be fixed, $0 < r < 1$. (Any r will do.) Let δ' be determined by the relation $|r - e(\delta/2)| = 1 - r + \delta'$. Thus $\delta' > 0$. Put $\mathcal{S} = \{z \in \mathbb{C} : |z| \leq 1 - \delta'/2\} \cup \{z \in \mathbb{C} : |z - 1| \leq 2\pi\delta\}$. Since $\mathcal{S}$ is a compact set contained within the domain of analyticity of f, the quantity $\mu = \max_{z \in \mathcal{S}} |f(z)|$ is finite. If δ is small then the disk $|z - re(\alpha)| \leq 1 - r + \delta'/3$ lies within $\mathcal{S}$ provided that $|\alpha| \leq \delta/2$. Hence by the Cauchy coefficient inequalities,

(10)
$$\left| \frac{f^{(k)}(re(\alpha))}{k!} \right| \leq \frac{\mu}{(1 - r + \delta'/3)^k}$$

when $|\alpha| \leq \delta/3$. But

$$\frac{f^{(k)}(re(\alpha))}{k!} = \sum_{n=k}^{\infty} \binom{n}{k} \frac{f^{(n)}(0)}{n!} z^{n-k},$$

so by Lemma 2 we see that

(11)
$$\left| \frac{f^{(k)}(re(\alpha))}{k!} - \sum_{n=0}^{Ck} \binom{n}{k} \frac{f^{(n)}(0)}{n!} r^{n-k} e((n-k)\alpha) \right| < 1$$

for all large k, uniformly in α. Let $N(X)$ denote the number of $\lambda_n \leq X$. That is, $N(X)$ is the number of $n \leq X$ such that $f^{(n)}(0) \neq 0$. By Lemma 1 it follows that

$$\max_{\alpha} \left| \sum_{n=0}^{Ck} \binom{n}{k} \frac{f^{(n)}(0)}{n!} r^{n-k} e((n-k)\alpha) \right|$$

$$\leq \left(\frac{2e}{\delta} \right)^{N(Ck)} \max_{|\alpha| \leq \delta/2} \left| \sum_{n=0}^{Ck} \binom{n}{k} \frac{f^{(n)}(0)}{n!} r^{n-k} e((n-k)\alpha) \right|.$$

Hence by (10), (11),

$$\max_{\alpha} \left| \frac{f^{(k)}(re(\alpha))}{k!} \right| \leq 1 + \left(\frac{2e}{\delta} \right)^{N(Ck)} \left(1 + \frac{\mu}{(1-r+\delta'/3)^k} \right).$$

By hypothesis, $N(X) = o(X)$ as $X \to \infty$. Hence

$$\left| \frac{f^{(k)}(re(\alpha))}{k!} \right| \leq \frac{1}{(1-r+\delta'/4)^k}$$

for all large k, uniformly in α. That is, the power series expansion of f about the point $re(\alpha)$ has radius of convergence $\geq 1 - r + \delta'/4$, for every α. Consequently f is regular in the disk $|z| < 1 + \delta'/4$. Since this contradicts the hypothesis that the power series (9) has radius of convergence 1, the proof is complete.

4. Longer Ranges of ν. We now consider how the constant in Turán's First Main Theorem might be improved if we allow ν to run over a longer range. For simplicity we restrict our attention to the case $M = 0$. To construct a polynomial with the desired properties, we first establish the following auxiliary result.

LEMMA 3. *For any positive integer d there is a polynomial $Q(z)$ of degree d such that $Q(0) = 1$, $Q(1) = 1$, and for which $\max_{|z| \leq 1} |Q(z)| \leq 1 + 2/d$.*

The constant 2 might be improved somewhat, but it can not be replaced by a number less than 1. To see this, note that

$$\sum_{k=0}^{d} Q\left(e(\frac{k}{d+1})\right) = d + 1$$

since the constant term of $Q(z)$ is 1. Since $Q(1) = 0$, the above sum has absolute value at most $d \max_{|z| \leq 1} |Q(z)|$, and hence $\max_{|z| \leq 1} |Q(z)| \geq 1 + 1/d$.

PROOF. We construct a polynomial $R(z)$ of degree d such that $R(0) = 0$, $R(1) \geq 1/2$, and $|R(z) - R(1)| \leq R(1) + 1/d$ when $|z| \leq 1$. Then

$$Q(z) = 1 - \frac{R(z)}{R(1)}$$

has the desired properties.

Let $f(z)$ be the linear fractional map for such that $f(-1) = -1/d$, $f(0) = 0$, $f(1) = 1$. Thus $f(z)$ maps the unit disk $|z| \leq 1$ to the disk $\mathcal{D}_1$ whose diameter is the line segment $[-1/d, 1]$. We may write $f(z)$ explicitly,

$$f(z) = \frac{2z}{d+1-(d-1)z} = \frac{2z}{d+1} \sum_{k=0}^{\infty} \left(\frac{d-1}{d+1}\right)^k z^k.$$

We take $R(z)$ to be a Cesàro partial-sum of this power series:

$$(12) \qquad R(z) = \frac{2z}{d+1} \sum_{k=0}^{d-1} \left(1 - \frac{k+1}{d+1}\right) \left(\frac{d-1}{d+1}\right)^k z^k$$

$$(13) \qquad = \frac{2z}{d+1-(d-1)z} - \frac{2z\left(1 - \left(\frac{d-1}{d+1}z\right)^{d+1}\right)}{(d+1-(d-1)z)^2}.$$

From (12) it is clear that $R(z)$ has degree d and that $R(0) = 0$, and from (13) it is clear that $R(1) = \frac{1}{2} + \frac{1}{2}\left(\frac{d-1}{d+1}\right)^{d+1} > 1/2$. On writing $z = re(\theta)$ we see also that

$$R(z) = \int_{\mathbb{T}} f(re(\phi)) \Delta_d(\theta - \phi) \, d\phi$$

for $r \leq 1$, where Δ_d is the Fejér kernel, as given in (16) of Chapter 1. Thus $R(z)$ is a weighted average of the values $f(re(\phi))$. Since these values are all in $\mathcal{D}_1$, and since $\mathcal{D}_1$ is convex, it follows that $R(z) \in \mathcal{D}_1$. Let $\mathcal{D}_2$ denote the disk with center $R(1)$ and radius $R(1) + 1/d$. Since $R(1) > 1/2$ we see that $\mathcal{D}_1 \subset \mathcal{D}_2$. That is, $|R(z) - R(1)| \leq R(1) + 1/d$ when $|z| \leq 1$. This completes the proof.

THEOREM 3. *Let s_ν be as in (1), and suppose that $|z_n| \geq 1$ for all n. If $N \leq H \leq N^2$ then*

$$\sum_{\nu=1}^{H} |s_\nu|^2 \geq e^{-8N^2/H} |s_0|^2.$$

If $H \geq N^2$ then

$$\sum_{\nu=1}^{H} |s_\nu|^2 \gg HN^{-2}|s_0|^2.$$

We note in particular that if $|z_n| \geq 1$ for all n then

$$\max_{1 \leq \nu \leq N^2} \gg \frac{|s_0|}{N}.$$

PROOF. Let numbers a_ν be chosen later. By Cauchy's inequality we see that

$$\left| \sum_{\nu=1}^{H} a_\nu s_\nu \right| \leq \left(\sum_{\nu=1}^{H} |a_\nu|^2 \right)^{1/2} \left(\sum_{\nu=1}^{H} |s_\nu|^2 \right)^{1/2}.$$

The sum on the left is

$$\sum_{\nu=1}^{H} a_\nu \sum_{n=1}^{N} b_n z_n^\nu = \sum_{n=1}^{N} b_n \sum_{\nu=1}^{H} a_\nu z_n^\nu = \sum_{n=1}^{N} b_n p(z_n)$$

where $p(z) = \sum_{\nu=1}^{H} a_\nu z^\nu$. Here $p(z)$ is a polynomial of degree $\leq H$ with $p(0) = 0$. If in addition, $p(z_n) = 1$ for all n, then the sum on the right above is s_0. We wish to find such a polynomial for which

$$\sum_{\nu=1}^{H} |a_\nu|^2 = \int_{\mathbb{T}} |p(e(\theta))|^2 \, d\theta$$

is small. We let $Q(z)$ be as in Lemma 3, and set

$$p(z) = 1 - \prod_{n=1}^{N} Q(z/z_n).$$

Then $p(z_n) = 1$ for all n, and $p(0) = 0$. To ensure that $\deg p \leq H$ we take $d = [H/N]$ in Lemma 3. Thus

$$1 + \sum_{\nu=1}^{H} |a_\nu|^2 = \int_{\mathbb{T}} \left| \prod_{n=1}^{N} Q(e(\theta)/z_n) \right|^2 d\theta \leq \left(1 + \frac{2}{d} \right)^{2N}$$

since $|z_n| \geq 1$ for all n. Since $d \geq \frac{1}{2} H N^{-1}$, it follows that

$$\sum_{\nu=1}^{H} |a_\nu|^2 \leq \left(1 + \frac{4N}{H} \right)^{2N} - 1 < e^{8N^2/H} - 1.$$

This suffices to prove the two asserted inequalities.

5. Turán's Second Main Theorem. Theorems 1 and 3 give lower bounds for $\max |s_\nu|$ in terms of $|s_0|$ and $\left(\min_n |z_n| \right)^\nu$. We now seek similar results, in which the lower bound involves $|s_0|$ and $\left(\max_n |z_n| \right)^\nu$. By homogeneity, we may assume that $\max_n |z_n| = 1$. We encounter an immediate obstacle.

EXAMPLE 1. Let $z_1 = 1$, $z_n = \epsilon$ for $n > 1$, $b_1 = \epsilon$, and $b_n = 1/(N-1)$ for $n > 1$. Then $s_0 = 1 + \epsilon$, but $s_\nu = \epsilon + \epsilon^\nu$ for all $\nu > 0$.

Thus we see that some compromise is necessary.

THEOREM 4. (Turán's Second Main Theorem) *Let s_ν be defined as in (1),
and suppose that $1 = |z_1| \geq |z_2| \geq \ldots \geq |z_N|$. Then for any non-negative integer
M there is an integer ν, $M + 1 \leq \nu \leq M + N$ such that*

$$|s_\nu| \geq 2\left(\frac{N}{8e(M+N)}\right)^N \min_{1 \leq j \leq N} \sum_{n=1}^{j} b_n.$$

PROOF. We may suppose that the z_n are distinct, for otherwise terms may
be combined and we can consider a smaller value of N. For arbitrary numbers
a_ν,

$$\sum_{\nu=0}^{N-1} a_\nu s_{M+1+\nu} = \sum_{n=1}^{N} b_n z_n^{M+1} \sum_{\nu=0}^{N-1} a_\nu z_n^\nu = \sum_{n=1}^{N} b_n z_n^{M+1} p(z_n)$$

where $p(z) = \sum_{\nu=0}^{N-1} a_\nu z^\nu$. Suppose that $p(z_n) = z_n^{-M-1}$ for $1 \leq n \leq j$, and that
$p(z_n) = 0$ for $j < n \leq N$. For any given j, there exists a unique such $p(z)$. Then

$$\left|\sum_{n=1}^{j} b_n\right| \leq \left(\sum_{\nu=0}^{N-1} |a_\nu|\right) \max_{M+1 \leq n \leq M+N} |s_\nu|.$$

To complete the proof it suffices to show that j can be chosen so that

(14)
$$\sum_{\nu=0}^{N-1} |a_\nu| \leq \frac{1}{2}\left(\frac{8e(M+N)}{N}\right)^N.$$

Write

$$p(z) = \sum_{k=0}^{N-1} c_k \prod_{n=1}^{k} (z - z_n).$$

If $R > 1$ then

$$c_k = \frac{1}{2\pi i} \oint_{|z|=R} \frac{p(z)}{\prod_{n=1}^{k+1}(z - z_n)} dz$$

$$= \frac{1}{2\pi i} \oint_{|z|=R} \frac{p(z) - z^{-M-1}}{\prod_{n=1}^{k+1}(z - z_n)} dz.$$

Suppose that $r < 1$, and that $|z_j| < r < |z_{j+1}|$. Since the integrand is regular in
the annulus $r \leq |z| \leq R$, the integral above is

$$= \frac{1}{2\pi i} \oint_{|z|=r} \frac{p(z) - z^{-M-1}}{\prod_{n=1}^{k+1}(z - z_n)} dz.$$

We choose r later as a function of $|z_2|, \ldots, |z_N|$. This choice then determines
the value of j. Since $p(z_n) = 0$ when $|z_n| < r$, we deduce that

$$c_k = \frac{-1}{2\pi i} \oint_{|z|=r} \frac{z^{-M-1}}{\prod_{n=1}^{k+1}(z - z_n)} dz.$$

Hence

$$|c_k| \le \frac{1}{r^M \prod_{n=1}^{k+1} \left| r - |z_n| \right|}.$$

But $0 < r < 1$ and $|z_n| \le 1$ for all n, so that $\left| r - |z_n| \right| \le 1$ for all n. Thus the above is

$$\le \frac{1}{r^M \prod_{n=1}^{N} \left| r - |z_n| \right|}.$$

We wish to find an r for which the product in the denominator is not too small. To this end we recall a theorem of Chebyshev (see p. 149 of Korneichuk [17], Theorem 7.3 of Powell [27], p. 31 of Rivlin [30], or pp. 41–42 of Szegö [34]) that asserts that if $F(z)$ is a monic polynomial of degree d and if I is an interval in $\mathbb{R}$ of length L then

$$\max_{z \in I} |F(z)| \ge 2\left(\frac{L}{4}\right)^N.$$

Take $F(z) = \prod_{n=1}^{N}(z - |z_n|)$ and put $I = [r_0, 1]$ where $0 < r_0 < 1$. Then there is an r, $r_0 \le r \le 1$, such that $|F(r)| \ge 2\left(\frac{1-r_0}{4}\right)^N$. For such an r we see that

$$|c_k| \le \frac{1}{2} r_0^{-M} \left(\frac{4}{1-r_0}\right)^N$$

for all k. Take $r_0 = M/(M+N)$. Since $r_0^{-M} = (1 + N/M)^M < e^N$, we see that $c_k| \le C$ for all k where

$$C = \frac{1}{2}\left(\frac{4e(M+N)}{N}\right)^N.$$

Put

$$P(z) = C \sum_{k=0}^{N-1}(z+1)^k = \sum_{\nu=0}^{N-1} A_\nu z^\nu,$$

say. Then $|a_\nu| \le A_\nu$ for all ν, and hence

$$\sum_{\nu=0}^{N-1} |a_\nu| \le \sum_{\nu=0}^{N-1} A_\nu = P(1) = C(2^N - 1) < \frac{1}{2}\left(\frac{8e(M+N)}{N}\right)^N.$$

Thus we have (14), and the proof is complete.

The constant we have obtained in the Second Main Theorem is not the best possible, but we see from the following two examples that it is not far from the truth.

EXAMPLE 2. An identity of Euler asserts that if $f(z) = \prod_{n=1}^{N}(z - z_n)$ with distinct z_n then

$$\sum_{n=1}^{N} \frac{z_n^\nu}{f'(z_n)} = \begin{cases} 0 & \text{for } \nu = 0,\dots,N-2, \\ 1 & \text{when } \nu = N-1. \end{cases}$$

(To prove this put

$$Q(z) = \sum_{n=1}^{N} \frac{z_n^{\nu} f(z)}{f'(z_n)(z - z_n)}.$$

Then $Q(z)$ is a polynomial of degree at most $N - 1$. Also, $Q(z_n) = z_n^{\nu}$ for $1 \le n \le N$. If $\nu < N$ then it follows that $Q(z) \equiv z^{\nu}$. The sum in question is the coefficient of z^{N-1} of $Q(z)$.) We let $z_n = 1 - (n - 1)/N$ for $1 \le n \le N$, and put $b_n = \left(z_n f'(z_n)\right)^{-1}$. Thus by Euler's identity $s_{\nu} = 0$ for $1 \le \nu \le N - 1$, and $s_N = 1$. To evaluate the partial sums of the b_n we note that

$$f'(z_n) = \prod_{\substack{1 \le m \le N \\ m \ne n}} (z_n - z_m) = \frac{(-1)^{n-1}(n - 1)!(N - n)!}{N^{N-1}},$$

so that

$$z_n f'(z_n) = \frac{(-1)^{n-1}(n - 1)!(N - n + 1)!}{N^N}.$$

Hence

$$\sum_{n=1}^{j} b_n = \frac{N^N}{N!} \sum_{n=1}^{j} (-1)^{n-1} \binom{N}{n - 1} = \frac{N^N}{N!}(-1)^j \binom{N - 1}{j - 1},$$

and we see that

$$\min_j \left| \sum_{n=1}^{j} b_n \right| = \frac{N^N}{N!} > \frac{e^N}{N}.$$

Thus we conclude that the constant on the right hand side in the Second Main Theorem can not be larger than N/e^N when $M = 0$.

We next consider an example that is instructive when M is large.

EXAMPLE 3. By the binomial theorem we see that

$$(\cos 2\pi\theta)^{N-1} = \sum_{n=1}^{N-1} 2^{-N+1} \binom{N - 1}{n - 1} e\big((2n - 1 - N)\theta\big).$$

Hence if we take $b_n = 2^{-N+1} \binom{N-1}{n-1}$ and $z_n = e\big((2n - 1 - N)\theta\big)$ then $s_{\nu} = (\cos 2\pi\nu\theta)^{N-1}$. We take $\theta = 1/(2(2M + N + 1))$, so that $|\nu\theta - 1/4| \le \frac{N-1}{4(2M+N+1)}$ when $M + 1 \le \nu \le M + N$. Thus

$$\max_{M+1 \le \nu \le M+N} |s_{\nu}| = \left(\sin \frac{\pi(N - 1)}{2(2M + N + 1)} \right)^{N-1} < \left(\frac{\pi(N - 1)}{2(2M + N + 1)} \right)^{N-1}.$$

Since $|z_n| = 1$ for all n, this example applies to both the First and Second Main Theorems. We note that in the present situation, $s_0 = 1$ and $\min_j \left| \sum_{n=1}^{j} b_n \right| = 2^{-N+1}$.

We conclude this discussion with an example that demonstrates that the factor $\min_j \left| \sum_{n=1}^{j} b_n \right|$ in the Second Main Theorem can not be replaced by the simpler quantity $\min_n |b_n|$.

EXAMPLE 4. Take $z_n = 1$ for all n, $b_1 = 1$, and $b_n = -1/(N-1)$ for $2 \leq n \leq N$. Then $s_\nu = 0$ for all ν, but $\min_n |b_n| > 0$.

6. Special Coefficients b_n. We begin by considering the case in which $b_n = 1$ for all n, so that

$$(15) \qquad s_\nu = \sum_{n=1}^{N} z_n^\nu.$$

For this sum we obtain much better lower bounds.

THEOREM 5. *If s_ν is given by (15), and if $|z_n| \geq 1$ for all n, then there is a ν, $1 \leq \nu \leq N$, such that $|s_\nu| \geq 1$.*

PROOF. For $1 \leq j \leq N$, let σ_j denote the jth elementary symmetric function of the numbers z_n. It is also convenient to set $\sigma_0 = 1$. The Newton-Girard identities assert that

$$(16) \qquad r\sigma_r = \sum_{\nu=1}^{r} (-1)^{\nu-1} \sigma_{r-\nu} s_\nu$$

for $1 \leq r \leq N$. Let r be the least positive integer for which $|\sigma_r| \geq 1$. We know that there is such an r with $1 \leq r \leq N$, since $|\sigma_N| = |z_1 \cdots z_N| \geq 1$. With r chosen in this way, it follows that

$$r \leq r|\sigma_r| = \left| \sum_{\nu=1}^{r} (-1)^{\nu-1} \sigma_{r-\nu} s_\nu \right| \leq \sum_{\nu=1}^{r} |s_\nu|.$$

Hence we must have $|s_\nu| \geq 1$ for at least one ν in the range $1 \leq \nu \leq r$.

EXAMPLE 5. Suppose that $z_n = e(n/(N+1))$ for $1 \leq n \leq N$. Then $s_\nu = -1$ for $1 \leq n \leq N$ where s_ν is defined by (15). Thus Theorem 5 is best possible.

THEOREM 6. *Let s_ν be defined by (15). If s_ν is real for all positive integers ν, then $s_\nu \geq 0$ for some integer ν in the range $1 \leq \nu \leq N+1$.*

PROOF. By (16) and induction we deduce that σ_j is real for all j, and hence we see that the hypothesis that the s_ν are real is equivalent to the assertion that the z_n occur in complex-conjugate pairs. Suppose that $s_\nu < 0$ for $1 \leq \nu \leq N$. By inducting in (16) we deduce that $(-1)^j \sigma_j > 0$ for $1 \leq j \leq N$. In addition to the identities (16), a second set of Newton-Girard identities assert that

$$s_{M+N+1} = \sum_{\nu=M+1}^{M+N} s_\nu (-1)^{M+N-\nu} \sigma_{M+N+1-\nu}$$

for $M \geq 0$. Taking $M = 0$, we see that $s_\nu < 0$ and $(-1)^{N-\nu} \sigma_{N+1-\nu} < 0$ for $1 \leq \nu \leq N$, so that all summands on the right hand side are positive. hence $s_{N+1} > 0$, and the proof is complete.

Although the result just proved might seem to be of rather special interest, we use it to prove the following more central result.

THEOREM 7. *Let s_ν be defined by* (15), *and suppose that* $\max_n |z_n| = 1$. *Then* $|s_\nu| \geq 1$ *for some ν in the range* $1 \leq \nu \leq 2N - 1$.

PROOF. Without loss of generality $|z_N| = 1$. By replacing z_n by z_n/z_N we may suppose further that $z_N = 1$. Put

$$t_\nu = \sum_{n=1}^{N-1} z_n^\nu + \overline{z_n}^{-\nu}.$$

By the preceding theorem we see that $t_\nu \geq 0$ for some ν, $1 \leq \nu \leq 2N - 1$. But $\Re s_\nu = 1 + t_\nu/2$, and hence $|s_\nu| \geq \Re s_\nu \geq 1$.

We now turn to a family of results that depend on the properties of Fejér's kernel.

THEOREM 8. *Let s_ν be given by* (1) *where $b_n \geq 0$ and $|z_n| = 1$ for all n. Then*

$$\sum_{\nu=1}^{K} |s_\nu|^2 \geq \frac{K+1}{2} \sum_{n=1}^{N} |b_n|^2 - \frac{1}{2}\left(\sum_{n=1}^{N} b_n\right)^2.$$

From this we see that if $b_n = 1$ and $|z_n| = 1$ for all n then for any $\epsilon > 0$ there is a $C(\epsilon) > 0$ such that $|s_\nu| \geq C(\epsilon)\sqrt{N}$ for some ν in the interval $1 \leq \nu \leq (1+\epsilon)N$. In particular,

$$(17) \qquad\qquad\qquad |s_\nu| \geq \sqrt{N/2}$$

for some ν, $1 \leq \nu \leq 2N$. Here for the first time we are able to confirm our intuition that a power sum must occasionally be as large as the ℓ^2-norm of its coefficients.

PROOF. Write $z_n = e(\theta_n)$. The left hand side above is

$$\geq \sum_{\nu=1}^{K}\left(1 - \frac{\nu}{K+1}\right)|s_\nu|^2 = \sum_{m,n} b_m b_n \sum_{\nu=1}^{K}\left(1 - \frac{\nu}{K+1}\right)e\big(\nu(\theta_m - \theta_n)\big).$$

This expression is real, and hence is unaffected if we take real parts of each term. Thus the above is

$$\sum_{m,n} b_m b_n \sum_{\nu=1}^{K}\left(1 - \frac{\nu}{K+1}\right)\cos 2\pi\nu(\theta_m - \theta_n)$$

$$= \sum_{m,n} b_m b_n \left(\frac{1}{2}\Delta_{K+1}(\theta_m - \theta_n) - \frac{1}{2}\right)$$

$$= \frac{1}{2}\sum_{m,n} b_m b_n \Delta_{K+1}(\theta_m - \theta_n) - \frac{1}{2}\left(\sum_n b_n\right)^2.$$

Here $\Delta_{K+1}(\theta)$ is Fejér's kernel, as given in (16) of Chapter 1. Since $\Delta_{K+1}(\theta) \geq 0$ for all θ, and since $\Delta_{K+1}(0) = K + 1$, it follows that the above is

$$\geq \frac{K+1}{2}\sum_n b_n^2 - \frac{1}{2}\left(\sum_n b_n\right)^2.$$

The following variant of Theorem 8 is useful.

THEOREM 9. *Let f be an even, continuous function of period 1, and suppose that $\widehat{f}(n) \geq 0$ for all non-zero n. Then for any real number θ,*

$$(18) \qquad \sum_{k=1}^{K} \left(1 - \frac{k}{K+1}\right) f(k\theta) \geq \frac{K+1}{2} \int_{\mathbb{T}} f(x)\,dx - \frac{1}{2} f(0).$$

Here the power sum is the Fourier expansion of f; it may involve infinitely many terms, but it is absolutely convergent.

PROOF. If we replace f by $f + c$ where c is some real constant, then both sides of (18) are increased by the amount $Kc/2$. Hence we may assume that $\widehat{f}(0) \geq 0$, so that $\widehat{f}(n) \geq 0$ for all n. Since f is continuous, the Cesàro partial sums of its Fourier expansion converge uniformly to $f(x)$. For $x = 0$ this gives the relation

$$f(0) = \lim_{N\to\infty} \sum_{n=-N}^{N} \left(1 - \frac{|n|}{N+1}\right) \widehat{f}(n).$$

Since the sum on the right is monotonically increasing in N, we deduce that the Fourier expansion of f converges absolutely to $f(x)$. Thus the left hand side of (18) is

$$\sum_n \widehat{f}(n) \sum_{k=-K}^{K} \left(1 - \frac{|k|}{K+1}\right) e(nk\theta).$$

This expression is real, so its value is unaltered if we replace each term by its real part. Consequently the above is

$$= \sum_n \widehat{f}(n) \left(\frac{1}{2}\Delta_{K+1}(n\theta) - \frac{1}{2}\right)$$

$$= \frac{1}{2}\sum_n \widehat{f}(n)\Delta_{K+1}(n\theta) - \frac{1}{2}\sum_n \widehat{f}(n).$$

In the first sum, the term $n = 0$ contributes the amount $\widehat{f}(0)(K+1)$, and the other terms are non-negative. The second sum is $f(0)$. Thus we have (18), and the proof is complete.

Suppose we take $f(x) = \max(0, 1 - \|x\|/\delta)$ in Theorem 9. Then $\widehat{f}(n) = (\pi n)^{-2}\delta^{-1}(\sin \pi n\delta)^2 \geq 0$, so the hypotheses are satisfied, $\int_{\mathbb{T}} f(x)\,dx = \delta$, and $f(0) = 1$. Hence the right hand side of (18) is $((K+1)\delta - 1)/2$, which is positive if $\delta > 1/(K+1)$. For such δ there must be at least one positive term on the left hand side of (18). That is, $\|k\theta\| < \delta$ for some k, $1 \leq k \leq K$. Since this holds for every $\delta > 1/(K+1)$, we conclude that $\|k\theta\| \leq 1/(K+1)$ for some k, $1 \leq k \leq K$. This is Dirichlet's theorem. Since Theorem 9 can be extended to functions of several variables, we can prove Dirichlet's theorem for simultaneous approximation in the same way. Thus we can use power sum techniques to derive the inequality (2) of our opening remarks. We now apply Theorem 8 with s_ν replaced by s_ν^m to obtain estimates intermediate between (2) and (17).

THEOREM 10. *Suppose that s_ν is defined by (15), and that $|z_n| = 1$ for all n. Suppose that m is a positive integer, $1 \le m \le N/2$. Then*

$$|s_\nu| \ge \frac{1}{4}(mN)^{1/2}$$

for at least one integral ν, $1 \le \nu \le (12N/m)^m$.

By taking $m = 1$ we obtain a slightly weakened version of (17); by taking $m = [N/2]$ we obtain a slightly weakened version of (2).

PROOF. Take $K = \left[(12N/m)^m\right]$, and set $\mu = \max_{1 \le \nu \le K} |s_\nu|$. Then

$$\frac{1}{2}\left(\frac{12N}{m}\right)^m \mu^{2m} \ge \frac{K}{2}\mu^{2m}$$

(19)
$$\ge \sum_{\nu=1}^{K}\left(1 - \frac{\nu}{K+1}\right)|s_\nu|^{2m}.$$

By the multinomial theorem we see that

$$s_\nu^m = \sum_{\mathbf{m}}\binom{m}{m_1 \ldots m_N}\left(z_1^{m_1}\cdots z_N^{m_N}\right)^\nu$$

where the sum extends over those $\mathbf{m} = (m_1, \ldots, m_N)$ with non-negative integral coordinates such that $m_1 + \cdots + m_N = m$. Thus by Theorem 8 we see that the expression (19) is

$$\ge \frac{K+1}{2}\sum_{\mathbf{m}}\binom{m}{m_1 \ldots m_N}^2 - \frac{1}{2}\left(\sum_{\mathbf{m}}\binom{m}{m_1 \ldots m_N}\right)^2.$$

Here the second sum is N^m, by the multinomial theorem. To derive a lower bound for the first sum, we restrict our attention to those $\mathbf{m}$ whose coordinates are all 0 or 1. There are precisely $\binom{N}{m}$ such $\mathbf{m}$, and for such $\mathbf{m}$ the multinomial coefficient is $m!$. Thus the expression above is

$$\ge \frac{K+1}{2}\binom{N}{m}m!^2 - \frac{1}{2}N^{2m}.$$

Here $K+1 \ge (12N/m)^m$. Also, $\binom{N}{m}m! = N(N-1)\cdots(N-m+1) \ge (N/2)^m$ since $m \le N/2$. Finally, $m! \ge (m/e)^m$. On multiplying these inequalities together we see that the above is

$$\ge \frac{1}{2}N^{2m}\left(\left(\frac{6}{e}\right)^m - 1\right)$$
$$\ge \frac{1}{2}N^{2m}$$

since $e < 3$ and $m \ge 1$. That is, $\mu \ge \sqrt{mN/12}$, which suffices.

It would be helpful to have examples to show that the above theorem is close to being best possible. The following example in this direction draws on arithmetic exponential sums, but is limited to $1 \leq \nu \leq N^{2-\epsilon}$.

EXAMPLE 6. Let χ be a Dirichlet character (mod p) of order $p-1$. Then from basic properties of Gauss sums (see pp. 30, 65–67 of Davenport [7]), we see that

$$\left| \sum_{n=1}^{p-1} \left(\chi(n)e(n/p) \right)^{\nu} \right| = \begin{cases} p^{1/2} & \text{if } p \nmid \nu, \ (p-1) \nmid \nu, \\ 0 & \text{if } p \mid \nu, \ (p-1) \nmid \nu, \\ 1 & \text{if } p \nmid \nu, \ (p-1) \mid \nu, \\ p-1 & \text{if } p \mid \nu, \ (p-1) \mid \nu. \end{cases}$$

Here $N = p - 1$ and $s_\nu \ll \sqrt{N}$ for $\nu < p(p-1)$. To extend this to general N let p_0 be the largest prime not exceeding N, and put $N_1 = N - p_0 + 1$. Then iterate this, so that p_i is the larges prime not exceeding N_i, and put $N_{i+1} = N_i - p_i + 1$. Repeat this until $N_k = 1$ or 2. Thus $N = \sum (p_i - 1)$ with $p_{i+1} - 1 \leq (p_i - 1)/2$. By applying the above construction to blocks of length $p_i - 1$, we deduce that $s_\nu \ll N^{1/2}$ for $\nu \leq N^{2-\epsilon}$.

We next consider how the Fejér kernel technique can be used when the hypothesis $|z_n| = 1$ is weakened to $\max_n |z_n| = 1$.

THEOREM 11. *Let s_ν be given by (1), where $b_1 > 0$, $b_n \geq 0$ for all n, and $\max_n |z_n| = |z_1| = 1$. If $c > 0$ then*

$$\max_{1 \leq \nu \leq K} \Re s_\nu \geq \frac{cb_1}{4(4+c)}$$

provided that $K \geq (4+c)s_0/b_1$.

PROOF. Let $P(z) = 1/2 + \sum_{\nu=1}^{K}(1 - \frac{\nu}{K+1})z^\nu$. Thus $\Re P(e(\theta)) = \Delta_{K+1}(\theta)/2 \geq 0$. But $\Re P(z)$ is a harmonic function, and hence $\Re P(z) \geq 0$ whenever $|z| \leq 1$. Write $z_n = r_n e(\theta_n)$. Then

$$\sum_{\nu=1}^{K} \left(1 - \frac{\nu}{K+1} \right)(1 + \cos 2\pi\nu\theta_1)\Re s_\nu$$

$$= \sum_{n=1}^{N} b_n \sum_{\nu=1}^{K} \left(1 - \frac{\nu}{K+1} \right) r_n^\nu (1 + \cos 2\pi\nu\theta_1) \cos 2\pi\nu\theta_n$$

$$= \sum_{n=1}^{N} b_n \Re \left(P(z_n) + \frac{1}{2}P(r_n e(\theta_n - \theta_1)) + \frac{1}{2}P(r_n e(\theta_n - \theta_1)) - 1 \right).$$

Since $P(r_1) = P(1) = (K+1)/2$, we deduce that the above is

$$\geq \frac{(K+1)b_1}{4} - s_0$$

$$\geq \frac{cKb_1}{4(4+c)}$$

since $s_0 \leq Kb_1/(4+c)$ by hypothesis. But

$$\sum_{\nu=1}^{K}\Big(1-\frac{\nu}{K+1}\Big)(1+\cos 2\pi\nu\theta_1) \leq 2\sum_{\nu=1}^{K}\Big(1-\frac{\nu}{K+1}\Big) = K,$$

so we have the stated result.

EXAMPLE 7. If $z_n = e(\frac{2n-1}{4N})$ for $1 \leq n \leq N$ and s_ν is defined by (15) then $\Re s_\nu = 0$ for $1 \leq \nu < 4N$ except that $s_{2N} = -N$. Thus $\Re s_\nu \leq 0$ when $0 < \nu < 4N$. Consequently the lower bound for K in Theorem 11 can not be reduced. A second example of this type is obtained by taking $z_n = e(\frac{n}{N}+\frac{1}{N})$.

For use in the next chapter, we conclude this section by formulating a two-dimensional analogue of Theorem 8.

THEOREM 12. *Let* $\mathbf{u}_1,\ldots,\mathbf{u}_N$ *be points in* $\mathbb{T}^2$. *Then*

$$\sum_{\substack{|k_1|\leq X_1 \\ |k_2|\leq X_2 \\ \mathbf{k}\neq\mathbf{0}}} \Big|\sum_{n=1}^{N} e(\mathbf{k}\cdot\mathbf{u}_n)\Big|^2 \geq NX_1X_2 - N^2$$

for any positive real numbers X_1, X_2.

PROOF. Let $K_i = [X_i]$ for $i = 1, 2$. It suffices to show that

$$\sum_{|k_1|\leq K_1}\sum_{|k_2|\leq K_2} \Big|\sum_{n=1}^{N} e(\mathbf{k}\cdot\mathbf{u}_n)\Big|^2 \geq N(K_1+1)(K_2+1).$$

Here the left hand side is

$$\geq \sum_{|k_1|\leq K_1}\sum_{|k_2|\leq K_2}\Big(1-\frac{|k_1|}{K_1+1}\Big)\Big(1-\frac{|k_2|}{K_2+1}\Big)\Big|\sum_{n=1}^{N} e(\mathbf{k}\cdot\mathbf{u}_n)\Big|^2.$$

Write $\mathbf{u}_n = (u_{n1}, u_{n2})$. We square out and invert the order of summation to see that the above is

$$= \sum_{m=1}^{N}\sum_{n=1}^{N}\Delta_{K_1+1}(u_{m1}-u_{n1})\Delta_{K_2+1}(u_{m2}-u_{n2}).$$

These terms are non-negative, and the diagonal terms $m = n$ contribute the amount $N(K_1+1)(K_2+1)$. This gives the result.

7. **Notes.** §1. For a complete account of the theory and applications of power sums, one should consult the book of Turán [42].

In connection with the problem of giving an effective upper bound for the first change of sign of $\pi(x) - \text{li}\,x$, Littlewood [21] considered the problem of showing that a sum

$$f(x) = 1 + \sum_{n=1}^{N} a_n \cos\lambda_n x$$

of cosines takes a large value in a specified range. Littlewood formulated a theorem in this direction, but Turán [38] produced examples to show that the theorem is false. The error lies in the fact that Littlewood asserted a lower bound for $\max_{x \in I} f(x)$, but his proof establishes a lower bound only for $\max_{x \in I} |f(x)|$. Much later, Knapowski [14, 15] succeeded in using power sums to give an effective upper bound for the first sign change of $\pi(x) - \operatorname{li} x$.

§2. Turán [37] established the First Main Theorem with a constant slightly smaller than in (5). Makai [24] and de Bruijn [5] independently determined the best constant by elementary manipulation of power series. Our use of contour integration follows the approach of Balkema and Tijdeman [3]. The characteristic feature of Turán's method is the introduction of coefficients a_ν that are subject to certain constraints, while consideration of the original coefficients b_n is eliminated. This type of reasoning—a sort of duality argument—is found again in the proofs of Theorems 3 and 4.

Since the s_ν given by (1) satisfies a linear recurrence, it is natural to consider general linear recurrence sequences; this amounts to allowing polynomial coefficients. Put

$$(20) \qquad s_\nu = \sum_{n=1}^{N} b_n(\nu) z_n^\nu$$

where $b_n(x)$ is a polynomial of degree d_n. Put $H = \sum_{n=1}^{N}(d_n + 1)$. Thus H is the total number of coefficients of all the polynomials b_n. Using the same method that we used to prove Theorem 1, Tijdeman [35] showed that there is a ν, $M + 1 \leq \nu \leq M + H$, such that $|s_\nu| \geq c(M, H)|s_0|$, provided that $|z_n| \geq 1$ for all n. It is natural to consider also the general solution of a linear differential equation with constant coefficients, namely an entire function of the form

$$(21) \qquad F(z) = \sum_{n=1}^{N} b_n(z) e^{\omega_n z}$$

where the b_n are polynomials. Let $M(R) = \max_{|z| \leq R} |F(z)|$. Tijdeman [35, 36] used the same method to derive an upper bound for $|F(z)|$ in terms of the maximum size of the power-sums $F^{(\nu)}(0)$. Since by the Cauchy inequalities these latter quantities are bounded in terms of $M(R_1)$, Tijdeman derived an upper bound for $M(R_2)/M(R_1)$ when $0 < R_1 < R_2$, expressed in terms of R_1, R_2, H, and $\Omega = \max_n |\omega_n|$. From this, Tijdeman deduced that the number of zeros of $F(z)$, in any disk of radius R, is not more than $\frac{10}{3}(\Omega R + H)$. Later, Voorhoeve [44, 45] found a different method to derive results of this kind. Such estimates have applications in transcendence theory.

§3. Lemma 1 is due to Turán [38]. It subsumes the result proved earlier by Littlewood. Turán [39] also discovered that Lemma 1 provides a natural proof of Fabry's Theorem; Wiener (see Paley & Wiener [26, p. 125]) had guessed that such a proof might exist. For a somewhat different derivation of Fabry's theorem using Turán's First Main Theorem see Landau and Gaier [19].

Since we are often interested in the behavior of infinite sums, truncation arguments such as that found in Lemma 2 are common to many applications of Turán's method.

§4. For better constants than we obtained in Lemma 3, see Rahman and Stenger [28], Rahman and Schmeisser [29], and Lachance, Saff, and Varga [18]. Theorem 3 is due to Halász [11], who showed more generally that if $|z_n| \geq 1$ for all n, $H \geq N$, and $M \geq 0$ then

$$|s_0| \leq \left(\frac{H\sqrt{M}}{N} + \sqrt{H} \right) \exp(4N^2 H^{-1} + 6NM^{1/2}H^{-1/2}) \max_{M+1 \leq \nu \leq M+H} |s_\nu|.$$

It would be interesting to know if the factor in parentheses here could be replaced by an absolute constant. Halász gave applications similar to our Lemma 1 (due to Turán). Halász and Montgomery [12] used these results to bound $\max_{0 \leq x \leq 1} |F'(x)|$ in terms of $\max_{0 \leq x \leq 1} |F(x)|$ where F is an almost-periodic polynomial. See also Lorch and Russell [22, 23].

§5. Turán [40] proved Theorem 4, but with e^{26} in place of $8e$. The constant $8e$ was first obtained by Uchiyama [43]. Our presentation follows that of Balkema and Tijdeman [3]. Kolesnik and Straus [16] have obtained the best constant $4e$.

Example 3 is essentially an example that Littlewood [21] attributes to P. Stein.

§6. Strictly speaking, the approaches used in this section do not involve Turán's method, since there is no appeal to duality. On the other hand, the results here conform to Turán's view that it is useful to have information concerning the behavior of power sums. Theorem 5 and Example 5 are due to Turán [41]. Theorems 6–8 are due to Cassels [6]. It is more difficult to derive a result like Theorem 7 but with ν restricted to $1 \leq \nu \leq N$. Atkinson [1, 2] has given an involved proof that hypotheses of Theorem 7 imply that $|s_\nu| \geq 1/6$ for some ν, $1 \leq \nu \leq N$. It is not known whether, in this situation, one can replace the constant $1/6$ by a function tending to 1 as $N \to \infty$. In the best known example, $\max_{1 \leq \nu \leq N} |s_\nu| < 1 - c(\log N)/N$. A. Biro (Acta Math. Acad. Sci. Hungar., to appear) has replaced Atkinson's $1/6$ by $1/2$. It is tempting to think that perhaps the hypothesis $|z_n| = 1$ in Theorem 8 could be replaced by the weaker assumption that $|z_n| \geq 1$ for all n, but this question seems to be difficult to resolve. Theorem 9 was formulated by Blanksby and Montgomery [4], for the purpose of studying roots of unity near the unit circle. Hindry and Silverman [13] applied Theorem 9 with

$$f(x) = \widehat{B}_2(x) = \{x\}^2 - \{x\} + 1/6 = \frac{1}{\pi^2} \sum_{n=1}^{\infty} \frac{\cos 2\pi n x}{n^2}$$

in proving Lang's height lower bound conjecture (conditionally for number fields, unconditionally for function fields). Elkies (see Lang [20, p. 150]) proved an analogue of Theorem 9 for Green's functions on curves. Theorem 10 is Theorem 5 of Montgomery [25]; Gonek [10] generalized it to arbitrary $b_n \geq 0$. Example 6 is due to Montgomery [25, p. 23]. Ruzsa has observed that the same effect can

be achieved by using a fat Sidon set of residue classes (mod q), and indeed that
if we write

$$\chi(n)e(n/p) = e\Big(\frac{b_n}{p(p-1)}\Big).$$

then the b_n form a fat Sidon set (mod $p(p-1)$). See also J. Fabrykowski (Acta
Acad. Sci. Hungar., to appear). In the direction of a complement to Theorem 10,
Erdős and Rényi [9] used probabilistic reasoning to demonstrate the existence
of numbers z_n with $|z_n| = 1$ for all n, with the property that

$$|s_\nu| \le (6N\log(\nu+1))^{1/2}$$

for all $\nu > 0$ where s_ν is defined by (15). Theorem 11 is due to Smyth [32].

The method used in proving Theorems 8, 9, and 12 is related to Siegel's analytic proof [31] of Minkowski's convex body theorem. Using Siegel's ideas, one
may show that if $\mathcal{C} \subseteq \mathbb{R}^2$, $\mathcal{C}$ is convex and symmetric about $\mathbf{0}$, then there exists a
trigonometric polynomial $T(\mathbf{x})$ in two variables such that $\operatorname{supp} \widehat{T} \subseteq \mathcal{C}$, $\widehat{T}(0) = 1$,
$T(\mathbf{x}) \ge 0$ for all $\mathbf{x} \in \mathbb{T}^2$, and $T(\mathbf{0}) \ge \frac{1}{4}\operatorname{area}(\mathcal{C})$. (To derive Minkowski's inequality from this, observe that if $\operatorname{area}(\mathcal{C}) > 4$ then $T(0) > \widehat{T}(0)$, and hence $T(\mathbf{x})$
is not constant. Consequently $\widehat{T}(\mathbf{k}) \ne 0$ for some $\mathbf{k} \ne \mathbf{0}$. But $\mathbf{k} \in \mathcal{C}$.) When
$\mathcal{C} = [-X_1, X_1] \times [-X_2, X_2]$ it suffices to take $T(\mathbf{x}) = \Delta_{K_1+1}(x_1)\Delta_{K_2+1}(x_2)$. Using the more general polynomial T in the same way as in the proof of Theorem 12,
we may show that

$$(22) \qquad \sum_{\substack{\mathbf{k}\in\mathcal{C}\\ \mathbf{k}\ne\mathbf{0}}} \left|\sum_{n=1}^{N} e(\mathbf{k}\cdot\mathbf{u}_n)\right|^2 \ge \tfrac{1}{4}\operatorname{area}(\mathcal{C})N - N^2$$

provided that $\mathcal{C}$ is convex and symmetric about $\mathbf{0}$.

References

1. F. V. Atkinson, *On sums of powers of complex numbers*, Acta Math. Hungar.
   12 (1961), 185–188.
2. _____, *Some further estimates concerning sums of powers of complex numbers*, Acta Math. Hungar. **20** (1969), 193–210.
3. A. A. Balkema and R. Tijdeman, *Some estimates in the theory of exponential
   sums*, Acta Math. Hungar. **24** (1973), 115–133.
4. P. E. Blanksby and H. L. Montgomery, *Algebraic integers near the unit circle*,
   Acta Arith. **18** (1971), 355–369.
5. N. G. de Bruijn, *On Turán's first main theorem*, Acta. Math. Hungar. **11**
   (1960), 213–216.
6. J. W. S. Cassels, *On the sums of powers of complex numbers*, Acta Math.
   Hungar. **7** (1957), 283–289.
7. H. Davenport, *Multiplicative Number Theory*, Second Edition, Springer-Verlag, New York, 1980.

8. L. Erdős, *On some problems of P. Turán concerning power sums of complex numbers*, Acta Math. Hungar. **59** (1992), 11–24.

9. P. Erdős and A. Rényi, *A probabilistic approach to problems of Diophantine approximation*, Illinois J. Math. **1** (1957), 303–315.

10. S. M. Gonek, *A note on Turán's method*, Michigan Math. J. **28** (1981), 83–87.

11. G. Halász, *On the first and second main theorems in Turán's theory of power sums*, Studies in Pure Mathematics To the Memory of Paul Turán (Paul Erdős, ed.), Birkhäuser Verlag, Basel, 1983, pp. 259–269.

12. G. Halász and H. L. Montgomery, *Bernstein's inequality for finite intervals*, Conference on harmonic analysis in honor of Antoni Zygmund (Chicago, 1981), Wadsworth, Belmont, CA, 1983, pp. 60–65.

13. M. Hindry and J. Silverman, *The canonical height and integral points on elliptic curves*, Invent. Math. **93** (1988), 419–450.

14. S. Knapowski, *On sign-changes of the difference $\pi(x) - \mathrm{Li}\,x$*, Acta Arith. **7** (1961), 107–119.

15. _____, *On sign-changes in the remainder-term in the prime-number formula*, J. London Math. Soc. **36** (1961), 451–460.

16. G. Kolesnik and E. G. Straus, *On the sum of powers of complex numbers*, Studies in Pure Mathematics To the Memory of P. Turán (P. Erdős, ed.), Birkhäuser Verlag, Basel, 1983, pp. 427–442.

17. N. Korneichuk, *Exact Constants in Approximation Theory*, Encyclopedia of Math. 38, Cambridge Univ. Press, Cambridge, 1991.

18. M. M. Lachance, E. B. Saff, and R. S. Varga, *Inequalities for polynomials with a prescribed zero*, Math. Z. **168** (1979), 105–116.

19. E. Landau and D. Gaier, *Darstellung und Begrundung einiger neuerer Ergebnisse der Funktionentheorie*, Third Edition, Springer-Verlag, Berlin, 1986.

20. S. Lang, *Introduction to Arakelov Theory*, Springer-Verlag, New York, 1988.

21. J. E. Littlewood, *Mathematical Notes (12): An inequality for a sum of cosines*, J. London Math. Soc. **12** (1937), 217–221; *Collected Papers*, Oxford Univ. Press, Oxford, 1982, pp. 838–842.

22. L. Lorch and D. Russell, *On some contributions of Halász to the Turán power-sum theory*, Approximation and optimization (Havana, 1987), Lecture Notes in Math. 1354, Springer-Verlag, Berlin, 1988, pp. 169–177.

23. _____, *On some contributions of Halász to the Turán power-sum theory, II*, Constructive theory of functions (Varna, 1987), Bulgar. Acad. Sci., Sofia, 1988, pp. 297–304.

24. E. Makai, *The first main theorem of P. Turán*, Acta Math. Hungar. **10** (1959), 405–411.

25. H. L. Montgomery, *Turán's Method*, Institut Mittag-Leffler Report No. 15 (1978), 26 pp.

26. R. E. A. C. Paley and N. Wiener, *Fourier Transforms in the Complex Domain*, Colloquium Publ. 19, Amer. Math. Soc., Providence, 1934.

27. M. J. D. Powell, *Approximation Theory and Methods*, Cambridge Univ. Press, Cambridge, 1981.

28. Q. I. Rahman and F. Stenger, *An extremum problem for polynomials with a prescribed zero*, Proc. Amer. Math. Soc. **43** (1974), 84–90.

29. Q. I. Rahman and G. Schmeisser, *Some inequalities for polynomials with a prescribed zero*, Trans. Amer. Math. Soc. **216** (1976), 91–103.

30. T. J. Rivlin, *An Introduction to the Approximation of Functions*, Dover, New York, 1981.

31. C. L. Siegel, *Über Gitterpunkte in convexen Körpern und ein damit zusammenhängendes Extremalproblem*, Acta Math. **65** (1935), 307–323; Gesammelte Abhandlungen, vol. I, Springer-Verlag, Berlin, 1966.

32. C. J. Smyth, *Some inequalities for certain power sums*, Acta Math. Hungar. **28** (1976), 271–273.

33. J. Suranyi and M. Szalay, *Some notes on the power sums of complex numbers whose sum is* 0, Studies in Pure Mathematics To the Memory of P. Turán (P. Erdős, ed.), Birkhäuser Verlag, Basel, 1983, pp. 711–717.

34. G. Szegö, *Orthogonal Polynomials*, 4th Edition, Colloquium Publications vol. 23, Amer. Math. Soc., Providence, 1975.

35. R. Tijdeman, *On the distribution of the values of certain functions* (Ph.D. Thesis), University of Amsterdam, 1969.

36. _____, *On the number of zeros of general exponential polynomials*, Nederl. Akad. Wetensch. Proc. Ser. A **74** (= Indag. Math. **33**) (1971), 1–7.

37. P. Turán, *Über die Verteilung der Primzahlen I*, Acta Sci. Math. (Szeged) **10** (1941), 81–104.

38. _____, *On a theorem of Littlewood*, J. London Math. Soc. **21** (1946), 268–275.

39. _____, *On the gap theorem of Fabry*, Acta Math. Hungar. **1** (1947), 21–29.

40. _____, *On Riemann's Hypothesis*, Izv. Akad. Nauk SSSR Ser. Mat. **11** (1947), 197–262.

41. _____, *On a certain limitation of eigenvalues of matrices*, Aequat. Math. **2** (1969), 184–189.

42. _____, *On a New Method of Analysis and its Applications*, Wiley-Interscience, New York, 1984.

43. S. Uchiyama, *A note on the second main theorem of P. Turán*, Acta Math. Hungar. **9** (1958), 379–380.

44. M. Voorhoeve, *On the oscillation of exponential polynomials*, Math. Z. **151** (1976), 277–294.

45. _____, *A generalization of Descartes' rule*, J. London Math. Soc. (2) **20** (1979), 446–456.

Chapter 6. Irregularities of Distribution

1. Introduction. Suppose that $\mathbf{u}_1, \ldots, \mathbf{u}_N$ is a sequence of points in $\mathbb{T}^2$. Our object is to show that these points can not be too well distributed. In order to obtain precise results we must first specify how the distribution is to be measured. To this end, let $\mathcal{S}$ denote a measurable set in $\mathbb{T}^2$, and put

$$
(1) \qquad D(\mathcal{S}) = \sum_{n=1}^{N} \chi_{\mathcal{S}}(\mathbf{u}_n) \quad - N \operatorname{area} \mathcal{S}
$$

where $\chi_{\mathcal{S}}(\mathbf{u})$ denotes the characteristic function of $\mathcal{S}$. For any given set $\mathcal{S}$, we can choose the points $\mathbf{u}_n$ so that $|D(\mathcal{S})| \leq 1$. However, we suppose that $\mathcal{S}$ is a member of a family $\mathcal{F}$ of sets, and we ask whether $|D(\mathcal{S})|$ can be small for every $\mathcal{S} \in \mathcal{F}$. We restrict out attention to families $\mathcal{F}$ that are closed under translation, so that if $\mathcal{S} \in \mathcal{F}$ then $\mathcal{S} + \boldsymbol{\alpha} \in \mathcal{F}$ for all $\boldsymbol{\alpha} \in \mathbb{T}^2$. Let the set $\mathcal{S}$ be fixed, and put

$$
(2) \qquad d_{\mathcal{S}}(\boldsymbol{\alpha}) = D(\mathcal{S} + \boldsymbol{\alpha}).
$$

Then $d_{\mathcal{S}}(\boldsymbol{\alpha}) \in L^1(\mathbb{T}^2)$, and by direct calculation we see that its Fourier coefficients

$$
\widehat{d_{\mathcal{S}}}(\mathbf{k}) = \int_{\mathbb{T}^2} d_{\mathcal{S}}(\boldsymbol{\alpha}) e(-\mathbf{k} \cdot \boldsymbol{\alpha}) \, d\boldsymbol{\alpha}
$$

are given by the formulæ

$$
(3) \qquad \widehat{d_{\mathcal{S}}}(\mathbf{k}) = \begin{cases} \widehat{\chi_{\mathcal{S}}}(-\mathbf{k}) \widehat{U}(\mathbf{k}) & \text{if } \mathbf{k} \neq \mathbf{0}, \\ 0 & \text{if } \mathbf{k} = \mathbf{0} \end{cases}
$$

where $\widehat{U}(\mathbf{k}) = \sum_{n=1}^{N} e(-\mathbf{k} \cdot \mathbf{u}_n)$. (This notation was used already in Chapter 1.) Hence by Parseval's identity,

$$
(4) \qquad \int_{\mathbb{T}^2} d_{\mathcal{S}}(\boldsymbol{\alpha})^2 \, d\boldsymbol{\alpha} = \sum_{\mathbf{k} \neq \mathbf{0}} |\widehat{\chi_{\mathcal{S}}}(\mathbf{k})|^2 |\widehat{U}(\mathbf{k})|^2.
$$

(Note the similarity of this to the identity (15) of Chapter 1.) Our strategy is to derive a lower bound for the right hand side above by appealing to Theorem 12 of the preceding chapter. However, this can be done only when a lower bound for $|\widehat{\chi_{\mathcal{S}}}(\mathbf{k})|$ can be given, for $\mathbf{k}$ near $\mathbf{0}$. Fortunately, $|\widehat{\chi_{\mathcal{S}}}(\mathbf{k})|$ is reasonably large on average, so that by further averaging one can obtain a good lower bound. This averaging may involve scaling the size of the set $\mathcal{S}$, rotating it, or both.

In §2 we take $\mathcal{F}$ to consist of squares with sides parallel to the coordinate axes. In §3 we take $\mathcal{F}$ to consist of disks of radius $1/4$ or $1/2$. In §4 we derive a general asymptotic estimate for the mean square rate of decay of the Fourier transform of the characteristic function of a set in the plane. Specifically, we show that if $\mathcal{S}$ is a closed set in $\mathbb{R}^2$ whose boundary is a piecewise C^1 curve $\mathcal{C}$, then

$$(5) \qquad \int_{|\mathbf{t}| \geq R} |\widehat{\chi}_{\mathcal{S}}(\mathbf{t})|^2 \, d\mathbf{t} \sim \frac{|\mathcal{C}|}{2\pi^2 R}$$

as $R \to \infty$. Here $|\mathcal{C}|$ denotes the arc-length of $\mathcal{C}$. In §5 this estimate is used to derive a lower bound for the regularity of distribution when the family $\mathcal{F}$ is generated by translating, scaling, and rotating a given set $\mathcal{S}_0$.

2. Squares. We prove the following result.

THEOREM 1. *For any sequence* $\mathbf{u}_1, \ldots, \mathbf{u}_N$ *of points in* $\mathbb{T}^2$, *there is a square* $\mathcal{S}$ *with sides parallel to the coordinate axes, such that*

$$(6) \qquad D(\mathcal{S}) \geq \tfrac{1}{17}(\log 2N)^{1/2}$$

where the discrepancy function $D(\mathcal{S})$ *is defined as in* (1) *above.*

If $\{u_n\}$ is an infinite sequence of points in $\mathbb{T}$, then for any N we may set $\mathbf{u}_n = (n/N, u_n)$, and we deduce that there is an $n \leq N$ for which

$$(7) \qquad D(n) > c\sqrt{\log N}.$$

Here c is a suitable positive absolute constant, and $D(n)$ is the discrepancy function as defined in Chapter 1.

PROOF. Let $\mathcal{S} = [-1/2, 1/2] \times [-1/2, 1/2]$, so that $s\mathcal{S}$ is a square of side-length s. In the notation of (2), it suffices to show that

$$(8) \qquad \int_0^1 \int_{\mathbb{T}^2} |d_{s\mathcal{S}}(\boldsymbol{\alpha})|^2 \, d\boldsymbol{\alpha} \, ds \geq \frac{e}{8\pi^4} \log 2N.$$

We suppose that $0 \leq s \leq 1$, and write $\mathbf{k} = (k_1, k_2)$. Then

$$\widehat{\chi}_{s\mathcal{S}}(\mathbf{k}) = \frac{\sin \pi k_1 s}{\pi k_1} \cdot \frac{\sin \pi k_2 s}{\pi k_2}$$

where it is understood that the first factor on the right should be replaced by s if $k_1 = 0$, and similarly for the second factor if $k_2 = 0$. Hence if $k_1 k_2 \neq 0$ then

$$\int_0^1 |\widehat{\chi}_{s\mathcal{S}}(\mathbf{k})|^2 \, ds = \frac{1}{4\pi^4 k_1^2 k_2^2} \int_0^1 (1 - \cos 2\pi k_1 s)(1 - \cos 2\pi k_2 s) \, ds$$

$$\geq \frac{1}{4\pi^4 k_1^2 k_2^2}.$$

If $k_1 \neq 0$ and $k_2 = 0$ then

$$\int_0^1 |\widehat{\chi}_{s\mathcal{S}}(\mathbf{k})|^2 \, ds = \frac{1}{2\pi^2 k_1^2} \int_0^1 s^2 (1 - \cos 2\pi k_1 s) \, ds$$

$$= \frac{1}{2\pi^2 k_1^2} \left(\frac{1}{3} - \frac{1}{2\pi^2 k_1^2} \right)$$

$$\geq \frac{1}{4\pi^4 k_1^2},$$

and similarly if $k_1 = 0, k_2 \neq 0$. Hence by (4),

$$(9) \qquad \int_0^1 \int_{\mathbb{T}^2} |d_{s\mathcal{S}}(\boldsymbol{\alpha})|^2 \, d\boldsymbol{\alpha} \geq \sum_{\mathbf{k} \neq \mathbf{0}} a(\mathbf{k}) |\widehat{U}(\mathbf{k})|^2$$

where

$$a(\mathbf{k}) = \frac{1}{4\pi^4 \max(1, k_1^2) \max(1, k_2^2)}.$$

Let X be a parameter to be chosen later, let $\mathcal{R}(x) = [-x, x] \times [-X/x, X/x]$ be a rectangle centered at $\mathbf{0}$ with area $4X$, and put

$$b(\mathbf{k}) = \frac{e}{2\pi^4 X^2} \int_1^X \chi_{\mathcal{R}(x)}(\mathbf{k}) \, \frac{dx}{x}.$$

From Theorem 5.12 we know that

$$\sum_{\substack{\mathbf{k} \in \mathcal{R}(x) \\ \mathbf{k} \neq \mathbf{0}}} |\widehat{U}(\mathbf{k})|^2 \geq XN - N^2.$$

On multiplying both sides by $e/(2\pi^4 X^2 x)$, and integrating over $1 \leq x \leq X$, we see that it follows that

$$(10) \qquad \sum_{\mathbf{k} \neq \mathbf{0}} b(\mathbf{k}) |\widehat{U}(\mathbf{k})|^2 \geq \frac{e}{2\pi^4 X^2} (XN - N^2) \log X.$$

By direct calculation we find that

$$b(\mathbf{k}) = \frac{e}{2\pi^4 X^2} \log^+ \left(\frac{X}{\max(1, |k_1|) \max(1, |k_2|)} \right)$$

where $\log^+ u = \max(0, \log u)$. Since $\log u \leq \frac{1}{2e} u^2$ for all $u \geq 1$, we see that $b(\mathbf{k}) \leq a(\mathbf{k})$ for all $\mathbf{k} \in \mathbb{Z}^2$. On combining (9) and (10), and taking $X = 2N$, we obtain (8), so the proof is complete.

3. Disks. Let $\mathcal{D} = \{\mathbf{x} \in \mathbb{R}^2 : x_1^2 + x_2^2 \leq 1\}$ be the unit disk in the plane, so that $r\mathcal{D}$ is a disk of radius r. Then

$$(11) \qquad \widehat{\chi}_{r\mathcal{D}}(\mathbf{t}) = \int_{|\mathbf{x}| \leq r} e(-\mathbf{t} \cdot \mathbf{x}) \, d\mathbf{x} = \frac{r}{|\mathbf{t}|} J_1(2\pi r |\mathbf{t}|)$$

where J_1 is a Bessel function of the first kind. Since J_1 has positive real zeros, it seems that our method fails if we insist on using a single radius r. On the other hand, we can obtain a good result by averaging over r. Indeed, it suffices

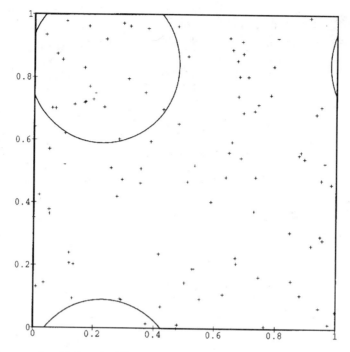

FIGURE 1.   Points in $\mathbb{T}^2$, and a disk considered as a subset of $\mathbb{T}^2$.

to consider just two radii r_1, r_2, provided that they are not proportional to two positive zeros of J_1.

THEOREM 2. *There is an absolute constant $c > 0$ such that for any N points $\mathbf{u}_1, \ldots, \mathbf{u}_N$ in $\mathbb{T}^2$ there is a disk $\mathcal{D}$ of radius $1/4$ or $1/2$ such that*

$$|D(\mathcal{D})| \geq cN^{1/4}.$$

Strictly speaking, $\mathcal{D}$ is a subset of $\mathbb{R}^2$, not of $\mathbb{T}^2$, so it makes no sense to say that a point $\mathbf{u} \in \mathbb{T}^2$ lies in $\mathcal{D}$. However, we consider $\mathbf{u}$ to be a member of $\mathcal{D}$ if $\mathbf{u} + \mathbf{m} \in \mathcal{D}$ for some lattice point $\mathbf{m} \in \mathbb{Z}^2$. In Figure 1, a disk of radius $1/4$ is depicted as a subset of $\mathbb{T}^2$.

PROOF. Since

$$J_1(x) = \left(\frac{2}{\pi x}\right)^{1/2} \cos(x - \tfrac{3}{4}\pi) + O(x^{-3/2}),$$

it follows that

$$\frac{\pi x}{2}\left(J_1(x)^2 + J_1(2x)^2\right) = \tfrac{3}{4} - \tfrac{1}{2}\sin 2x - \tfrac{1}{4}\sin 4x + O(x^{-1}).$$

The main term on the right lies between $\tfrac{3}{4}(1 - \tfrac{\sqrt{3}}{2})$ and $\tfrac{3}{4}(1 + \tfrac{\sqrt{3}}{2})$, and hence

$$(12) \qquad\qquad J_1(x)^2 + J_1(2x)^2 \approx \frac{1}{x}$$

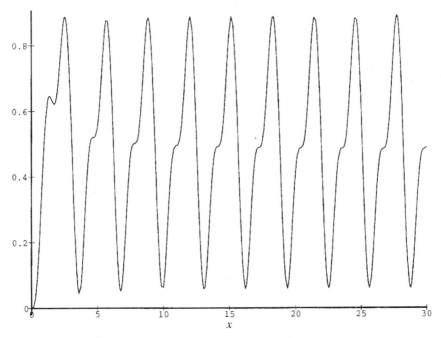

FIGURE 2.   Graph of $x(J_1(x)^2 + J_1(2x)^2)$ for $0 \leq x \leq 30$.

for all sufficiently large x. By using a device found at the end of the proof of
Theorem 4 one could make this suffice, but for our present purpose it is more
convenient to show that (12) holds for all $x \geq 1$. Here the upper bound offers
no difficulty, but we must take some care with the lower bound. Hankel [**23**, pp.
491–494] wrote

$$J_1(x) = \left(\frac{2}{\pi x}\right)^{1/2} \left(P(x)\cos(x - \tfrac{3}{4}x) - Q(x)\sin(x - \tfrac{3}{4}x)\right)$$

where $P(x)$ and $Q(x)$ are certain functions for which he gave asymptotic expansions. These expansions, though divergent, have the attractive property that at
each stage the error term is of the same size as, and not larger than the first
term omitted (see §7.3 of Watson [**39**]). Thus we know that

$$1 + \frac{15}{128x^2} - \frac{4725}{2^{15}x^4} \leq P(x) \leq 1 + \frac{15}{128x^2},$$

and that

$$\frac{3}{8x} - \frac{105}{2^{10}x^3} \leq Q(x) \leq \frac{3}{8x}.$$

Hence $|P(x) - 1| \leq \frac{15}{128x^2}$ and $|Q(x)| \leq \frac{3}{8x}$ for $x \geq 1$. Define $r(x)$ by the relation
$J_1(x) = (\frac{2}{\pi x})^{1/2}\left(\cos(x - \tfrac{3}{4}x) + r(x)\right)$, and put $R(x) = 1/(2x)$. Thus $|r(x)| \leq R(x)$
for $x \geq 1$. Since

$$\frac{\pi x}{2}J_1(x)^2 = \cos(x - \tfrac{3}{4}x)^2 + 2r(x)\cos(x - \tfrac{3}{4}x) + r(x)^2 \geq \cos(x - \tfrac{3}{4}x)^2 - 2R(x),$$

it follows that

$$\frac{\pi x}{2}\left(J_1(x)^2 + J_2(2x)^2\right) \geq \tfrac{2}{3} - \tfrac{1}{2}\sin 2x - \tfrac{1}{4}\sin 4x - 2R(x) - R(2x)$$

for $x \geq 1$. Here the main term is $\geq \tfrac{3}{4}(1 - \tfrac{\sqrt{3}}{2})$, so the right hand side above is $\geq 1/25$ uniformly for $x \geq 25$.

To treat the remaining interval $1 \leq x \leq 25$, it suffices to note that there is no x in this range for which $J_1(x) = J_1(2x) = 0$ (the zeros $j_{1,s}$ of J_1 are recorded in Table 9.5 on p. 409 of Abramowitz and Stegun [3]). Alternatively, one may consult a graph of $x\left(J_1(x)^2 + J_1(2x)^2\right)$, as in Figure 2. In any case, we conclude that (12) holds uniformly for all $x \geq 1$.

By (4) and (11) we deduce that

$$\int_{\mathbb{T}^2} d_{\frac{1}{2}\mathcal{D}}(\boldsymbol{\alpha})^2 + d_{\frac{1}{4}\mathcal{D}}(\boldsymbol{\alpha})^2\, d\boldsymbol{\alpha} \gg \sum_{\mathbf{k}\neq 0} \frac{1}{|\mathbf{k}|^3}|\widehat{U}(\mathbf{k})|^2.$$

$$\gg N^{-3/2} \sum_{\substack{\mathbf{k}\neq 0 \\ |\mathbf{k}_1|\leq\sqrt{2N} \\ |\mathbf{k}_2|\leq\sqrt{2N}}} |\widehat{U}(\mathbf{k})|^2,$$

and by Theorem 5.12 this is $\gg N^{1/2}$. This gives the desired lower bound.

4. Decay of the Fourier Transform. When we are allowed to rotate and rescale a set $\mathcal{S}$, the lower bound we obtain depends on the mean square decay of the Fourier transform of the characteristic function of our set. We find that the behavior is remarkably similar for a wide class of sets. To understand why this might be the case, we first reason informally. We seek to understand the asymptotic behavior of the integral

$$\widehat{\chi}_{\mathcal{S}}(\mathbf{t}) = \int_{\mathcal{S}} e(-\mathbf{t}\cdot\mathbf{x})\, d\mathbf{x}$$

when $|\mathbf{t}|$ is large. Let

$$f(\mathbf{x}) = -\frac{e(-\mathbf{t}\cdot\mathbf{x})}{4\pi^2|\mathbf{t}|^2},$$

so that

$$\boldsymbol{\nabla}f(\mathbf{x}) = -\frac{e(-\mathbf{t}\cdot\mathbf{x})}{2\pi i|\mathbf{t}|^2}\mathbf{t}$$

and

$$\nabla^2 f(\mathbf{x}) = e(-\mathbf{t}\cdot\mathbf{x}).$$

We suppose that the boundary of $\mathcal{S}$ is the smooth curve $\mathcal{C}$. Then by Green's theorem,

$$\widehat{\chi}_{\mathcal{S}}(\mathbf{t}) = \int_{\mathcal{S}} \nabla^2 f\, d\mathbf{x} = \int_{\mathcal{C}} \boldsymbol{\nabla}f\cdot\mathbf{N}\, ds$$

where $\mathbf{N}$ is the outward unit normal to $\mathcal{C}$; if $\mathbf{T} = (\cos\alpha, \sin\alpha)$ is the unit tangent to $\mathcal{C}$ then $\mathbf{N} = (\sin\alpha, -\cos\alpha)$. Writing $\mathbf{t} = (r\cos\phi, r\sin\phi)$ in polar coordinates, we see that

$$\boldsymbol{\nabla} f \cdot \mathbf{N} = -\frac{e(-\mathbf{t}\cdot\mathbf{x})}{2\pi i |\mathbf{t}|}\sin(\alpha - \phi).$$

Consequently

$$(13) \qquad \widehat{\chi}_{\mathcal{S}}(\mathbf{t}) = \frac{-1}{2\pi i |\mathbf{t}|}\int_{\mathcal{C}} e(-\mathbf{t}\cdot\mathbf{x})\sin(\alpha - \phi)\, ds.$$

We expect this integral to be small when $|\mathbf{t}|$ is large, because the argument in the exponential is rapidly changing. Precisely,

$$\frac{d}{dx}(\mathbf{t}\cdot\mathbf{x}) = \mathbf{t}\cdot\frac{d\mathbf{x}}{ds} = \mathbf{t}\cdot\mathbf{T} = r\cos(\alpha - \phi).$$

Thus the integral (13) has a stationary phase at points on $\mathcal{C}$ where $\mathbf{t}\perp\mathbf{T}$. Let $\mathcal{X}(\phi) = \{\mathbf{x}\in\mathcal{C} : \alpha = \phi \pm \pi/2\}$. The magnitude of the contribution of the stationary phase is governed by the second derivative,

$$\frac{d^2}{ds^2}(\mathbf{t}\cdot\mathbf{x}) = \mathbf{t}\cdot\frac{d\mathbf{T}}{ds} = \mathbf{t}\cdot(-\kappa N) = \pm\kappa r$$

where κ denotes the curvature of $\mathcal{C}$ at $\mathbf{x}$. Thus we expect that

$$(14) \qquad \widehat{\chi}_{\mathcal{S}}(\mathbf{t}) \doteq \frac{1}{r^{3/2}}\sum_{\mathbf{x}\in\mathcal{X}(\phi)} c(\mathbf{x})e(\lambda(\mathbf{x})r)$$

where

$$|c(\mathbf{x})| = \frac{1}{2\pi\sqrt{\kappa}}, \qquad \lambda(\mathbf{x}) = \mathbf{x}\cdot(\cos\phi, \sin\phi).$$

In the approximate relation (14) we have ignored the error terms that would arise from the stationary phase analysis. If we consider ϕ to be fixed, and $r\to\infty$ then the right hand side of (14) is an almost periodic polynomial. For most ϕ the frequencies $\lambda(\mathbf{x})$ are distinct, so we expect that

$$\int_{R_1}^{R_2}\left|\sum_{\mathbf{x}\in\mathcal{X}(\phi)} c(\mathbf{x})e(\lambda(\mathbf{x})r)\right|^2 dr \sim (R_2 - R_1)\sum_{\mathbf{x}}|c(\mathbf{x})|^2$$

when $R_2 - R_1$ is large. Such approximate forms of Parseval's identity will be a topic discussed in the next chapter. By integrating by parts it would follow that

$$\int_R^\infty |\widehat{\chi}_{\mathcal{S}}(\mathbf{t})|^2\, r\,dr \sim \int_R^\infty \frac{1}{r^2}\left|\sum_{\mathbf{x}} c(\mathbf{x})e(\lambda(\mathbf{x})r)\right|^2 dr$$

$$\sim \frac{1}{R}\sum_{\mathbf{x}}|c(\mathbf{x})|^2$$

$$(15) \qquad\qquad = \frac{1}{4\pi^2 R}\sum_{\mathbf{x}}\frac{1}{|\kappa(\mathbf{x})|}$$

as $R \to \infty$. Since in polar coordinates

$$\int_{|\mathbf{t}| \geq R} |\widehat{\chi}_S(\mathbf{t})|^2 \, d\mathbf{t} = \int_0^{2\pi} \int_R^\infty |\widehat{\chi}_S(\mathbf{t})|^2 \, r dr \, d\phi,$$

it remains to integrate both sides of (15) with respect to ϕ. But

$$\int_0^{2\pi} \sum_{\mathbf{x}} \frac{1}{|\kappa(\mathbf{x})|} = \int_0^{2\pi} \left| \frac{ds}{d\phi} \right| d\phi = \int_{\mathcal{C}} 1 \, ds = |\mathcal{C}|,$$

and thus we are led to expect that the asymptotic relation (5) holds as R tends to infinity. This heuristic argument would be difficult to justify unless rather stringent conditions were placed on the curve $\mathcal{C}$. By taking a different line of approach, we are able to show that (5) holds under rather weak hypotheses.

THEOREM 3. *Let $\mathcal{C}$ be a simple, closed, piecewise C^1 curve in the plane, let S denote its interior, and let $\widehat{\chi}_S(\mathbf{t})$ denote the Fourier transform of the characteristic functions of S. Then the asymptotic relation (5) holds as $R \to \infty$.*

As will be apparent from the proof, we could allow S to have several components or even be multiply-connected set, though in such a situation we should insist that S is closed, and we would replace $\mathcal{C}$ by the boundary ∂S of S. Moreover the condition that $\mathcal{C}$ is C^1 could be relaxed, although we do need to know that $\mathcal{C}$ is tame at least to the extent that

$$(16) \qquad \lim_{\delta \to 0} \frac{\text{meas}\{\mathbf{x} \in \mathbb{R}^2 : d(\mathbf{x}, \mathcal{C}) \leq \delta\}}{\delta}$$

should exist and be finite.

PROOF. Let $f(\mathbf{x}) = e^{-\pi R^2 |\mathbf{x}|^2}$, where R is large. This kernel offers some smoothing which is undone with a Tauberian argument at the end of the proof. By Plancherel's theorem,

$$(17) \qquad \int_{\mathbb{R}^2} |\chi_S * \nabla^2 f|^2 \, d\mathbf{x} = \int_{\mathbb{R}^2} |\widehat{\chi}_S \widehat{\nabla^2 f}|^2 \, d\mathbf{t}.$$

We integrate by parts to see that

$$\widehat{\nabla^2 f}(\mathbf{t}) = -4\pi^2 |\mathbf{t}|^2 \widehat{f}(\mathbf{t}).$$

Also, $\widehat{f}(\mathbf{t}) = R^{-2} e^{-\pi R^{-2} |\mathbf{t}|^2}$, so the right hand side of (17) is

$$(18) \qquad 16\pi^4 R^{-4} \int_{\mathbb{R}^2} |\widehat{\chi}_S|^2 |\mathbf{t}|^4 e^{-2\pi R^{-2}} \, d\mathbf{t}.$$

As for the left hand side of (17), we see by Green's theorem that

$$\chi_S * \nabla^2 f(\mathbf{x}) = \int_S \nabla^2 f(\mathbf{x} - \mathbf{y}) \, d\mathbf{y} = \int_{\mathcal{C}} \frac{\partial f}{\partial \mathbf{n}}(\mathbf{x} - \mathbf{y}) \, ds$$

where $\mathbf{y}$ is the position vector on the curve $\mathcal{C}$. From the definition of f we see that $\nabla f(\mathbf{w}) = -2\pi R^2 f(\mathbf{w})\mathbf{w}$, and hence

$$\frac{\partial f}{\partial \mathbf{n}}(\mathbf{x} - \mathbf{y}) = -2\pi R^2 f(\mathbf{x} - \mathbf{y})\big((\mathbf{x} - \mathbf{y}) \cdot \mathbf{n}\big).$$

Thus the left hand side of (17) is

$$= 4\pi^2 R^4 \int_{\mathbb{R}^2} \left| \int_{\mathcal{C}} f(\mathbf{x} - \mathbf{y})\big((\mathbf{x} - \mathbf{y}) \cdot \mathbf{n}\big)\, ds \right|^2 d\mathbf{x}.$$

On expanding and taking the integral $d\mathbf{x}$ inside, we see that this is

$$= 4\pi^2 R^4 \int_{\mathcal{C}} \int_{\mathcal{C}} I(\mathbf{y}_1, \mathbf{y}_2)\, ds_1\, ds_2$$

where

$$I(\mathbf{y}_1, \mathbf{y}_2) = \int_{\mathbb{R}^2} f(\mathbf{x} - \mathbf{y}_1) f(\mathbf{x} - \mathbf{y}_2)\big((\mathbf{x} - \mathbf{y}_1) \cdot \mathbf{n}_1\big)\big((\mathbf{x} - \mathbf{y}_2) \cdot \mathbf{n}_2\big)\, d\mathbf{x}.$$

We put $\mathbf{d} = \mathbf{y}_1 - \mathbf{y}_2$ and complete the square in the exponents to see that

$$f(\mathbf{x} - \mathbf{y}_1) f(\mathbf{x} - \mathbf{y}_2) = f(\mathbf{d}/\sqrt{2}) f\big(\sqrt{2}(\mathbf{x} - \tfrac{1}{2}(\mathbf{y}_1 + \mathbf{y}_2))\big).$$

We change variables, writing $\mathbf{w} = \mathbf{x} - \tfrac{1}{2}(\mathbf{y}_1 + \mathbf{y}_2)$. Thus

$$(\mathbf{x} - \mathbf{y}_i) \cdot \mathbf{n}_i = \mathbf{w} \cdot \mathbf{n}_i + (-1)^i \tfrac{1}{2}\mathbf{d} \cdot \mathbf{n}_i$$

for $i = 1, 2$, and the product of these two expressions is

$$(\mathbf{w} \cdot \mathbf{n}_1)(\mathbf{w} \cdot \mathbf{n}_2) + \tfrac{1}{2}(\mathbf{d} \cdot \mathbf{n}_2)(\mathbf{w} \cdot \mathbf{n}_1) - \tfrac{1}{2}(\mathbf{d} \cdot \mathbf{n}_1)(\mathbf{w} \cdot \mathbf{n}_2) - \tfrac{1}{4}(\mathbf{d} \cdot \mathbf{n}_1)(\mathbf{d} \cdot \mathbf{n}_2)$$
$$= T_1 + T_2 + T_3 + T_4,$$

say. We express $\mathbf{w}$ in polar coordinates, $\mathbf{w} = (r\cos\theta, r\sin\theta)$, so that

$$I(\mathbf{y}_1, \mathbf{y}_2) = f(\mathbf{d}/\sqrt{2}) \int_0^\infty e^{-2\pi r^2 r^2} r \int_0^{2\pi} T_1 + \cdots + T_4\, d\theta\, dr.$$

On writing $\mathbf{n}_i = (\cos\phi_i, \sin\phi_i)$ for $i = 1, 2$, we see that

$$\int_0^{2\pi} T_1\, d\theta = \pi r^2 \cos(\phi_1 - \phi_2).$$

Similarly we see that $\int_0^{2\pi} T_j\, d\theta = 0$ for $j = 2, 3$, and also that

$$\int_0^{2\pi} T_4\, d\theta = -\tfrac{1}{2}\pi(\mathbf{d} \cdot \mathbf{n}_1)(\mathbf{d} \cdot \mathbf{n}_2).$$

Since $\int_0^\infty e^{-ar^2} r^3\, dr = \tfrac{1}{2}a^{-2}$ and $\int_0^\infty e^{-ar^2} r\, dr = \tfrac{1}{2}a^{-1}$, we conclude that

$$I(\mathbf{y}_1, \mathbf{y}_2) = f(\mathbf{d}/\sqrt{2}) \left(\frac{\cos(\phi_1 - \phi_2)}{8\pi R^4} - \frac{(\mathbf{d} \cdot \mathbf{n}_1)(\mathbf{d} \cdot \mathbf{n}_2)}{8R^2} \right).$$

Hence the left hand side of (17) is

$$= \frac{\pi}{2} \int_{\mathcal{C}} \int_{\mathcal{C}} f(\mathbf{d}/\sqrt{2}) \cos(\phi_1 - \phi_2) \, ds_1 \, ds_2$$

$$- \frac{1}{2}\pi^2 R^2 \int_{\mathcal{C}} \int_{\mathcal{C}} f(\mathbf{d}/\sqrt{2})(\mathbf{d} \cdot \mathbf{n}_1)(\mathbf{d} \cdot \mathbf{n}_2) \, ds_1 \, ds_2.$$

If $\mathbf{y}_1 \in \mathcal{C}$ then meas $\{s_2 : |\mathbf{d}| \le \delta\} \ll \delta$ for all small δ, uniformly in $\mathbf{y}_1$. Hence if $\mathbf{y}_1 \in \mathcal{C}$ then

$$(19) \qquad\qquad \int_{\mathcal{C}} f(\mathbf{d}/\sqrt{2}) \, ds \ll R^{-1},$$

and

$$(20) \qquad\qquad \int_{\mathcal{C}} f(\mathbf{d}/\sqrt{2})|\mathbf{d}|^2 \, ds \ll R^{-3}.$$

Suppose that $0 \le s \le |\mathcal{C}|$, and that the interval $[0, |\mathcal{C}|]$ is partitioned into finitely many subintervals $\mathcal{I}_i$ in such a way that $\mathbf{y} = \mathbf{y}(s)$ is C^1 in each $\mathcal{I}_i$. Choose $\delta > 0$. Let $\mathcal{G}$, the 'good' points on $\mathcal{C}$, be the set of those $\mathbf{y}(s)$ on $\mathcal{C}$ for which s is at least δ away from the endpoints of the interval $\mathcal{I}_i$ in which it falls. Let $\mathcal{B} = \mathcal{C} \setminus \mathcal{G}$ be the complementary set of 'bad' points on $\mathcal{C}$. By (19) we see that

$$\int_{\mathcal{B}} \int_{\mathcal{C}} f(\mathbf{d}/\sqrt{2}) \cos(\phi_1 - \phi_2) \, ds_1 \, ds_2 \ll \int_{\mathcal{B}} R^{-1} \, ds_1 \ll \delta R^{-1},$$

and similarly from (20) we see that

$$\int_{\mathcal{B}} \int_{\mathcal{C}} f(\mathbf{d}/\sqrt{2}) f(\mathbf{d}/\sqrt{2})(\mathbf{d} \cdot \mathbf{n}_1)(\mathbf{d} \cdot \mathbf{n}_2) \, ds_1 \, ds_2 \ll \delta R^{-3}.$$

If $\mathbf{y}_i \in \mathcal{G}$ for $i = 1, 2$ then $|\mathbf{d}| \sim |s_1 - s_2|$ and $\cos(\phi_1 - \phi_2) \to 0$ uniformly as $|\mathbf{d}| \to 0$. Consequently

$$\int_{\mathcal{G}} \int_{\mathcal{G}} f(\mathbf{d}/\sqrt{2}) \cos(\phi_1 - \phi_2) \, ds_1 \, ds_2 \sim \left(|\mathcal{C}| + O(\delta)\right) \int_{-\infty}^{\infty} e^{-\pi R^2 y^2 / 2} \, dy$$

$$= \left(|\mathcal{C}| + O(\delta)\right) 2^{1/2} R^{-1}$$

as $R \to \infty$. Since $\mathbf{d}$ is approximately a tangent vector when $|\mathbf{d}|$ is small, $\mathbf{d} \cdot \mathbf{n}_i = o(|\mathbf{d}|)$ uniformly as $|\mathbf{d}| \to 0$ with $\mathbf{y}_i \in \mathcal{G}$. Hence

$$\int_{\mathcal{G}} \int_{\mathcal{G}} f(\mathbf{d}/\sqrt{2})(\mathbf{d} \cdot \mathbf{n}_1)(\mathbf{d} \cdot \mathbf{n}_2) \, ds_1 \, ds_2 = o(R^{-3})$$

as $R \to \infty$. By letting δ tend to 0, we conclude that the left hand side of (17) is

$$(21) \qquad\qquad \sim \pi 2^{-1/2} |\mathcal{C}| R^{-1}$$

as $R \to \infty$.

Now let

$$g(r) = \int_0^{2\pi} |\widehat{\chi}_{\mathcal{S}}(r \cos\theta, r \sin\theta)|^2 \, d\theta.$$

On combining (18) and (21) in (17), we find that

$$\int_0^\infty g(r)r^5 e^{-2\pi r^2/R^2}\, dr \sim \pi^{-3}2^{-9/2}|\mathcal{C}|R^3$$

as $R \to \infty$. If we put $r^2 = u$, $2\pi R^{-2} = \delta$, this takes the form

$$\int_0^\infty g(\sqrt{u})u^2 e^{-\delta u}\, du \sim \pi^{-3/2}2^{-2}|\mathcal{C}|\delta^{-3/2}$$

as $\delta \to 0$. By the Hardy-Littlewood Tauberian Theorem (take $\sigma = 3/2$, $\alpha(t) = \int_0^t g(\sqrt{u})u^2\, du$ in Theorem 108 of Hardy [**24**]) it follows that

$$\int_0^U g(\sqrt{u})u^2\, du \sim \tfrac{1}{3}\pi^{-2}|\mathcal{C}|U^{3/2}$$

as $U \to \infty$. Putting $r = \sqrt{u}$, we see that this can be rewritten as

$$\int_0^R g(r)r^5\, dr \sim \tfrac{1}{6}\pi^{-2}|\mathcal{C}|R^3$$

as $R \to \infty$. By integrating by parts we obtain (5), and the proof is complete.

5. Families allowing translation, scaling and rotation. We now apply the information gained in the preceding section to derive a general theorem relating to irregularities of distribution.

THEOREM 4. *Let $\mathcal{C}$ be a simple, closed, piecewise C^1 curve in the plane, let $\mathcal{S}_0$ be the interior of $\mathcal{C}$, and suppose that $\mathcal{S}_0$ has diameter not exceeding 1. Let $\mathcal{S}_0(\theta)$ denote the set obtained by rotating $\mathcal{S}_0$ through an angle θ, and let $\mathcal{F}$ be the family of all sets of the form $s\mathcal{S}_0(\theta) + \boldsymbol{\alpha}$ where $0 \le s \le 1$. Then there is a constant $c = c(\mathcal{C}) > 0$ such that for any sequence of points $\mathbf{u}_1, \ldots, \mathbf{u}_N$ in $\mathbb{T}^2$ there is a set $\mathcal{S} \in \mathcal{F}$ for which*

$$D(\mathcal{S}) > cN^{1/4}.$$

The condition on the diameter of $\mathcal{S}_0$ ensures that no overlapping occurs when $\mathcal{S}_0(\theta)$ is considered mod $\mathbb{Z}^2$.

PROOF. By integrating both sides of (4) with respect to s and θ, we find that

$$(22) \qquad \int_0^1 \int_0^{2\pi} \int_{\mathbb{T}^2} D(s\mathcal{S}_0(\theta) + \boldsymbol{\alpha})^2\, d\boldsymbol{\alpha}\, d\theta\, ds = \sum_{\mathbf{k} \neq 0} c(\mathbf{k})|\widehat{U}(\mathbf{k})|^2$$

where

$$c(\mathbf{k}) = \int_0^1 \int_0^{2\pi} |\widehat{\chi}_{s\mathcal{S}_0(\theta)}(\mathbf{k})|^2\, d\theta\, ds$$

$$= |\mathbf{k}|^{-5} \int_{|\mathbf{t}| \le |\mathbf{k}|} |\widehat{\chi}_{\mathcal{S}_0}(\mathbf{t})|^2 |\mathbf{t}|^3\, dt.$$

By Theorem 3 and integration by parts we deduce that

$$c(\mathbf{k}) \sim \frac{|\mathcal{C}|}{4\pi^2 |\mathbf{k}|^3}$$

as $|\mathbf{k}| \to \infty$. Hence there is a constant k_0 depending only on $\mathcal{C}$ such that

(23) $c(\mathbf{k}) \gg |\mathbf{k}|^{-3}$

uniformly for $|\mathbf{k}| \geq k_0$.

Without loss of generality, k_0 is an integer. By replacing $\mathbf{u}_n$ by $k_0 \mathbf{u}_n$ and X_i by X_i/k_0 in Theorem 5.12, we find that

$$\sum_{\substack{|k_i| \leq X_i \\ \mathbf{k} \neq \mathbf{0} \\ k_0 | k_i}} |\widehat{U}(\mathbf{k})|^2 \geq N X_1 X_2 k_0^{-2} - N^2.$$

Hence

$$\sum_{\substack{|k_i| \leq X_i \\ |\mathbf{k}| \geq k_0}} |\widehat{U}(\mathbf{k})|^2 \geq N X_1 X_2 k_0^{-2} - N^2.$$

We take $X_1 = X_2 = 2k_0 N^{1/2}$. By (23) we see that $c(k) \gg k_0^{-3} N^{-3/2}$ uniformly for all $\mathbf{k}$ in the above sum. Thus we conclude that the right hand side of (22) is $\gg k_0^{-3} N^{1/2}$. This gives the desired result.

6. Notes. For a comprehensive account of the subject of irregularities of distribution, one should consult the book of Beck and Chen [14]. The approach that we have adopted in this chapter follows Montgomery [28].

In 1935, van der Corput [18, 19] conjectured that $\limsup_{N\to\infty} D(N) = \infty$ for any infinite sequence $\{u_n\}$ of points in $\mathbb{T}$. This was first proved in 1945 by van Aardenne-Ehrenfest [1], and in 1949 she [2] gave the quantitative bound

$$\limsup_{N\to\infty} \frac{D(N)}{(\log\log N)/(\log\log\log N)} > 0.$$

In 1954, Roth [30] gave the better lower bound

$$\limsup_{N\to\infty} \frac{D(N)}{\sqrt{\log N}} > c > 0.$$

Finally, in 1972, Schmidt [35] showed that

$$\limsup_{N\to\infty} \frac{D(N)}{\log N} > c > 0.$$

This resolved the issue, since Ostrowski [29] had long before observed that $D(N) \ll \log N$ if $u_n = n\sqrt{2}$.

Roth [30] formulated the irregularity problem as follows. Let $\{\mathbf{u}_n\}_{n=1}^N$ be a sequence of points of $\mathbb{T}^k$, and for simplicity suppose that all their coordinates lie in the interval $[0, 1)$. let $\boldsymbol{\alpha}$ be a point whose coordinates also lie in this interval, and let $Z(\boldsymbol{\alpha})$ denote the number of the $\mathbf{u}_n$ that lie in the box $[0, \alpha_1] \times \cdots \times [0, \alpha_k]$. Finally, let

$$D(\boldsymbol{\alpha}) = Z(\boldsymbol{\alpha}) - N \prod_{i=1}^{k} \alpha_i$$

be the difference between the number of points counted and the expected number. How small can this function be? Roth [30] proved that

$$\|D\|_2 \geq c_k (\log N)^{(k-1)/2}.$$

Schmidt [36] showed more generally that

$$\|D\|_p > c_{k,p} (\log N)^{(k-1)/2}$$

for any $p > 1$. Halász [21] extended this to $p = 1$, but only when $k = 2$. All these results are best possible, since Chen [17] has shown that for any finite $p > 0$ and any $k > 1$ there is a constant $C_{k,p}$ and a point distribution for which

$$\|D\|_p \leq C_{k,p} (\log N)^{(k-1)/2}.$$

The case $p = \infty$ is more resistant. Schmidt [35] showed that $\|D\|_\infty > c \log N$ when $k = 2$, and Halász [21] gave a different proof of this, but neither proof provides a stronger lower bound in higher dimensions. In the opposite direction, Halton [22] has shown that for any $k > 1$ there is a point distribution for which

$$\|D\|_\infty < C_k (\log N)^{k-1}.$$

The main unsolved problem remaining in this area is to close the gap between these bounds for $\|D\|_\infty$ when $k > 2$.

Suppose that $\{u_n\}$ is an infinite sequence of points in $\mathbb{T}$, and let $D(N; \alpha)$ be the associated discrepancy function introduced in Chapter 1 (see p. 1). Erdős [20] asked whether there must exist an α for which the sequence $\{D(N; \alpha)\}$ is unbounded. Schmidt [33] that such α must exist, and later he proved [34] the set of α for which $\{D(N; \alpha)\}$ is bounded is at most countable. In addition, Tijdeman and Wagner [37] showed that there is a constant $c > 0$ such that

$$\limsup_{N \to \infty} \frac{D(N; \alpha)}{\log N} > c$$

for almost all α, and Halász [21] proved that the set of α for which $D(N; \alpha) = o(\log N)$ is a set of Hausdorff dimension 0.

Suppose that $\{z_n\}$ is an infinite sequence of unimodular complex numbers, put $P_N(z) = \prod_{n=1}^{N} (z - z_n)$, and set $M_N = \max_{|z| \leq 1} |P_N(z)|$. Erdős [20] asked whether the numbers z_n can be so well distributed around the unit circle that the sequence of numbers $\{M_N\}$ is bounded. This was answered in the negative by Wagner [38], who showed that there is a $\delta > 0$ such that

$$\limsup_{N \to \infty} \frac{M_N}{(\log N)^\delta} > 0.$$

The best possible result in this direction was obtained recently by Beck [12], who showed that there is a $\delta > 0$ such that

$$\limsup_{N \to \infty} \frac{M_N}{N^\delta} > 0.$$

§1. Antecedents of the approach developed here can be seen in the earlier work of Kendall [27] and Herz [25] concerning the number of lattice points inside a convex curve, and a lower bound of Roth [31] for the mean square distribution of a set of integers in arithmetic progressions.

§2. Theorem 1 is due to Halász [21], who devised a variant of Roth's method quite different from the method we have used. Theorem 1 implies the result of Roth [30]. Ruzsa [32] has shown that squares and rectangles have the same discrepancy, up to a constant factor.

§3. Theorem 2 is due to Montgomery [28]. Beck [5] obtained a similar result involving an average over radii.

§4. Theorem 3 is due to Montgomery [28]. Herz [25] obtained similar results in the case that S is convex.

§5. Theorem 4 is due to Montgomery [28]. Beck [5] independently obtained the same result when S is convex, using a similar method.

For further developments in this area, see Beck [4–12] and Beck and Chen [13, 15, 16].

References

1. T. van Aardenne-Ehrenfest, *Proof of the impossibility of a just distribution of an infinite sequence of points over an interval*, Proc. Kon. Ned. Akad. Wetensch. **48** (1945), 266–271.

2. _____, *On the impossibility of a just distribution*, Proc. Kon. Ned. Akad. Wetensch. **52** (1949), 734–739.

3. M. Abramowitz and I. Stegun, *Handbook of Mathematical Functions*, Dover, New York, 1965.

4. J. Beck, *Uniformity and irregularity*, Proceedings of the International Congress of Mathematicians (Berkeley, 1986), Amer. Math. Soc., Providence, 1987, pp. 1400–1407.

5. _____, *Irregularities of distribution I*, Acta Math. **159** (1987), 1–49.

6. _____, *On a problem of Erdős in the theory of irregularities of distribution*, Math. Ann. **277** (1987), 233–247.

7. _____, *On the discrepancy of convex plane sets*, Monatsh. Math. **105** (1988), 91–106.

8. _____, *A two-dimensional van Aardenne-Ehrenfest theorem in irregularities of distribution*, Compositio Math. **72** (1989), 269–339.

9. _____, *On a problem of W. M. Schmidt concerning one-sided irregularities of point distributions*, Math. Ann. **285** (1989), 29–55.

10. _____, *Irregularities of distribution II*, Proc. London Math. Soc. (3) **56** (1988), 1–50.

11. _____, *Irregularities of distribution and category theorem*, Studia Sci. Math. Hungar. **26** (1991), 81–86.

12. _____, *The modulus of polynomials with zeros on the unit circle: a problem of Erdős*, Ann. of Math. (2) **134** (1991), 609–651.

13. J. Beck and W. W. L. Chen, *Note on irregularities of distribution*, Mathematika **33** (1986), 148–163.

14. _____, *Irregularities of Distribution*, Cambridge Tract 89, Cambridge University Press, Cambridge, 1987.

15. _____, *Irregularities of point distributions relative to convex polygons*, Irregularities of partitions (Fertod, 1986), Springer-Verlag, Berlin, 1989, pp. 1–22.

16. _____, *Note on irregularities of distribution II*, Proc. London Math. Soc. (3) **61** (1990), 251–272.

17. W. W. L. Chen, *On irregularities of distribution*, Mathematika **27** (1980), 153–170.

18. J. C. van der Corput, *Verteilungsfunktionen. I*, Proc. Kon. Ned. Akad. Wetensch. **38** (1935), 813–821.

19. _____, *Verteilungsfunktionen. II*, Proc. Kon. Ned. Akad. Wetensch. **38** (1935), 1058–1066.

20. P. Erdős, *Problems and results on Diophantine approximation*, Compositio Math. **16** (1964), 52–66.

21. G. Halász, *On Roth's method in the theory of irregularities of point distributions*, Recent Progress in Analytic Number Theory, Vol. 2, Academic Press, London, 1981, pp. 79–94.

22. J. H. Halton, *On the efficiency of certain quasirandom sequences of points in evaluating multidimensional integrals*, Num. Math. **2** (1960), 84–90.

23. H. Hankel, *Die Cylinderfunctionen erster und zweiter Art*, Math. Ann. **1** (1869), 467–501.

24. G. H. Hardy, *Divergent Series*, Oxford University Press, Oxford, 1963.

25. C. S. Herz, *Fourier transforms related to convex sets*, Ann. of Math. (2) **75** (1961), 81–92.

26. _____, *On the number of lattice points in a convex set*, Amer. J. Math. **84** (1962), 126–133.

27. D. G. Kendall, *On the number of lattice points inside a random oval*, Quart. J. Math. (Oxford) **19** (1948), 1–26.

28. H. L. Montgomery, *On irregularities of Distribution*, Congress of Number Theory (Zarautz, 1984), Universidad del País Vasco, Bilbao, 1989, pp. 11–27.

29. A. Ostrowski, *Bemerkungen zur Theorie der Diophantischen Approximationen I*, Abh. Math. Sem. Hamburg **1** (1922), 77–98; *II* **1** (1922), 250–251; *III* **4** (1926), 224.

30. K. F. Roth, *On irregularities of distribution*, Mathematika **1** (1954), 73–79.

31. _____, *Remark concerning integer sequences*, Acta Arith. **9** (1964), 257–260.

32. I. Z. Ruzsa, *The discrepancy of rectangles and squares*, Ber. Math-Statist. Sekt. Forsch. Graz **318** (1992), 135–140.

33. W. M. Schmidt, *Irregularities of distribution*, Quart. J. Math. (Oxford) (2) **19** (1968), 181–191.

34. _____, *Irregularities of distribution VI*, Compositio Math. **24** (1972), 63–74.

35. _____, *Irregularities of distribution VII*, Acta Arith. **21** (1972), 45–50.

36. _____, *Irregularities of distribution X*, Number Theory and Algebra, Academic Press, New York, 1977, pp. 311–329.

37. R. Tijdeman and G. Wagner, *A sequence has almost nowhere small discrepancy*, Monatsh. Math. **90** (1980), 315–329.

38. G. Wagner, *On a problem of Erdős in Diophantine approximation*, Bull. London Math. Soc. **12** (1980), 81–88.

39. G. N. Watson, *A treatise on the Theory of Bessel Functions*, Second Edition, Cambridge University Press, Cambridge, 1966.

Chapter 7. Mean and Large Values
of Dirichlet Polynomials

1. Introduction. Let $D(s)$ be a *Dirichlet polynomial*, say

$$\text{(1)} \qquad D(s) = \sum_{n=1}^{N} a_n n^{-s}.$$

We write $s = \sigma + it$, and note that $D(\sigma + it)$ is an almost periodic function of t, when σ is fixed. On a finite interval $0 \le t \le T$, the function n^{-it} is not quite uniformly distributed on the unit circle, but its distribution tends toward the uniform when $T \to \infty$. Thus the asymptotic distribution function of values of $D(\sigma + it)$ is the same as for a corresponding sum of random variables,

$$\text{(2)} \qquad \mathbf{X} = \sum_{n=1}^{N} a_n n^{-\sigma} \mathbf{X}_n,$$

in which each $\mathbf{X}_n$ is uniformly distributed on the unit circle. Unfortunately, these variables are not independent, since, for example, the value of 6^{-it} is determined by that of 2^{-it} and 3^{-it}. On the other hand, the numbers $\log p$ are linearly independent over $\mathbb{Q}$ (this is the Fundamental Theorem of Arithmetic), and hence by the strong form of Kronecker's theorem it follows that the numbers p^{-it} are asymptotically independent, as p runs over any finite collection of primes. Consequently, if the $\mathbf{X}_p$ are independent random variables uniformly distributed on the unit circle, and if we put

$$\mathbf{X}_n = \prod_{p^\alpha \| n} \mathbf{X}_p^\alpha,$$

then the asymptotic distribution of $D(\sigma + it)$ is the distribution of the random variable $\mathbf{X}$ given in (2). Thus we know, for example, that $|D(\sigma + it)|$ is rarely large, asymptotically. However, for practical purposes we need to know how quickly the asymptotic behavior is approached. That is, how often in an interval $0 \le t \le T$ is $|D(\sigma+it)|$ large? One way to estimate the frequency of large values is by estimating *moments*,

$$\int_0^T \left| \sum_{n=1}^{N} a_n n^{-\sigma-it} \right|^q dt.$$

In the case $q = 2$ it suffices to square out and integrate term-by-term, since

$$\int_0^T \left(\frac{m}{n}\right)^{it} dt = \begin{cases} T & \text{if } m = n, \\ O_{m,n}(1) & \text{otherwise.} \end{cases}$$

Thus we see that

$$\lim_{T \to \infty} \frac{1}{T} \int_0^T \left| \sum_{n=1}^N a_n n^{-\sigma - it} \right|^2 dt = \sum_{n=1}^N |a_n|^2 n^{-2\sigma}.$$

In this situation also, we need to know how quickly the limit is approached.

Since the behavior of a Dirichlet polynomial $D(it)$ has an air of harmonic analysis about it, to gain perspective it is useful to compare and contrast the properties of a trigonometric polynomial $T(x) = \sum_{n=1}^N a_n e(nx)$ with those of $D(it)$. In Table 1 we list some characteristic properties of $T(x)$, and in Table 2 we list the corresponding properties of $D(it)$. In both cases we assume that $|a_n| \le 1$ for all n.

TABLE 1. Properties of $T(x) = \sum_1^N a_n e(nx)$ with $|a_n| \le 1$

NUMBER OF TERMS: N

GAP BETWEEN FREQUENCIES: 2π

$\max_x |T(x)| \le N$

IF $a_n = 1$ FOR ALL n THEN $T(0) = N$,
     AND THE WIDTH OF THIS PEAK IS $\approx 1/N$

$\max_x |T'(x)| \ll N \max_x |T(x)|$

$\deg(T^2) \le 2N$

$\# \text{terms}\,(T^2) = 2N - 1$

$\|T\|_2 \ll N^{1/2}$

$\|T\|_4 \ll N^{3/4}$

In §2 we apply principles of trigonometric approximation to derive an approximate form of Parseval's identity. Such results apply not just to ordinary Dirichlet polynomials, but also to *generalized Dirichlet polynomials*, which are sums of the form

$$(3) \qquad\qquad D(s) = \sum_{n=1}^N a_n e^{-\lambda_n s}$$

where the λ_n are distinct real numbers. When $\lambda_n = \log n$, this is just an ordinary Dirichlet polynomial; and when $\lambda_n = n$ this is a power series in e^{-s}. We find that the error term in the approximate Parseval identity depends on the degree of well-spacing of the frequencies λ_n.

In §3 we determine those exponents q for which

$$\int_{-T}^{T}\left|\sum_{n=1}^{N}a_n e^{-i\lambda_n t}\right|^q dt \ll \int_{-T}^{T}\left|\sum_{n=1}^{N}A_n e^{-i\lambda_n t}\right|^q dt$$

when $|a_n| \le A_n$ for all n. We find that such a principle holds only when q is a positive even integer.

In §4 we review some basic inequalities concerning matrices, especially those relating to eigenvalues. We apply this information in §5 to derive a bilinear form inequality that provides an alternative approach to the study of the mean values of Dirichlet polynomials. In §6 we apply the matrix theory of §4 to obtain upper bounds for the frequency of large values of Dirichlet polynomials. For ordinary Dirichlet polynomials (but not for generalized Dirichlet polynomials) we derive much better upper bounds than those that follow from mean value estimates.

TABLE 2. Properties of $D(it) = \sum_{1}^{N} a_n n^{-it}$ with $|a_n| \le 1$

NUMBER OF TERMS: N

GAP BETWEEN FREQUENCIES: $\sim 1/n$

$\max_t |D(it)| \le N$

IF $a_n = 1$ FOR ALL n THEN $D(0) = N$,
    AND THE WIDTH OF THIS PEAK IS ≈ 1

$\max_t |D'(it)| \ll (\log N) \max_t |D(it)|$

$\deg(D^2) = N^2$

$N^2(\log N)^{-A} < \#\,\text{terms}\,(D^2) < N^2(\log N)^{-a}$

$\lim_{T\to\infty}\sqrt{\frac{1}{T}\int_0^T |D(it)|^2\,dt} \ll N^{1/2}$

$\lim_{T\to\infty}\left(\frac{1}{T}\int_0^T |D(it)|^4\,dt\right)^{1/4} \ll N^{1/2}(\log N)^{3/4}$

2. Mean Values via Trigonometric Approximation. We begin by constructing the *Selberg functions* $s^+(x)$ and $s^-(x)$ for a given interval $\mathcal{I} = [\alpha, \beta]$ of the real line. These functions are analogous to the Selberg polynomials $S^\pm(x)$ given in $(1.21^\pm)$. These functions respectively majorize and minorize the characteristic function of $\mathcal{I}$, so that $s^-(x) \le \chi_{\mathcal{I}}(x) \le s^+(x)$ for all x. They have Fourier transforms supported in $(-1,1)$, $\operatorname{supp} s^\pm \subseteq (-1,1)$, and also $\int_{\mathbb{R}} s^\pm(x)\,dx = \beta - \alpha \pm 1$. These functions are easily derived by utilizing our construction of the Selberg polynomials in Chapter 1. Let $S_K^+(x)$ be the Selberg majorant polynomial of order K associated with the arc $[\alpha/(K+1), \beta/(K+1)]$ of $\mathbb{T}$, and put

$$\sigma_K(x) = S_K^+\left(\frac{x}{K+1}\right).$$

Thus σ_k has period $K + 1$, and $\chi_{_J}(x) \leq \sigma_K(x)$ for all real x. On combining (1.16), (1.18), (1.20), and (1.21$^+$), we find that

$$\sigma_K(x) = \frac{\beta - \alpha}{K + 1} + \frac{1}{2(K + 1)} \sum_{k=-K}^{K} \left(1 - \frac{|k|}{K + 1}\right)\left(e\left(\tfrac{k(x-\beta)}{K+1}\right) + e\left(\tfrac{k(\alpha-x)}{K+1}\right)\right)$$

$$+ \frac{1}{K + 1} \sum_{k=1}^{K} f\left(\tfrac{k}{K+1}\right)\left(\sin \tfrac{2\pi k(x-\beta)}{K+1} + \sin \tfrac{2\pi k(\alpha-x)}{K+1}\right).$$

where $f(u) = -(1 - u)\cot \pi u - 1/\pi$. Here the first term tends to 0 as $K \to \infty$, while the latter two terms may be considered to be Riemann sums. Thus we see that

$$\sigma_K(x) \longrightarrow \frac{1}{2}\int_{-1}^{1} (1 - |u|)\left(e\big(u(x - \beta)\big) + e\big(u(\alpha - x)\big)\right) dx$$

$$+ \int_{0}^{1} f(u)\big(\sin 2\pi u(x - \beta) + \sin 2\pi u(\alpha - x)\big)\, du$$

as $K \to \infty$, uniformly for x in a compact set. Take $s^+(x)$ to be the above limit. Then $\chi_{_J}(x) \leq s^+(x)$ for all real x, supp $s^+ \subseteq (-1, 1)$, and $\int_{\mathbb{R}} s^+(x)\, dx = \widehat{s}^+(0) = \beta - \alpha + 1$. The construction of $s^-(x)$ is similar.

With the Selberg functions in hand, it is a simple matter to derive an approximate Parseval identity for generalized Dirichlet polynomials.

THEOREM 1. *Suppose that $\lambda_1, \ldots, \lambda_N$ are distinct real numbers, and suppose that $\delta > 0$ is chosen so that $|\lambda_m - \lambda_n| \geq \delta$ whenever $m \neq n$. Then for any coefficients a_n, and any $T > 0$,*

$$(4) \qquad \int_0^T \left| \sum_{n=1}^N a_n e(\lambda_n t) \right|^2 dt = \left(T + \frac{\theta}{\delta}\right) \sum_{n=1}^N |a_n|^2$$

for some θ, $-1 \leq \theta \leq 1$.

By applying this with a_n replaced by $a_n e(\lambda_n T_0)$, we see that the interval $[0, T]$ of integration may be replaced by any interval of length T.

In §5 we give a second proof of Theorem 1, and we describe there a more delicate estimate in which the error term associated with $|a_n|^2$ depends on the distance from λ_n to the other λ's. For the ordinary Dirichlet polynomial $D(s)$ defined in (1), the above yields the estimate

$$(5) \qquad \int_0^T |D(it)|^2 dt = \big(T + O(N)\big) \sum_{n=1}^N |a_n|^2.$$

Suppose that $|a_n| \leq 1$ for all n. By applying this with $D(s)$ replaced by $D(s)^k$, we find that

$$(6) \qquad \int_0^T |D(it)|^{2k} dt \ll \big(T + N^k\big)N^{k+\epsilon}$$

for any fixed positive integer k. It is tempting to think that this estimate holds for all real exponents ≥ 2.

CONJECTURE 1. *Let $D(s)$ be defined by (1), and suppose that $|a_n| \leq 1$ for all n. Then*

(7)
$$\int_0^T |D(it)|^q \, dt \ll (T + N^{q/2}) N^{q/2 + \epsilon}$$

uniformly for $2 \leq q \leq 4$.

Estimates such as (5), (6), and (7) provide information concerning the measure of the set of t for which $|D(it)|$ is large. If $N = T$ then from (5) we find that

$$\text{meas}\,\{t \in [0, T] : |D(it)| \geq V\} \ll T^2/V^2,$$

which is best possible. Similarly, if $N = T^{1/2}$ then by taking $k = 2$ in (6) we find that

$$\text{meas}\,\{t \in [0, T] : |D(it)| \geq V\} \ll T^{2+\epsilon}/V^4.$$

On the other hand, if $T^{1/2} < N < T$, then from (6) we learn only that

$$\text{meas}\,\{t \in [0, T] : |D(it)| \geq V\} \ll \min\left(\frac{TN}{V^2}, \frac{N^{3+\epsilon}}{V^4}\right),$$

while from (7) we would obtain the superior estimate

$$\text{meas}\,\{t \in [0, T] : |D(it)| \geq V\} \ll T^{2+\epsilon} V^{-2(\log T)/\log N}.$$

PROOF OF THEOREM 1. Let s^+ be the Selberg majorizing function for the interval $\mathfrak{I} = [0, \delta T]$, and put $K(t) = s^+(\delta t)$. Then $\chi_{\mathfrak{I}}(t) \leq K(t)$ for all t, and $\widehat{K}(u) = \widehat{s}^+(u/\delta)/\delta$, so that $\text{supp}\,\widehat{K} \subseteq (-\delta, \delta)$ and $\int_{\mathbb{R}} K(t) \, dt = \widehat{K}(0) = T + 1/\delta$. Thus the left hand side of (4) is

$$\leq \int_{\mathbb{R}} K(t) \left| \sum_{n=1}^N a_n e(\lambda_n t) \right|^2 dt.$$

On squaring out and integrating term-by-term, we see that this is

$$= \sum_{m=1}^N \sum_{n=1}^N a_m \overline{a_n} \widehat{K}(\lambda_n - \lambda_m).$$

But $\widehat{K}(\lambda_n - \lambda_m) = 0$ when $m \neq n$, and $\widehat{K}(0) = T + 1/\delta$, so the above is

$$= \left(T + \frac{1}{\delta}\right) \sum_{n=1}^N |a_n|^2.$$

This is the upper bound portion of (4). The lower bound is proved similarly, using s^- instead of s^+.

We now show that Conjecture 1 is valid when $a_n = 1$ for all n.

THEOREM 2. *If $N \geq 2$ and $T \geq 2$, then*

(8) $$\int_0^T \left| \sum_{n=1}^N n^{-it} \right|^q dt \ll N^q + TN^{q/2} (\log T)^{(5q-4)/2}$$

uniformly for $2 \leq q \leq 4$.

PROOF. If $N < T^{1/2}$ then by applying (5) to $(\sum_{n \leq N} n^{-it})^2$ we find that

$$\int_0^T \left| \sum_{n=1}^N n^{-it} \right|^4 dt \ll TN^2 (\log N)^3.$$

By Hölder's inequality it follows that the left hand side of (8) is

$$\ll TN^{q/2} (\log T)^{3q/4},$$

which is more than enough.

If $N > T$ then we observe that the left hand side of (8) is

$$\leq N^{q-2} \int_0^T \left| \sum_{n=1}^N n^{-it} \right|^2 dt.$$

By (5) we see that this new integral is $\ll N^2$, and so the left hand side of (8) is $\ll N^q$ in this case.

We now suppose that $T^{1/2} \leq N \leq T$. By the truncated Perron formula (see p. 105 of Davenport [6]) we know that

$$\sum_{n=1}^N n^{-it} = \frac{1}{2\pi i} \int_{a-2iT}^{a+2iT} \zeta(w+it) N^w \frac{dw}{w} + O(NT^{-1} \log T)$$

where $a = 1 + 1/\log T$. We move the path of integration to the line $\Re w = 1/2$. To estimate the contribution of the horizontal segments we use the old estimate $\zeta(s) \ll t^{(1-\sigma)/2} \log t$, which is valid uniformly for $0 \leq \sigma \leq 1$ and $t \geq 2$. Our contour encloses a pole at $w = 1 - it$, and thus we find that

$$\sum_{n=1}^N n^{-it} = \frac{1}{2\pi} \int_{-2T}^{2T} \zeta\left(\frac{1}{2} + i(t+v)\right) \frac{N^{1/2+iv}}{1/2+iv} dv$$
$$+ \frac{N^{1-it}}{1-it} + O(NT^{-1} \log T)$$
$$= T_1 + T_2 + T_3,$$

say. By Hölder's inequality,

$$|T_1|^q \leq N^{q/2} \left(\int_{-2T}^{2T} |1/2 + iv|^{-1} dv \right)^{q-1} \int_{-2T}^{2T} |\zeta(1/2 + i(t+v))|^q |1/2 + iv|^{-1} dv,$$

and hence

$$\int_0^T |T_1|^q dt \ll N^{q/2} (\log T)^q \int_{-3T}^{3T} |\zeta(1/2 + it)|^q dt.$$

When $q = 2$ this last integral is $\ll T \log T$, and when $q = 4$ this integral is $\ll T(\log T)^4$ (see Theorems 7.2(A) and 7.16 of Titchmarsh [**56**]). Hence by Hölder's inequality, this integral is $\ll T(\log T)^{(3q-4)/2}$, uniformly for $2 \leq q \leq 4$. Thus we see that

$$\int_0^T |T_1|^q \, dt \ll TN^{q/2}(\log T)^{(5q-2)/2}.$$

On the other hand, it is clear that

$$\int_0^T |T_2|^q \, dt \ll N^q$$

uniformly for $2 \leq q \leq 4$, and that

$$\int_0^T |T_3|^q \, dt \ll T(\log T)^{2q}.$$

On combining these estimates we obtain the stated result.

3. Majorant Principles. We begin with a useful positive result.

THEOREM 3. *Let* $\lambda_1, \ldots, \lambda_N$ *be real numbers, and suppose that* $|a_n| \leq A_n$ *for all* n. *Then*

$$(9) \qquad \int_{-T}^T \left| \sum_{n=1}^N a_n e(\lambda_n t) \right|^2 dt \leq 3 \int_{-T}^T \left| \sum_{n=1}^N A_n e(\lambda_n t) \right|^2 dt.$$

By applying this with a_n replaced by $a_n e(\lambda_n T_0)$ we see that the interval of integration on the left hand side can be replaced by any interval of length $2T$. As an application, suppose that $|a_n| \leq 1$ for all n. Then by (9) we see that

$$\int_{T_0-1}^{T_0+1} \left| \sum_{n=1}^\infty a_n n^{-\sigma-it} \right|^2 dt \leq 3 \int_{-1}^1 |\zeta(\sigma + it)|^2 dt$$

for $\sigma > 1$. Here the sums have infinitely many terms, but this is not a problem since these series are uniformly convergent. Since $\zeta(s) \ll 1/|s-1|$ for s in a bounded set, it follows that the above is

$$(10) \qquad \ll \frac{1}{\sigma - 1}$$

uniformly for $1 < \sigma \leq 2$.

PROOF. Let $K(t) = \max(0, 1 - |t|/T)$. We show first that

$$(11) \qquad \int_{-\infty}^\infty K(t) \left| \sum_{n=1}^N a_n e(\lambda_n t) \right|^2 dt \leq \int_{-\infty}^\infty K(t) \left| \sum_{n=1}^N A_n e(\lambda_n t) \right|^2 dt.$$

To see this, we multiply out and integrate term-by-term. Thus the left hand side is

$$\sum_{m=1}^N \sum_{n=1}^N a_m \overline{a_n} \widehat{K}(\lambda_n - \lambda_m)$$

But $\widehat{K}(u) = \pi^{-2}(\sin \pi T u)^2 T^{-1} u^{-2} \geq 0$ for all u, and hence the above is

$$\leq \sum_{m=1}^{N} \sum_{n=1}^{N} A_m A_n \widehat{K}(\lambda_n - \lambda_m).$$

But this is the right hand side of (11), so (11) is proved.

By replacing a_n by $a_n e(\lambda_n T_0)$ in (11), we see that

(12) $$\int_{-\infty}^{\infty} K(t - T_0) \left| \sum_{n=1}^{N} a_n e(\lambda_n t) \right|^2 dt \leq \int_{-\infty}^{\infty} K(t) \left| \sum_{n=1}^{N} A_n e(\lambda_n t) \right|^2 dt$$

for any real number T_0. But

$$\chi_{[-T,T]}(t) \leq K(t - T) + K(t) + K(t + T)$$

for all t, so that the left hand side of (9) is

$$\leq \int_{-\infty}^{\infty} \left(K(t - T) + K(t) + K(t + T) \right) \left| \sum_{n=1}^{N} a_n e(\lambda_n t) \right|^2 dt.$$

By three applications of (12) we see that this is

$$\leq 3 \int_{-\infty}^{\infty} K(t) \left| \sum_{n=1}^{N} A_n e(\lambda_n t) \right|^2 dt$$

$$\leq 3 \int_{-T}^{T} \left| \sum_{n=1}^{N} A_n e(\lambda_n t) \right|^2 dt.$$

This completes the proof.

It is instructive to consider the inequality (12) on which the above proof depends. The reason that this inequality holds with the kernel $K(t)$ is that $K(t)$ is the convolution of a function with itself. In the abstract, this principle can be cast in the following form.

THEOREM 4. *Suppose that $Y = [y_{nr}]$ is an arbitrary $N \times R$ matrix, and that $|a_n| \leq A_n$ for all n. Then*

(13) $$\sum_{r=1}^{R} \sum_{s=1}^{R} \left| \sum_{n=1}^{N} a_n y_{nr} \overline{y_{ns}} \right|^2 \leq \sum_{r=1}^{R} \sum_{s=1}^{R} \left| \sum_{n=1}^{N} A_n y_{nr} \overline{y_{ns}} \right|^2.$$

PROOF. On squaring out the left hand side and inverting the order of summation, we see that the left hand side above is

$$= \sum_{m=1}^{N} \sum_{n=1}^{N} a_m \overline{a_n} \sum_{r=1}^{R} y_{mr} \overline{y_{nr}} \sum_{s=1}^{R} \overline{y_{ms}} y_{ns}$$

$$= \sum_{m=1}^{N} \sum_{n=1}^{N} a_m \overline{a_n} \left| \sum_{r=1}^{R} y_{mr} \overline{y_{nr}} \right|^2.$$

We may similarly rewrite the right hand side of (13), and of the two expressions, the one involving A_n is clearly the larger. This completes the proof.

We observe that Conjecture 1 could be derived from Theorem 2 if a suitable majorant principle could be established for qth powers. Such a principle, which would suffice in this connection, was proposed by Hardy and Littlewood [16] (see also p. 23 of Littlewood [43]), who conjectured that for any real number $q \geq 2$ there is a constant C_q such that

$$(14) \qquad \int_{\mathbb{T}} |f(x)|^q \, dx \leq C_q \int_{\mathbb{T}} |F(x)|^q \, dx.$$

for any trigonometric polynomials

$$f(x) = \sum_{-N}^{N} a_n e(nx), \qquad F(x) = \sum_{-N}^{N} A_n e(nx),$$

for which $|a_n| \leq A_n$ for all n. By Parseval's identity we see that this holds when q is an even integer, say $q = 2k$, and that we may take $C_{2k} = 1$ in this case. We now show that these are the only q for which such an inequality holds.

THEOREM 5. *If $q > 2$, and q is not an even integer, then there is no constant C_q such that (14) holds uniformly for all choices of the trigonometric polynomials f and F.*

PROOF. First we show that if there is such a C_q, then necessarily $C_q > 1$ when q is not an even integer. Secondly we show that if there is such a C_q then (14) holds with $C_q = 1$. These two results combine to give the proof.

We take advantage of the fact that the power series coefficients of $(1+z)^{q/2}$ are not all positive. Indeed, let k be the unique integer such that $2k-4 < q < 2k-2$. Then the first negative coefficient is the coefficient of z^k. Let $f(z) = 1 + z - z^k$, and put $F(z) = 1 + z + z^k$. We show that

$$(15) \qquad \int_{\mathbb{T}} |f(re(\theta))|^q \, d\theta > \int_{\mathbb{T}} |F(re(\theta))|^q \, d\theta$$

for all sufficiently small r, $r > 0$. By the binomial theorem,

$$(1 + z \pm z^k)^{q/2} = \sum_{j=0}^{\infty} \binom{q/2}{j} (z \pm z^k)^j$$

$$= \sum_{j=0}^{k-1} \binom{q/2}{j} z^j + \left(\binom{q/2}{k} \pm 1 \right) z^k + \text{higher order terms}$$

provided that $|z| < 1/2$. We set $z = re(\theta)$ and apply Parseval's identity to see that the respective sides of (15) are

$$\left(\sum_{j=0}^{k-1} \binom{q/2}{j}^2 r^{2j} \right) + \left(\binom{q/2}{k} \pm 1 \right)^2 r^{2k} + O(r^{2k+2}).$$

Since $\binom{q/2}{k} < 0$, the coefficient of r^{2k} is larger when the negative sign is used. Thus we have (15) for all sufficiently small $r > 0$. This completes the first portion of the proof.

For the second portion of the proof we begin by observing that if $g(x)$ and $h(x)$ are properly Riemann-integrable functions on $[0, 1]$, and if $h(x)$ has period 1, then

$$(16) \qquad \lim_{K \to \infty} \int_0^1 g(x)h(Kx)\,dx = \int_0^1 g(x)\,dx \cdot \int_0^1 h(x)\,dx.$$

Suppose now that $c > 1$, and that f and F are trigonometric polynomials such that $\int_{\mathbb{T}} |f(x)|^q\,dx > c \int_{\mathbb{T}} |F(x)|^q\,dx$, with the coefficients of f majorized by those of F. Put $f_1(x) = f(x)f(Kx)$ and $F_1(x) = F(x)F(Kx)$. Then the coefficients of f_1 are majorized by those of F_1. By (16) we see that $\int |f_1|^q \to \left(\int |f|^q \right)^2$ as $K \to \infty$, and similarly for F_1. Thus $\int_{\mathbb{T}} |f_1(x)|^q\,dx > c^2 \int_{\mathbb{T}} |F_1(x)|^q\,dx$ if K is sufficiently large. Finally, suppose that C_q is the optimal constant in (14). We have shown that if $c < C_q$ then $c^2 < C_q$. But this can be the case only if $C_q \leq 1$. Since it is trivial that $C_q \geq 1$, we conclude that $C_q = 1$. This completes the proof.

4. Review of Elementary Operator Theory. Let A be an $M \times N$ matrix, so that $\mathbf{y} \mapsto A\mathbf{y}$ is a linear map from $\mathbb{C}^N$ to $\mathbb{C}^M$. We are interested in knowing how long the image vector $A\mathbf{y}$ is, relative to the length of $\mathbf{y}$. The *operator norm* of A, denoted $\|A\|$, is the maximum of the ratio $\|A\mathbf{y}\|/\|\mathbf{y}\|$ over all non-zero vectors $\mathbf{y} \in \mathbb{C}^N$. (By homogeneity we may restrict $\mathbf{y}$ to be a unit vector.) Associated with A is the *adjoint* matrix $A^* = [\overline{a_{nm}}]$; this is an $N \times M$ matrix that determines a linear map from $\mathbb{C}^M$ to $\mathbb{C}^N$. By means of the following elementary duality principle, we see that the operator norms of A and A^* are equal.

THEOREM 6. (Duality) *Let* $A = [a_{mn}]$ *be a given* $M \times N$ *matrix. Then the following three assertions concerning the constant c are equivalent:*

(1) *For all* $\mathbf{y} \in \mathbb{C}^N$, *we have*

$$\sum_{m=1}^{M} \left| \sum_{n=1}^{N} a_{mn} y_n \right|^2 \leq c^2 \sum_{n=1}^{N} |y_n|^2;$$

(2) *For all* $\mathbf{x} \in \mathbb{C}^N$ *and all* $\mathbf{y} \in \mathbb{C}^M$ *we have*

$$\left| \sum_{m=1}^{M} \sum_{n=1}^{N} a_{mn} x_m y_n \right| \leq c \left(\sum_{m=1}^{M} |x_m|^2 \right)^2 \left(\sum_{n=1}^{N} |y_n|^2 \right)^2;$$

(3) *For all* $\mathbf{x} \in \mathbb{C}^M$ *we have*

$$\sum_{n=1}^{N} \left| \sum_{m=1}^{M} a_{mn} x_m \right|^2 \leq c^2 \sum_{m=1}^{M} |x_m|^2.$$

PROOF. To see that (1) implies (2) we observe that by Cauchy's inequality,

$$\left| \sum_{m=1}^{M} x_m \sum_{n=1}^{N} a_{mn} y_n \right|^2 \leq \left(\sum_{m=1}^{M} |x_m|^2 \right) \left(\sum_{m=1}^{M} \left| \sum_{n=1}^{N} a_{mn} y_n \right|^2 \right).$$

We use (1) to estimate the second factor, and thus we have (2).

To see that (2) implies (1), put $x_m = \sum_{n=1}^{N} a_{mn} y_n$. Thus the left hand side of (1) is $\sum_{m=1}^{M} |x_m|^2 = S$, say. Thus

$$S = \sum_{m=1}^{M} \overline{x_m} \sum_{n=1}^{N} a_{mn} y_n,$$

and by (2) this is

$$\leq c \left(\sum_{m=1}^{M} |x_m|^2 \right)^{1/2} \left(\sum_{n=1}^{N} |y_n|^2 \right)^{1/2}$$

$$= c S^{1/2} \left(\sum_{n=1}^{N} |y_n|^2 \right)^{1/2}.$$

If $S = 0$ then there is nothing to prove. If $S > 0$ then we cancel $S^{1/2}$ and square both sides to obtain (1).

We have established that (1) and (2) are equivalent. By symmetry we see similarly that (2) and (3) are equivalent. This completes the proof.

Since the optimal constant in (1) is $\|A\|$, and the optimal constant in (3) is $\|A^*\|$, it follows that

(17) $$\|A\| = \|A^*\|$$

for any matrix A.

In the case that A is a square matrix, there are further numbers associated with it. The *spectral radius* of A is $\rho(A) = \max |\lambda|$, where the maximum is over all eigenvalues λ of A. Also, the *numerical radius* of A, denoted $\nu(A)$, is the optimal constant c in the inequality

$$\left| \sum_{m=1}^{N} \sum_{n=1}^{N} a_{mn} x_m \overline{x_n} \right| \leq c \sum_{n=1}^{N} |x_n|^2.$$

Alternatively, $\nu(A) = \max |(A\mathbf{x}, \mathbf{x})|$ where the maximum is extended over all unit vectors $\mathbf{x} \in \mathbb{C}^N$. On comparing the definition of the numerical radius with the more general inequality (2) of Theorem 6, we see that $\nu(A) \leq \|A\|$. Also, if $\mathbf{x}$ is a unit eigenvector associated with the eigenvalue λ, then $|(A\mathbf{x}, \mathbf{x})| = |(\lambda \mathbf{x}, \mathbf{x})| = |\lambda|$, and hence we see that $\rho(A) \leq \nu(A)$. That is,

(18) $$\rho(A) \leq \nu(A) \leq \|A\|$$

for all square matrices A. For the latter two quantities there is also an inequality in the opposite direction. To see this, we first note the identity

$$(A\mathbf{x}, \mathbf{y}) = \tfrac{1}{4}(A(\mathbf{x} + \mathbf{y}), \mathbf{x} + \mathbf{y}) - \tfrac{1}{4}(A(\mathbf{x} - \mathbf{y}), \mathbf{x} - \mathbf{y})$$
$$+ \tfrac{i}{4}(A(\mathbf{x} + i\mathbf{y}), \mathbf{x} + i\mathbf{y}) - \tfrac{i}{4}(A(\mathbf{x} - i\mathbf{y}), \mathbf{x} - i\mathbf{y}),$$

from which it follows that

$$|(A\mathbf{x}, \mathbf{y})| \le \tfrac{1}{4}\nu(A)\big(\|\mathbf{x} + \mathbf{y}\|^2 + \|\mathbf{x} - \mathbf{y}\|^2 + \|\mathbf{x} + i\mathbf{y}\|^2 + \|\mathbf{x} - i\mathbf{y}\|^2\big)$$
$$= \nu(A)\big(\|\mathbf{x}\|^2 + \|\mathbf{y}\|^2\big).$$

If $\|\mathbf{x}\| = \|\mathbf{y}\| = 1$ then this is $= 2\nu(A)$, and hence we deduce that

$$\tfrac{1}{2}\|A\| \le \nu(A).$$

On the other hand, the gap between the spectral radius and the operator norm can be enormous. For example, if A is strictly upper triangular then $\rho(A) = 0$ while $\|A\|$ may be large. In general we expect these inequalities to be strict, but it is easy to see that equality holds throughout (18) when A is a diagonal matrix.

We recall that a square matrix U is *unitary* if its columns form an orthonormal system, and we say that two square matrices A and B are *unitarily similar* if there is a unitary matrix U such that $B = U^*AU$. Since $\|U\mathbf{x}\| = \|\mathbf{x}\|$ for all $\mathbf{x} \in \mathbb{C}^N$, it follows that if A and B are unitarily similar then $\|A\| = \|B\|$, $\nu(A) = \nu(B)$, and $\rho(A) = \rho(B)$. (This last identity holds also under the less stringent assumption that A and B are merely similar.) Schur's Lemma (whose proof we omit) asserts that every square matrix A is unitarily similar to an upper triangular matrix T. It is easy to verify that T commutes with its adjoint, $TT^* = T^*T$, if and only if T is diagonal. Moreover, $TT^* = T^*T$ if and only if $AA^* = A^*A$. A matrix with this property is called *normal*, and we conclude that normal matrices are precisely those matrices that are unitarily similar to a diagonal matrix. Thus we see that if A is normal then equality holds throughout (18). The class of normal matrices contains two other noteworthy classes of matrices, namely the *Hermitian* matrices (those H for which $H^* = H$), and the unitary matrices U (characterized by the property that $U^* = U^{-1}$).

If A is a square matrix then $(A\mathbf{x}, \mathbf{x}) = (\mathbf{x}, A^*\mathbf{x})$. Hence if H is Hermitian and $\mathbf{x}$ is an eigenvector associated with the eigenvector λ, then

$$\lambda\|\mathbf{x}\|^2 = (\lambda\mathbf{x}, \mathbf{x})$$
$$= (H\mathbf{x}, \mathbf{x})$$
$$= (\mathbf{x}, H^*\mathbf{x})$$
$$= (\mathbf{x}, H\mathbf{x})$$
$$= (\mathbf{x}, \lambda\mathbf{x})$$
$$= \overline{\lambda}\|\mathbf{x}\|^2.$$

Since $\|\mathbf{x}\| > 0$, it follows that all eigenvalues λ of a Hermitian matrix H are real. From the identity $\|U\mathbf{x}\| = \|\mathbf{x}\|$ it is obvious that the eigenvalues of a unitary matrix are all unimodular.

If we multiply out the left hand side of (1) in Theorem 6, we find that the constant c^2 is a bound for the numerical radius of the matrix A^*A. That is, the left hand side of (1) is $(A\mathbf{x}, A\mathbf{x}) = (A^*A\mathbf{x}, \mathbf{x})$. But A^*A is Hermitian, so

$$\|A\|^2 = \nu(A^*A) = \|A^*A\| = \rho(A^*A),$$

and by Theorem 6 this common value is also equal to

$$\|A^*\|^2 = \nu(AA^*) = \|AA^*\| = \rho(AA^*).$$

This completes our review of basic operator theory, prerequisite to the following sections.

5. Mean Values via Hilbert's Inequality. Let A be a matrix with an unspecified number of rows and columns, perhaps infinitely many. Let R denote the maximum of the ℓ^1 norms of the rows of A, and C be the maximum of the ℓ^1 norms of the columns of A. That is,

$$R = \sup_m \sum_n |a_{mn}|, \qquad C = \sup_n \sum_m |a_{mn}|.$$

By Cauchy's inequality we see that

$$\left| \sum_{m,n} a_{mn} x_m y_n \right| \leq \left(\sum_{m,n} |a_{mn}||x_m|^2 \right)^{1/2} \left(\sum_{m,n} |a_{mn}||y_n|^2 \right)^{1/2}$$

$$= \left(\sum_m |x_m|^2 \sum_n |a_{mn}| \right)^{1/2} \left(\sum_n |y_n|^2 \sum_m |a_{mn}| \right)^{1/2}$$

$$(19) \qquad \leq (RC)^{1/2} \left(\sum_m |x_m|^2 \right)^{1/2} \left(\sum_n |y_n|^2 \right)^{1/2}.$$

Thus a matrix A has finite operator norm whenever the quantities R and C are finite. In order to give an example of a bounded operator that is not trivially bounded in this way, Hilbert (see Weyl [**58**]) proved that there is a constant c such that

$$(20) \qquad \left| \sum_{m \neq n} \frac{x_m y_n}{m - n} \right| \leq c \left(\sum_m |x_m|^2 \right)^{1/2} \left(\sum_n |y_n|^2 \right)^{1/2}.$$

Later, Schur [**53**] proved that one can take $c = \pi$. This constant is best possible, but equality is attained only when $\mathbf{x} = \mathbf{y} = \mathbf{0}$. This inequality can be generalized as follows.

THEOREM 7. *Let* $\lambda_1, \ldots, \lambda_N$ *be distinct real numbers, and suppose that* $\delta > 0$ *is chosen so that* $|\lambda_m - \lambda_n| \geq \delta$ *whenever* $m \neq n$. *Then*

$$(21) \qquad \left| \sum_{\substack{1 \leq m \leq N \\ 1 \leq n \leq N \\ m \neq n}} \frac{x_m y_n}{\lambda_m - \lambda_n} \right| \leq \frac{\pi}{\delta} \left(\sum_{m=1}^{N} |x_m|^2 \right)^{1/2} \left(\sum_{n=1}^{N} |y_n|^2 \right)^{1/2}.$$

As will be evident from the proof, equality occurs only when $\mathbf{x} = \mathbf{y} = \mathbf{0}$. Returning to Theorem 1, if we multiply out the left hand side of (4) and integrate term-by-term, then the diagonal terms contribute the amount $T \sum |a_n|^2$, while the non-diagonal terms contribute two bilinear forms of the shape in (21), one each for the endpoints at which the indefinite integral is evaluated. Thus by two applications of Theorem 7 we obtain Theorem 1 again.

PROOF. In view of Theorem 6, it suffices to show that

$$(22) \qquad \sum_{m=1}^{N} \left| \sum_{\substack{1 \leq n \leq N \\ n \neq m}} \frac{y_n}{\lambda_m - \lambda_n} \right|^2 \leq \frac{\pi^2}{\delta^2} \sum_{n=1}^{N} |y_n|^2.$$

On expanding, we see that the left hand side is

$$= \sum_{n=1}^{N} \sum_{\nu=1}^{N} y_n \overline{y_\nu} \sum_{\substack{1 \leq m \leq N \\ m \neq n \\ m \neq \nu}} \frac{1}{(\lambda_m - \lambda_n)(\lambda_m - \lambda_\nu)}.$$

We write the diagonal terms $n = \nu$ separately, and for the non-diagonal terms we apply the identity

$$\frac{1}{(x-a)(x-b)} = \frac{1}{a-b} \left(\frac{1}{x-a} - \frac{1}{x-b} \right)$$

to see that our expression is

$$= \sum_{n=1}^{N} |y_n|^2 \sum_{\substack{1 \leq m \leq N \\ m \neq n}} \frac{1}{(\lambda_m - \lambda_n)^2}$$

$$+ \sum_{\substack{1 \leq n, \nu \leq N \\ n \neq \nu}} \frac{y_n \overline{y_\nu}}{\lambda_n - \lambda_\nu} \sum_{\substack{1 \leq m \leq N \\ m \neq n \\ m \neq \nu}} \left(\frac{1}{\lambda_m - \lambda_n} - \frac{1}{\lambda_m - \lambda_\nu} \right)$$

$$= T_1 + T_2,$$

say. In T_2 we write the innermost sum as the difference of two sums. In the first of these sums we drop the constraint $m \neq \nu$, and in the second of these sums we drop the constraint $m \neq n$. After introducing a new term to compensate for these alterations, we find that

$$T_2 = \sum_{\substack{1 \leq n, \nu \leq N \\ n \neq \nu}} \frac{y_n \overline{y_\nu}}{\lambda_n - \lambda_\nu} \sum_{\substack{1 \leq m \leq N \\ m \neq n}} \frac{1}{\lambda_m - \lambda_n}$$

$$- \sum_{\substack{1 \leq n, \nu \leq N \\ n \neq \nu}} \frac{y_n \overline{y_\nu}}{\lambda_n - \lambda_\nu} \sum_{\substack{1 \leq m \leq N \\ m \neq \nu}} \frac{1}{\lambda_m - \lambda_\nu}$$

$$+ 2 \sum_{\substack{1 \leq n, \nu \leq N \\ n \neq \nu}} \frac{y_n \overline{y_\nu}}{(\lambda_n - \lambda_\nu)^2}$$

$$(23) \qquad\qquad = \Sigma_1 - \Sigma_2 + 2\Sigma_3,$$

say. Here

$$(24) \qquad \Sigma_1 = \sum_{n=1}^{N} y_n \left(\sum_{\substack{1 \leq m \leq N \\ m \neq n}} \frac{1}{\lambda_m - \lambda_n} \right) \left(\sum_{\substack{1 \leq \nu \leq N \\ \nu \neq n}} \frac{\overline{y_\nu}}{\lambda_n - \lambda_\nu} \right)$$

and

$$(25) \qquad \Sigma_2 = \sum_{\nu=1}^{N} \overline{y_\nu} \left(\sum_{\substack{1 \leq m \leq N \\ m \neq \nu}} \frac{1}{\lambda_m - \lambda_\nu} \right) \left(\sum_{\substack{1 \leq n \leq N \\ n \neq \nu}} \frac{y_n}{\lambda_n - \lambda_\nu} \right).$$

Since we have no evident means to bound these sums, we seem to be stuck. To salvage the argument we appeal again to the ideas developed in the preceding section. Let A denote the coefficient matrix of the bilinear form under consideration. Then A is skew-Hermitian, $A^* = -A$, which is to say that iA is Hermitian. Hence the operator norm of A is equal to its spectral radius, and thus we may suppose that the y_n are the coordinates of an eigenvector. Since the eigenvalues of A are all purely imaginary, we may assume that

$$(26) \qquad\qquad \sum_{\substack{1 \leq n \leq N \\ n \neq m}} \frac{y_n}{\lambda_m - \lambda_n} = i\lambda y_m$$

for all m, where λ is a real number. On taking complex conjugates, and using the fact that λ is real, we see that the innermost sum in (24) is $= -i\lambda \overline{y_n}$, and hence that

$$\Sigma_1 = -i\lambda \sum_{n=1}^{N} |y_n|^2 \sum_{\substack{1 \leq m \leq N \\ m \neq n}} \frac{1}{\lambda_m - \lambda_n}.$$

Since the innermost sum in (25) is the negative of the sum in (26), we deduce also that

$$\Sigma_2 = -i\lambda \sum_{\nu=1}^{N} |y_\nu|^2 \sum_{\substack{1 \leq m \leq N \\ m \neq \nu}} \frac{1}{\lambda_m - \lambda_\nu}.$$

That is, $\Sigma_1 = \Sigma_2$, the contributions of these terms cancels in (23), and $T_2 = 2\Sigma_3$. Marvelous!

To bound Σ_3 we invoke the inequality $|y_n \overline{y_\nu}| \leq \frac{1}{2}|y_n|^2 + \frac{1}{2}|y_\nu|^2$, and thus we see that

$$|\Sigma_3| \leq \sum_{n=1}^{N} |y_n|^2 \sum_{\substack{1 \leq \nu \leq N \\ \nu \neq n}} \frac{1}{(\lambda_n - \lambda_\nu)^2} = T_1.$$

Hence altogether we see that the left hand side of (22) is $\leq 3T_1$.

To bound T_1 we suppose, as we may, that the λ_n are in increasing order, so that $|\lambda_n - \lambda_\nu| \geq \delta|n - \nu|$. Hence the inner sum in T_1 is

$$\leq \frac{2}{\delta^2}\zeta(2) = \frac{\pi^2}{3\delta^2}.$$

Thus we have (22), and the proof is complete.

By the same method it can also be shown that

$$(27) \qquad \left| \sum_{\substack{1 \leq m \leq N \\ 1 \leq n \leq N \\ m \neq n}} \frac{x_m y_n}{\lambda_m - \lambda_n} \right| \leq \frac{3\pi}{2} \left(\sum_m |x_m|^2/\delta_m \right)^{1/2} \left(\sum_n |y_n|^2/\delta_n \right)^{1/2}$$

where

$$\delta_n = \min_{\substack{1 \leq m \leq N \\ m \neq n}} |\lambda_m - \lambda_n|.$$

In the same way that we derived Theorem 1 from Theorem 6, from (27) it follows that

$$(28) \qquad \int_0^T \left| \sum_{n=1}^{N} a_n e(\lambda_n t) \right|^2 dt = T \sum_{n=1}^{N} |a_n|^2 + O\left(\sum_{n=1}^{N} |a_n|^2/\delta_n \right).$$

The implicit constant here can be taken to be $3/2$. For the ordinary Dirichlet polynomial $D(s)$ in (1), this takes the form

$$(29) \qquad \int_0^T |D(it)|^2 dt = T \sum_{n=1}^{N} |a_n|^2 + O\left(\sum_{n=1}^{N} n|a_n|^2 \right).$$

6. Large Value Estimates. In addition to mean value estimates in which t runs continuously over an interval, we can establish useful estimates for the mean square of a Dirichlet polynomial as t ranges discretely over a relatively small collection of points. Such estimates yield new information regarding the number of times that a Dirichlet polynomial can be large.

THEOREM 8. *Suppose that $0 \leq t_1 < t_2 < \ldots < t_R \leq T$ where $t_{r+1} - t_r \geq 1$ for all r, and let $D(s)$ be defined as in (1). Then*

$$(30) \qquad \sum_{r=1}^{R} |D(it_r)|^2 \ll (N + RT^{1/2})(\log T) \sum_{n=1}^{N} |a_n|^2.$$

PROOF. By Theorem 5 it suffices to establish the dual inequality

$$\sum_{n=1}^{N}\left|\sum_{r=1}^{R} y_r n^{-it_r}\right|^2 \ll (N + RT^{1/2})(\log T)\sum_{r=1}^{R}|y_r|^2.$$

On expanding and inverting the order of summation, we find that the left hand side is

$$(31) \qquad = N\sum_{r=1}^{R}|y_r|^2 + \sum_{\substack{1\le q,\,r\le R\\ q\neq r}} Z\big(i(t_q - t_r)\big) y_q \overline{y_r}$$

where

$$Z(s) = \sum_{n=1}^{N} n^{-s}$$

is a partial sum of the Dirichlet series for the zeta function $\zeta(s)$. The second term in (31) is a bilinear form whose spectral analysis remains obscure. To estimate it we take the very crude approach offered by the inequality (19). Thus we see that the expression (31) is

$$(32) \qquad \le \left(N + \max_{1\le q\le R}\sum_{\substack{1\le r\le R\\ r\neq q}}\big|Z\big(i(t_q - t_r)\big)\big|\right)\sum_{r=1}^{R}|y_r|^2.$$

To complete the proof it suffices to show that

$$(33) \qquad Z(it) \ll N/t + t^{1/2}\log t$$

for $t \ge 2$. To this end we show that

$$(34) \qquad \sum_{U}^{2U} n^{-it} \ll \begin{cases} U/t & \text{if } U > t \\ t^{1/2} & \text{if } t^{1/2} \le U \le t \\ U & \text{if } U \le t^{1/2} \end{cases}$$

which suffices, since (33) follows by summing over diadic blocks. In the first case we apply the truncated Poisson process, Theorem 3.8, and then use Lemma 3.1 to estimate the resulting integrals. In the second case above we proceed similarly, but instead use Lemma 3.2 to estimate the integrals. The third estimate is trivial. This completes the proof.

Our bound (33) for $Z(it)$ is presumably somewhat far from the truth, since if the Lindelöf Hypothesis is true then we would have the better estimate $Z(it) \ll N/t + N^{1/2}t^\epsilon$ for all $t > t_0(\epsilon)$. This in turn would yield the better estimate

$$(35) \qquad \sum_{r=1}^{R}|D(it_r)|^2 \ll (N + RN^{1/2})T^\epsilon \sum_{n=1}^{N}|a_n|^2$$

in place of (30). To see how this might be applied, suppose that $|a_n| \le 1$ for all n, that

$$(36) \qquad N^{3/4}T^\epsilon < V,$$

and that $|D(it_r)| \geq V$ for all r. From (25) we deduce (assuming the Lindelöf Hypothesis) that $R \ll N^2/V^2$. By comparison, if we used instead the mean value estimate provided by Theorem 1, we would obtain the bound $R \ll TN/V^2$, which is much larger when N is small compared with T.

The condition (36) is disappointing, since it leave open the question of whether some similar bound might hold when $N^{1/2}T^\epsilon < V < N^{3/4}T^\epsilon$. The presumed defect in our argument lies in our appeal to the bound (19), since the bilinear form in (31) might be expected to be smaller. Indeed, it would be tempting to conjecture that

$$\sum_{r=1}^{R} |D(it_r)|^2 \ll (N+R)T^\epsilon \sum_{n=1}^{N} |a_n|^2$$

were it not for the following.

EXAMPLE. (Bourgain) Suppose that $T^{1/2} < N < T$. Put $H = [cN/T^{1/2}]$, and set $a_n = 1$ for $N < n \leq N+H$, with $a_n = 0$ otherwise. Put $J = [T/(2\pi N)]$, $K = [T^{1/2}]$, and suppose that $t = 2\pi j N - k$ where j and k are integers, $1 \leq j \leq J$, $1 \leq k \leq K$. Thus $0 \leq t \leq T$, and we note that

$$
\begin{aligned}
t \log n &= t \log N + t \log \left(1 + \frac{n-N}{N}\right) \\
&= t \log N + \frac{t(n-N)}{N} + O(TH^2/N^2) \\
&= t \log N + 2\pi j(n-N) - \frac{k(n-N)}{N} + O(TH^2/N^2) \\
&= t \log N + 2\pi j(n-N) + O(c),
\end{aligned}
$$

assuming that $0 < c < 1$. Hence for such a t we have

$$\left| \sum_{n=N+1}^{N+H} n^{-it} \right| \gg H$$

if c is small. Moreover there are $JK \gg T^{3/2}/N$ such t, so we can choose well-spaced t_r so that

$$\sum_{r=1}^{R} \left| \sum_{n=N+1}^{N+H} n^{-it_r} \right|^2 \gg NT^{1/2}$$

while

$$\sum |a_n|^2 = H \ll N/T^{1/2}.$$

By couching our conjectural improvement of Theorem 8 in terms of the sup-norm of the coefficients, we avoid any conflict with the above Example.

CONJECTURE 2. *Suppose that* $0 \leq t_1 < t_2 < \ldots < t_R \leq T$ *where* $t_{r+1} - t_r \geq 1$ *for all* r, *and let* $D(s)$ *be defined as in (1). If* $|a_n| \leq 1$ *for all* n *then*

$$\sum_{r=1}^{R} |D(it_r)|^2 \ll (N+R)NT^\epsilon.$$

If $V^2 < T^{1/2}N$ then (30) provides no upper bound for the number R of well-spaced points t_r at which $|D(it_r)| > V$. However, we can obtain such a bound from Theorem 8 by adding a further idea.

THEOREM 9. *Suppose that $0 \le t_1 < t_2 < \ldots < t_R \le T$ where $t_{r+1} - t_r \ge 1$ for all r, let $D(s)$ be defined as in (1), and suppose that $|D(it_r)| \ge V$ for all r. If $|a_n| \le 1$ for all n then*

$$R \ll N^2 V^{-2} + TN^4 V^{-6}(\log T)^2.$$

From Theorem 1 we can obtain the estimate $R \ll TN/V^2$, and we see that Theorem 9 improves on this when $V > N^{3/4}(\log T)^{1/2}$. The large value theory, as it stands, contributes nothing when $V \le N^{3/4}$.

PROOF. If $V^2 \ge CT^{1/2}(\log T)N$ and C is a large constant, then from (30) we obtain the upper bound $r \ll N^2/V^2$, which suffices. Suppose now that $V^2 < CT^{1/2}(\log T)N$. Let T_0 be determined by the relation $V^2 = CT_0^{1/2}(\log T_0)N$. Then by (30), the number of well-spaced t_r at which $|D(it_r)| \ge V$ is $\ll N^2/V^2$. We divide the interval $[0,T]$ into $\ll T/T_0$ subintervals of length T_0, and apply (30) to each of the subintervals to see that

$$R \ll N^2 V^{-2} T T_0^{-1} \ll TN^4 V^{-6}(\log T)^2.$$

7. Notes. §2. For a more customary construction of the Selberg functions $s^\pm$, see Montgomery [48] or Vaaler [57]. Theorem 1 is due to Montgomery and Vaughan [50], who used Hilbert's inequality as outlined in §5. Prior to that, somewhat weaker estimates had been given by Titchmarsh [55] and Montgomery [45, Theorem 6.1]. Conjecture 1 is a weakened form of Conjecture 9.2 of Montgomery [45]; see the comments below relating to §6. The proof of Theorem 2 succeeds because the sum can be written as the sum of two functions, $f_1 + f_2$, where

$$\int_0^T |f_1(t)|^2\, dt \ll T^{1+\epsilon}N, \qquad \int_0^T |f_1(t)|^4\, dt \ll T^{1+\epsilon}N^2,$$
$$\int_0^T |f_2(t)|^2\, dt \ll T^\epsilon N^2, \qquad \int_0^T |f_2(t)|^4\, dt \ll T^\epsilon N^4.$$

A possible strategy for proving Conjecture 1 would involve establishing such a decomposition for the general sum $D(it)$.

§3. The method of proof of Theorem 3 gives, more generally,

$$\int_{CT}^{CT} \left| \sum_{n=1}^N a_n e(\lambda_n t) \right|^2 dt \le (1 - [-2C]) \int_{-T}^T \left| \sum_{n=1}^N A_n e(\lambda_n t) \right|^2 dt.$$

In many applications the special case

$$\int_{T_0-T}^{T_0+T} \left| \sum_{n=1}^N A_n e(\lambda_n t) \right|^2 dt \le 3 \int_{-T}^T \left| \sum_{n=1}^N A_n e(\lambda_n t) \right|^2 dt$$

is all that is required. Inequalities such as these have been derived by many
people, among them Wiener (unpublished—see Theorem 12.6.12 of Boas [2]),
Erdős and Fuchs [8], Wiener and Wintner [59], and Halász [12]. The argument
giving the constant 3 was shown to me by E. Wirsing (unpublished). Logan
[44] has shown that this constant is best possible. For an extensive discussion
of majorant principles see Shapiro [54]. By Theorem 4 we see that if $|a_n| \leq 1$
for all n then

$$(37) \qquad \sum_{r=1}^{R}\sum_{s=1}^{R} |D(i(t_r - t_s))|^2 \leq \sum_{r=1}^{R}\sum_{s=1}^{R} \left| \sum_{n=1}^{N} n^{-i(t_r - t_s)} \right|^2,$$

an estimate that is useful in discussing large values. Inequalities of this type
were introduced to the subject by Jutila [40]. The same manipulation used in
the proof of Theorem 4 can be used to show that

$$(38) \quad \sum_{m=1}^{M}\sum_{n=1}^{N} |(\mathbf{u}_m, \mathbf{v}_n)|^2 \leq \left(\sum_{m=1}^{M}\sum_{\mu=1}^{M} |(\mathbf{u}_m, \mathbf{u}_\mu)|^2 \right)^{1/2} \left(\sum_{n=1}^{N}\sum_{\nu=1}^{N} |(\mathbf{v}_n, \mathbf{v}_\nu)|^2 \right)^{1/2}$$

where $\mathbf{u}_1, \dots, \mathbf{u}_M$ and $\mathbf{v}_1, \dots, \mathbf{v}_N$ are arbitrary vectors in an inner product
space. This is due to P. Enflo (unpublished). P. Halmos has observed that this
inequality is Schwartz's inequality in a suitably defined space. Enflo used this
inequality to give a new proof of Weyl's bound for the quadratic Weyl sum. (Let
the kth coordinate of $\mathbf{u}_m$ be $e((m+k)^2\alpha)$, and the kth coordinate of $\mathbf{v}_n$ be
$e(2kn)$.) It is not known whether further inequalities of this nature might be
contrived, to give bounds for Weyl sums of higher degree. Theorem 5 is due
to Bachelis [1]. Hardy and Littlewood [16] had earlier noted that $C_3 > 1$, and
Boas [3] had shown that $C_q > 1$ when q is not an even integer. It seems that
the counter-example to the Hardy-Littlewood majorant conjecture could even be
constructed with coefficients restricted to the set $\{-1, 0, 1\}$, since, for example,

$$\int_0^1 |1 + e(x) - e(3x)|^3 \, dx = 6.509619759\ldots,$$

while

$$\int_0^1 |1 + e(x) + e(3x)|^3 \, dx = 6.394078779\ldots.$$

In addition to the literature on majorants, there is an extensive literature on rearrangements of Fourier coefficients. Let $f \in L^1(\mathbb{T})$ have Fourier coefficients $\widehat{f}(k)$.
Suppose that the numbers $|\widehat{f}(k)|$ are permuted so as to form a monotonically
decreasing sequence, and suppose that these are the Fourier coefficients of some
new function, F. Then $\|f\|_q \leq C_q\|F\|_q$ for every $q \geq 2$, and $\|F\|_p \leq C_p\|f\|_p$
for $1 < p \leq 2$. See Montgomery [47] for a simple proof of the first part. If
an analogue of this could be constructed for Dirichlet series then presumably
Conjecture 1 would follow.

§4. Theorem 6 can be extended to other norms; see p. 205 of Hardy, Littlewood and Pólya [**17**]. For further discussion in the spirit of this section, see Hochwald [**26**].

§5. The proofs of Hilbert and Schur are reproduced in Hardy, Littlewood and Pólya [**17**], on pp. 235–236 and p. 213, respectively. The proof of Theorem 7 follows Schur's method up to (25); the observation that (26) allows one to deduce that $\Sigma_1 = \Sigma_2$ is due to Selberg. Montgomery and Vaughan [**51**] derived Theorem 7 from an analogue appropriate for the torus, namely

$$(39) \qquad \left| \sum_{\substack{1 \le m, n \le N \\ m \ne n}} \frac{x_m y_n}{\sin \pi(\lambda_m - \lambda_n)} \right| \le \frac{1}{\delta} \left(\sum_{m=1}^N |x_m|^2 \right)^{1/2} \left(\sum_{n=1}^N |y_n|^2 \right)^{1/2}$$

where $0 < \delta \le \|\lambda_m - \lambda_n\|$ whenever $m \ne n$. They also proved the corresponding weighted version,

$$(40) \qquad \left| \sum_{\substack{1 \le m, n \le N \\ m \ne n}} \frac{x_m y_n}{\sin \pi(\lambda_m - \lambda_n)} \right| \le \frac{3}{2} \left(\sum_{m=1}^N |x_m|^2/\delta_m \right)^{1/2} \left(\sum_{n=1}^N |y_n|^2/\delta_n \right)^{1/2}$$

where $0 < \delta_n \le \|\lambda_m - \lambda_n\|$ whenever $m \ne n$. It is probably simpler to derive Theorem 7 and (27) first, and then derive (39) and (40) by the method adopted in §6 of Montgomery [**48**]. The constants in (27) and (40) are not sharp. Preissmann [**51**] has replaced 3/2 by a constant a little smaller than 4/3, and Selberg (unpublished) claims to have proved (27) with the constant 3.2. The proof of (27) follows the lines of the proof of Theorem 7 up to the stage at which $\Sigma_1 = \Sigma_2$ so that $T_2 = 2\Sigma_3$. At this point new difficulties arise, as it becomes necessary to show that

$$\sum_{\substack{1 \le n, \nu \le N \\ n \ne \nu}} (\delta_n + \delta_\nu) \frac{|y_n y_\nu|}{(\lambda_n - \lambda_\nu)^2} \le 17 \sum_{n=1}^N |y_n|^2/\delta_n.$$

Montgomery and Vaaler [**49**] used this bound, together with the theory of H^2 functions in a half-plane, to show that if $\rho_n = \beta_n + i\gamma_n$ with $\beta_n \ge 0$ for all n, then

$$(41) \qquad \left| \sum_{\substack{1 \le m, n \le N \\ m \ne n}} \frac{x_m y_n}{\rho_m + \overline{\rho_n}} \right| < 84 \left(\sum_{m=1}^N |x_m|^2/\delta_m \right)^{1/2} \left(\sum_{n=1}^N |y_n|^2/\delta_n \right)^{1/2}$$

where $0 < \delta_n \le |\gamma_m - \gamma_n|$ whenever $m \ne n$. If we take $\beta_n = 0$ for all n then we recover (27), apart from the value of the constant. With regard to (28) we note that Gallagher [**11**] has given a very simple proof of the less precise bound

$$\int_0^T \left| \sum_{n=1}^N a_n e(\lambda_n t) \right|^2 dt \ll \sum_{n=1}^N |a_n|^2 (T + \delta_n^{-1}).$$

For an informative account of some further conjectures relating to mean values of Dirichlet series, see Ramachandra [52].

§6. The results in the preceding sections offered only small refinements of classical estimates, but in this section the improvements are much more dramatic. The innovative step was taken by Halász and Turán [14, 15]; their work led Montgomery [45] to develop Theorem 8. The bound (34) is classical but not well-known. Its q-analogue is the familiar Pólya-Vinogradov inequality. Fujii, Gallagher and Montgomery [10] constructed a hybrid bound that combines these estimates. The conjectures were originally formulated by Montgomery [46] in a stronger form that involved the ℓ^2-norm instead of the ℓ^∞-norm. The Example, due to Bourgain [4], shows that these conjectures are false in the stronger form. Bourgain also showed that Conjecture 2 implies that if $\mathcal{A}$ is a subset of $\mathbb{R}^d$ that contains a translate of every line in $\mathbb{R}^d$, then $\mathcal{A}$ has Hausdorff dimension d. This was proved by Davies [7] when $d = 2$ (see p. 103 of Falconer [9]), but remains a conjecture when $d > 2$. In addition, Bourgain showed that the factor T^ϵ must be included in the conjectured estimates. See also Bourgain [5]. Theorem 9 is due to Huxley [27]. It is easy to construct an analogue of Theorem 8 for Dirichlet characters, but to obtain such an analogue of Theorem 9 one must introduce further ideas, found in papers of Huxley [28–35], Huxley and Jutila [36], Jutila [37–41], and Heath-Brown [18–25].

References

1. G. F. Bachelis, *On the upper and lower majorant properties in $L^p(G)$*, Quart. J. Math. (Oxford) (2) **24** (1973), 119–128.

2. R. P. Boas, Jr., *Entire Functions*, Academic Press, New York, 1954.

3. _____, *Majorant problems for Fourier series*, J. d'Analyse Math. **10** (1962–63), 253–271.

4. J. Bourgain, *Remarks on Montgomery's conjectures on Dirichlet series*, Geometric Aspects of Functional Analysis (1989–1990), Springer-Verlag, Berlin, 1991, pp. 153–165.

5. _____, *Remarks on Halász-Montgomery type inequalities* (to appear).

6. H. Davenport, *Multiplicative Number Theory*, Springer-Verlag, New York, 1980.

7. R. O. Davies, *Some remarks on the Kakeya problem*, Proc. Cambridge Philos. Soc. **69** (1971), 417–421.

8. P. Erdős and W. H. J. Fuchs, *On a problem in additive number theory*, J. London Math. Soc. **31** (1956), 67–73.

9. K. J. Falconer, *The Geometry of Fractal Sets*, Cambridge University Press, Cambridge, 1986.

10. A. Fujii, P. X. Gallagher, and H. L. Montgomery, *Some hybrid bounds for character sums and Dirichlet L-series*, Topics in Number Theory (Debrecen,

1974), Colloq. Math. Soc. János Bolyai 13, North-Holland, Amsterdam, 1976, pp. 41–57.

11. P. X. Gallagher, *A large sieve density estimate near* $\sigma = 1$, Invent. Math. **11** (1970), 329–339.

12. G. Halász, *Über die Mittelwerte multiplikativer zahlentheoretischer Funktionen*, Acta Math. Acad. Sci. Hungar. **19** (1968), 365–403.

13. _____, *On the average order of magnitude of Dirichlet series*, Acta Math. Acad. Sci. Hungar. **21** (1970), 227–233.

14. G. Halász and P. Turán, *On the distribution of roots of Riemann zeta and allied functions I*, J. Number Theory **1** (1969), 121–137.

15. _____, *On the distribution of roots of Riemann zeta and allied functions II*, Acta Math. Acad. Sci. Hungar. **21** (1970), 403–419.

16. G. H. Hardy and J. E. Littlewood, *Notes on the theory of series* (XIX): *a problem concerning majorants of Fourier series*, Quart. J. Math. (Oxford) **6** (1935), 304–315.

17. G. H. Hardy, J. E. Littlewood, and G. Pólya, *Inequalities, Second Edition*, Cambridge Univ. Press, Cambridge, 1988.

18. D. R. Heath-Brown, *The differences between consecutive primes*, J. London Math. Soc. (2) **18** (1978), 7–13.

19. _____, *The differences between consecutive primes, II*, J. London Math. Soc. (2) **19** (1979), 207–220.

20. _____, *Zero density estimates for the Riemann zeta-function and Dirichlet L-functions*, J. London Math. Soc. (2) **19** (1979), 221–232.

21. _____, *A large values estimate for Dirichlet polynomials*, J. London Math. Soc. (2) **20** (1979), 8–18.

22. _____, *The differences between consecutive primes, III*, J. London Math. Soc. (2) **20** (1979), 177–178.

23. _____, *The density of zeros of Dirichlet's L-functions*, Canad. J. Math. **31** (1979), 231–240.

24. _____, *Prime numbers in short intervals and a generalized Vaughan identity*, Canad. J. Math. **34** (1982), 1365–1377.

25. _____, *The difference between consecutive primes, IV*, A Tribute to Paul Erdős, Cambridge Univ. Press, Cambridge, 1990, pp. 277–287.

26. S. Hochwald, *Linear algebra by analogy*, Amer. Math. Monthly **98** (1991), 918–926.

27. M. N. Huxley, *On the difference between consecutive primes*, Invent. Math. **15** (1972), 164–170.

28. _____, *The difference between consecutive primes*, Analytic Number Theory (St. Louis, 1972), Proc. Sympos. Pure Math. 24,, Amer. Math. Soc., Providence, 1973, pp. 141–146.

29. _____, *Large values of Dirichlet polynomials*, Acta Arith. **24** (1973), 329–346.

30. _____, *Large values of Dirichlet polynomials, II*, Acta Arith. **27** (1975), 159–169.

31. _____, *Large values of Dirichlet polynomials, III*, Acta Arith. **26** (1975), 435–444.

32. _____, *An imperfect hybrid zero-density theorem*, J. London Math. Soc. (2) **13** (1976), 53–56.

33. _____, *Small differences between consecutive primes, II*, Mathematika **24** (1977), 142–152.

34. _____, *A note on large gaps between prime numbers*, Acta Arith. **38** (1980), 63–68.

35. _____, *Dirichlet polynomials*, Elementary and analytic theory of numbers (Warsaw, 1982), PWN, Warsaw, 1985, pp. 307–316.

36. M. N. Huxley and M. Jutila, *Large values of Dirichlet polynomials, IV*, Acta Arith. **32** (1977), 297–312.

37. M. Jutila, *A statistical density theorem for L-functions with applications*, Acta Arith. **16** (1969), 207–216.

38. _____, *On a density theorem of H. L. Montgomery for L-functions*, Ann. Acad. Sci. Fenn. Ser. A I (1972), No. 520, 13 pp.

39. _____, *On large values of Dirichlet polynomials*, Topics in Number Theory (Debrecen, 1974), Colloq. Math. Soc. Janos Bolyai 13, North-Holland, Amsterdam, 1976, pp. 129–140.

40. _____, *Zero-density estimates for L-functions*, Acta Arith. **32** (1977), 55–62.

41. _____, *Transformation formulae for Dirichlet polynomials*, J. Number Theory **18** (1984), 135–156.

42. J. E. Littlewood, *On a theorem of Paley*, J. London Math. Soc. **29** (1954), 387–395.

43. _____, *Some Problems in Real and Complex Analysis*, D. C. Heath, New York, 1968.

44. B. F. Logan, *An interference problem for exponentials*, Michigan Math. J. **35** (1988), 369–393.

45. H. L. Montgomery, *Mean and large values of Dirichlet polynomials*, Invent. Math. **8** (1969), 334–345.

46. _____, *Topics in Multiplicative Number Theory*, LNM 227, Springer-Verlag, Berlin, 1971.

47. _____, *A note on rearrangements of Fourier coefficients*, Ann. Inst. Fourier **26** (1976), 29–34.

48. _____, *The analytic principle of the large sieve*, Bull. Amer. Math. Soc. **84** (1978), 547–567.

49. H. L. Montgomery and J. D. Vaaler, *A further generalization of Hilbert's inequality*, 5 pp. (to appear).

50. H. L. Montgomery and R. C. Vaughan, *Hilbert's Inequality*, J. London Math. Soc. (2) **8** (1974), 73–82.

51. E. Preissmann, *Sur une inégalité de Montgomery-Vaughan*, Enseign. Math. (2) **30** (1984), 95–113.

52. K. Ramachandra, *On Riemann Zeta-Function and Allied Questions*, Journées Arithmétiques (Geneva, 1991), Astérisque 209, Société Mathématique de France, Paris, 1992, pp. 57–72.

53. I. Schur, *Bemerkungen zur Theorie der beschränkten Bilinearformen mit unendlich vielen Veränderlichen*, J. Reine Angew Math. **140** (1911), 1–28.

54. H. S. Shapiro, *Majorant problems for Fourier coefficients*, Quart. J. Math. (Oxford) (2) **26** (1975), 9–18.

55. E. C. Titchmarsh, *An inequality in the theory of series*, J. London Math. Soc. **3** (1928), 81–83.

56. _____, *The Theory of the Riemann Zeta Function*, Second Edition (D. R. Heath-Brown, ed.), Oxford University Press, Oxford, 1986.

57. J. D. Vaaler, *Some extremal functions in Fourier analysis*, Bull. Amer. Math. Soc. **12** (1985), 183–216.

58. H. Weyl, *Singuläre Integralgleichungen mit besonderer Berücksichtigung des Fourierschen Integraltheorems*, Inaugural Dissertation, Göttingen, 1908.

59. N. Wiener and A. Wintner, *On a local L^2-variant of Ikehara's Theorem*, Rev. Math. Cuyana **2** (1956), 53–59; *Norbert Wiener: Collected Works*, vol. II, MIT Press, Cambridge, 1979, pp. 758–764; 788–790.

Chapter 8. Distribution of Reduced Residue Classes in Short Intervals

1. Introduction. Let p_i denote the ith prime number. We expect that the difference $p_{i+1} - p_i$ between one prime and the next is usually comparable to the mean $\log p_i$, and indeed we might conjecture that

$$(1) \qquad \sum_{p_i \leq x} (p_{i+1} - p_i)^\gamma \ll x(\log x)^{\gamma - 1}$$

for each fixed $\gamma > 0$. Concerning the the more precise statistical distribution of the differences between consecutive primes, on probabilistic grounds we might conjecture that

$$(2) \qquad \operatorname{card}\{p_i \leq x : p_{i+1} - p_i > c\log p_i\} \sim e^{-c}\frac{x}{\log x}$$

for each fixed $c > 0$. As for the maximum gap between primes we have the famous conjecture of Cramér, which asserts that

$$(3) \qquad \limsup_{p_i \to \infty} \frac{p_{i+1} - p_i}{(\log p_i)^2} = 1.$$

Our present knowledge is almost non-existent. In the hope of developing tools with which to approach such issues, we consider instead the distribution of reduced residue classes (mod q). Here we fare a little better.

Let $1 = a_1 < a_2 < \ldots$ be the integers relatively prime to q, so that $a_{\varphi(q)} = q - 1$ and $a_{\varphi(q)+1} = q + 1$. Set $P = \varphi(q)/q$, so that P is the probability that a randomly chosen residue class is reduced. By analogy with (1) we may expect that

$$(4) \qquad \sum_{i=1}^{\varphi(q)} (a_{i+1} - a_i)^\gamma \ll_\gamma \varphi(q)P^{-\gamma}.$$

We approach such an estimate by first estimating the moment

$$(5) \qquad M_k(q;h) = \sum_{n=1}^{q} \left(\operatorname{card}\{a_i : n < a_i \leq n+h\} - Ph\right)^k.$$

Here k is a positive real number. Based on the presumption that the reduced residue classes are fairly randomly distributed, we may expect that

$$(6) \qquad M_k(q;h) \ll_k q(Ph)^{k/2}$$

when $h \geq 1/P$. For $k = 2$ this is easy, since by an elementary calculation we find that

$$(7) \qquad M_2(q;h) = qP^2 \sum_{\substack{r|q \\ r>1}} \mu(r)^2 \left(\prod_{\substack{p|q \\ p\nmid r}} \frac{p(p-2)}{(p-1)^2} \right) \frac{r^2}{\varphi(r)^2} \{h/r\} \left(1 - \{h/r\}\right)$$

By the inequality $\{\alpha\}(1 - \{\alpha\}) \leq \alpha$ we see that the above is

$$\leq phP^2 \sum_{r|q} \mu(r)^2 \frac{r}{\varphi(r)^2} \prod_{\substack{p|q \\ p\nmid r}} \frac{p(p-2)}{(p-1)^2}$$

$$= qhP^2 \left(\prod_{p|q} \frac{p(p-2)}{(p-1)^2} \right) \sum_{r|q} \mu(r)^2 \frac{r}{\varphi(r)^2} \prod_{p|r} \frac{(p-1)^2}{p(p-2)}$$

$$= qhP^2 \left(\prod_{p|q} \frac{p(p-2)}{(p-1)^2} \right) \prod_{p|q} \left(1 + \frac{1}{p-2}\right)$$

$$= qhP.$$

This is (6) when $k = 2$. To deduce an estimate of the form (4) suppose that γ is fixed, and that k is a fixed real number for which (6) holds. Let

$$n(l) = \operatorname{card}\{a_i : 0 < a_i < q, \ a_{i+1} - a_i = l\},$$

and

$$N(l) = \operatorname{card}\{a_i : 0 < a_i < q, \ a_{i+1} - a_i \geq l\}$$
$$= n(l) + n(l+1) + \cdots .$$

Take $h \sim l/2$. If $a_{i+1} - a_i \geq l$ then $\operatorname{card}\{a_i : n < a_i \leq n + h\} = 0$ for $a_i \leq n < a_i + l - h$. Hence

$$N(l)h(Ph)^k \ll M_k(q;h) \ll q(Ph)^{k/2},$$

which gives the bound

$$(8) \qquad\qquad N(l) \ll \varphi(q)(Pl)^{-1-k/2}$$

when $l \geq 2/P$. To apply this to (4) we note that

$$\sum_{i=1}^{\varphi(q)} (a_{i+1} - a_i)^\gamma = \sum_{l=1}^{\infty} n(l) l^\gamma,$$

which by partial summation is

$$\approx \sum_{l=1}^{\infty} N(l) l^{\gamma-1}$$

$$= \sum_{1 \leq l \leq 2/P} N(l) l^{\gamma-1} + \sum_{l > 2/P} N(l) l^{\gamma-1}.$$

In the first sum we use the trivial bound $N(l) \le \varphi(q)$, and in the second we use the estimate (8), to see that the above is

$$\ll \varphi(q)P^{-\gamma} + \varphi(q)P^{-1-k/2} \sum_{l>2/P} l^{\gamma-2-k/2}.$$

If $k/2 > \gamma - 1$ then this last sum is $\ll P^{1-\gamma+k/2}$, which gives (4). Thus we see that (6) implies (4) for all $\gamma < 1+k/2$. In particular, since (6) holds when $k = 2$, we see that (4) holds for all $\gamma < 2$.

To prove (6) when $k > 2$ involves considerably more effort. In this chapter we only outline the argument, dwelling on some of its more intriguing features. We have two distinct methods. In the first of these, discussed in §2, we compare the situation to a probabilistic model; this works well when all the prime factors of q are large. In the second method, outlined in §3, we apply Fourier expansions. This works well when all the prime factors of q are small. Fortunately we can decompose a general q into two parts so that the two methods may be combined to provide a proof of (6) for all q and all $k > 0$. The Fourier method depends on an interesting inequality whose proof we give in §4.

Before embarking on the main arguments we make some preliminary reductions. If q' is the largest squarefree divisor of q then

$$M_k(q; h) = \frac{q}{q'} M_k(q'; h),$$

so it suffices to prove (6) when q is squarefree. Also, by Hölder's inequality we see that if (6) holds for k then it also holds for all $k' < k$. Hence to prove (6) for all k it suffices to prove (6) for a sequence of k tending to infinity, and consequently from now on we suppose that k is a positive integer.

2. A probabilistic model.

If all the prime factors dividing q are large then we may expect that the number of reduced residues in an interval will be distributed much as in the following probabilistic model: Let $\mathbf{X}_1, \ldots, \mathbf{X}_h$ be independent random variables with the distribution

$$\mathbf{P}(\mathbf{X}_m = 1) = P,$$
$$\mathbf{P}(\mathbf{X}_m = 0) = 1 - P,$$

and put $\mathbf{X} = \mathbf{X}_1 + \cdots + \mathbf{X}_h$. Thus $\mathbf{X}$ is a random variable with expectation hP, so that

(9) $$\mu_k = \mathbf{E}\Big((\mathbf{X} - hP)^k\Big)$$

is the kth moment of $\mathbf{X}$ about its mean. It is not hard to show that

$$\mu_k \ll_k (hP)^{k/2}$$

when $hP \geq 1$. To compare this with $M_k(q;h)$ we apply the binomial theorem to see that

$$(10) \qquad M_k(q;h) = \sum_{r=0}^{k} \binom{k}{r} \left(\sum_{n=1}^{q} \left(\sum_{\substack{m=1 \\ (m+n,q)=1}}^{h} 1 \right) \right)^{r} (-hP)^{k-r}.$$

On writing the rth power of the sum over m as an r-fold sum, and taking the sum over n inside, we see that the expression in large parentheses above is

$$\sum_{\substack{m_1,\dots,m_r \\ 1 \leq m_i \leq h}} \sum_{\substack{1 \leq n \leq q \\ (m_i+n,q)=1 \\ 1 \leq i \leq r}} 1.$$

Let $\mathcal{B} = \{m_1, \dots, m_r\}$, and put $s = \operatorname{card} \mathcal{B}$. Suppose that $h < y$ and that $p > y$ for all primes p dividing q. Then the inner sum above is

$$(11) \qquad \prod_{p|q}(p - s) = q \prod_{p|q}\left(1 - \frac{s}{q}\right).$$

Since the primes dividing q are large, this is approximately

$$(12) \qquad q \prod_{p|q}\left(1 - \frac{1}{p}\right)^{s} = qP^{s}.$$

It is not hard to show that if we replace the expression in large parentheses in (10) by qP^s then the resulting expression is exactly $q\mu_k$. Thus $M_k(q;h)$ differs from $q\mu_k$ by an amount that depends on the difference between the two expressions (11) and (12). Precisely, it can be shown that if $y > h$ and $p > y$ for every prime divisor p of q, then

$$M_k(q;h) = q\mu_k + O_k\left(\frac{q}{y}(hP)^k\right) + O_k\left(\frac{q}{y}hP\right).$$

3. An approach by Fourier techniques. If $f(n)$ has period q then we define the Fourier coefficients

$$\widehat{f}(a/q) = \frac{1}{q} \sum_{n=1}^{q} f(n)e(-an/q),$$

and we have the Fourier expansion

$$f(n) = \sum_{a=1}^{q} \widehat{f}(a/q)e(an/q).$$

For the functions we shall be considering, the size of the Fourier coefficient depends largely on the size of the least denominator of the rational number a/q. Thus it is helpful to note that the above is

$$= \sum_{r|q} \sum_{\substack{a=1 \\ (a,r)=1}}^{r} \widehat{f}(a/r)e(an/r).$$

With complete residue systems and reduced residue systems in mind, we put

(13)
$$\mathcal{C}(r) = \{a/r : a \in \mathbb{Z}\}/\mathbb{Z},$$

and

(14)
$$\mathcal{R}(r) = \{a/r : a \in \mathbb{Z}, (a,r) = 1\}/\mathbb{Z}.$$

In this notation, we may write the Fourier expansion of $f(n)$ as

(15)
$$f(n) = \sum_{r|q} \sum_{\rho \in \mathcal{R}(q)} \widehat{f}(\rho) e(\rho n).$$

Suppose that we wish to estimate the kth moment of f. Then we raise both sides to the kth power, and sum over n. After expanding the power on the right hand side and interchanging the order of summation, we see that

$$\sum_{n=1}^{q} f(n)^k = \sum_{\substack{r_i|q \\ 1 \le i \le k}} \sum_{\substack{\rho_i \in \mathcal{R}(r_i) \\ 1 \le i \le k}} \left(\prod_{i=1}^{k} \widehat{f}(\rho_i) \right) \sum_{n=1}^{q} e\big((\rho_1 + \cdots + \rho_k)n\big)$$

(16)
$$= q \sum_{\substack{r_i|q \\ 1 \le i \le k}} S(\mathbf{r})$$

where

$$S(\mathbf{r}) = \sum_{\substack{\rho_i \in \mathcal{R}(r_i) \\ 1 \le i \le k \\ \sum \rho_i \in \mathbb{Z}}} \prod_{i=1}^{k} \widehat{f}(\rho_i).$$

To estimate this expression we employ the following basic inequality.

FUNDAMENTAL LEMMA. (First Form) *Let* $r_1, \ldots, r_k$ *be positive squarefree integers, and put* $r = [r_1, \ldots, r_k]$. *In the notation of* (13), *for* $1 \le i \le k$ *we let* G_i *be a complex-valued function defined on* $\mathcal{C}(r_i)$. *Suppose also that every prime factor of* r *divides at least two of the* r_i. *Then*

(17)
$$\left| \sum_{\substack{\rho_i \in \mathcal{C}(r_i) \\ 1 \le i \le k \\ \sum \rho_i \in \mathbb{Z}}} \prod_{i=1}^{k} G_i(\rho_i) \right| \le \frac{1}{r} \prod_{i=1}^{k} \left(r_i \sum_{\rho_i \in \mathcal{C}(r_i)} |G_i(\rho_i)|^2 \right)^{1/2}.$$

The final hypothesis may at first seem peculiar. To appreciate its importance suppose that $p|r_1$ and that $p\nmid r_i$ for $i > 1$. Then the conditions $\rho_i \in \mathcal{C}(r_i)$, $\sum \rho_i \in \mathbb{Z}$ imply that $\rho_1 \in \mathcal{C}(r_1/p)$. Thus all mention of p can be removed from the left hand side, without affecting the value of the expression. On the other hand, if $G_1(\rho) = 0$ for $\rho \in \mathcal{C}(r_1) \setminus \mathcal{C}(r_1/p)$, then the right hand side is—as far as its dependence on p is concerned—of the form $C/\sqrt{p}$. Since p could be arbitrarily large, this leads to obvious nonsense. As for the degree of precision offered by (17), we may first note that we have equality if the G_i are all constant. More significantly, we have equality when k is even, $r_{2i-1} = r_{2i}$, $G_{2i-1}(\rho) = \overline{G}_{2i}(-\rho)$, and $r_2, r_4, \ldots, r_k$ are pairwise coprime. We think of this configuration as giving a "diagonal" term; then the Fundamental Lemma asserts that no term contributes more than it would if it were diagonal.

In the next section we construct a more general formulation of the Fundamental Lemma in which the r_i are no longer required to be squarefree.

To apply this machinery to reduced residues, we take

$$f(n) = \operatorname{card}\{a_i : n < a_i \le n + h\} - Ph.$$

Then

$$f(n) = P \sum_{\substack{r|q \\ r>1}} \frac{\mu(r)}{\varphi(r)} \sum_{\rho \in \mathcal{R}(r)} E(\rho)e(\rho n)$$

where $E(\rho) = \sum_{m=1}^{h} e(\rho m)$. This fits the pattern of (15). Since $E(\rho) \ll \min(h, 1/\|\rho\|)$ (recall (3.2) on p. 40), it follows that

$$\sum_{\substack{\rho \in \mathcal{C}(r) \\ \rho \ne 0}} |E(\rho)|^2 \ll rh.$$

Hence by (16) and the Fundamental Lemma we find that

$$M_k(q; h) \ll qh^{k/2}P^k \sum_{r|q} \frac{1}{r} \sum_{\substack{r_i|r \\ 1 \le i \le k}} \frac{r_i}{\varphi(r_i)}$$

$$= qh^{k/2}P^k \prod_{p|q}\left(1 + \frac{1}{p}\left(2 + \frac{1}{p-1}\right)^k\right)$$

$$\ll qh^{k/2}P^{-2^k+k}.$$

When combined with the probabilistic method of the preceding section, this gives not (6), but instead the weaker estimate

$$M_k(q; h) \ll_k q(hP)^{k/2}\left(1 + P^{k/2}(\log h)^{2^k}\right)$$

for $hP \ge 1$. This is still strong enough to prove (4) for all $\gamma > 0$, but to obtain (6) one must establish a complicated elaboration of the Fundamental Lemma, in which the upper bound given is smaller when the configuration is far from diagonal.

4. The fundamental lemma. We now formulate a more general version of the Fundamental Lemma.

FUNDAMENTAL LEMMA. (Second Form) *Let* $r_1, \ldots, r_k$ *be positive integers, and put* $r = [r_1, \ldots, r_k]$. *In the notation of* (13), *for* $1 \le i \le k$ *we let* G_i *be* *a complex-valued function defined on $\mathcal{C}(r_i)$. Suppose also that if $p^a | r$ then p^a divides at least two of the r_i. Then for any real number ρ,*

$$(18) \qquad \left| \sum_{\substack{\rho_i \in \mathcal{C}(r_i) \\ 1 \le i \le k \\ \sum \rho_i \equiv \rho \ (\mathrm{mod}\ 1)}} \prod_{i=1}^{k} G_i(\rho_i) \right| \le \frac{1}{r} \prod_{i=1}^{k} \left(r_i \sum_{\rho_i \in \mathcal{C}(r_i)} |G_i(\rho_i)|^2 \right)^{1/2}.$$

We may suppose that $\rho \in \mathcal{C}(r)$, since otherwise the sum is empty. If we choose numbers c_i so that $(c_i, r_i) = 1$ for all i then the map $\rho_i \mapsto c_i \rho_i$ (mod 1) permutes the $\rho_i \in \mathcal{C}(r_i)$. Since the right hand side of (18) is invariant under such permutations, it follows that (18) holds with the more general side condition

$$(19) \qquad \sum_{i=1}^{k} c_i \rho_i \equiv \rho \quad (\mathrm{mod}\ 1).$$

Suppose that r is squarefree, and consider the k-tuples $\mathbf{r} = (r_1, \dots, r_k)$ such that $[r_1, \dots, r_k] = r$. There are precisely $\left(2^k - k - 1 \right)^{\omega(r)}$ such k-tuples for which the last hypothesis in the Fundamental Lemma is satisfied. If k is odd then there are no diagonal terms, and if k is even then there are $(k/2)^{\omega(r)}$ diagonal terms, which is rather small, even when compared with the number $\binom{k}{2}^{\omega(r)}$ of terms for which every prime divisor p of r divides exactly 2 of the r_i. For such terms we see that

$$\prod_{i=1}^{k} r_i = r^2,$$

and hence the bound provided by the Fundamental Lemma is the same for these terms as for a diagonal term. It would be nice to have a form of the Fundamental Lemma that would give a better bound for these non-diagonal terms, but the following example suggests that this may be difficult to achieve.

EXAMPLE 1. Suppose that r is squarefree, and that each prime divisor p of r divides exactly 2 of the r_i. For each i, choose a particular $\rho_i' \in \mathcal{C}(r_i)$, and put $\rho = \sum \rho_i'$. Set

$$G_i(\rho_i) = \begin{cases} 1 & \text{if } \rho_i = \rho_i' \\ 0 & \text{otherwise.} \end{cases}$$

Then equality is achieved in the Fundamental Lemma, even though the configuration may be far from diagonal.

From the standpoint of applications the G_i above are not very natural, since we are primarily interested in functions with a peak in the neighborhood of the origin. However, even for such G_i we may encounter difficulties, as we see below.

EXAMPLE 2. Suppose that $k = 3$, and put $r_1 = (s-1)s$, $r_2 = s(s+1)$, $r_3 = (s+1)(s-1)$ where s is a large integer chosen so that $(s-1)s(s+1)$ is squarefree. Thus $s \equiv 2 \pmod 4$, $r = (s-1)s(s+1)$, and every prime factor of r divides exactly two of the r_i. Put

$$G_i(\rho_i) = \begin{cases} 1 & \text{if } \rho_i \in \mathcal{R}(r_i), \|\rho_i\| \le 3/s^2, \\ 0 & \text{otherwise.} \end{cases}$$

On the left hand side of (18) the term $\rho_1 = 1/r_1$, $\rho_2 = 1/r_2$, $\rho_3 = 1 - 2/r_3$ contributes the amount 1, and thus we see that the upper bound provided in (18) is of the correct order of magnitude. (Note that $2/r_3 \in \mathcal{R}(r_3)$ since r_3 is odd.) Of course this construction succeeds only because the r_i are of a very special sort. For general r_i we do not expect to experience such tight clustering of the ρ_i near the origin.

PROOF. Without loss of generality we may suppose that $\rho \in \mathcal{C}(r)$, and that the G_i are non-negative.

We first prove the result for squarefree r, arguing by induction on k. If $k = 2$ then $r_1 = r_2$, and the bound follows from Cauchy's inequality. Now suppose that $k > 2$. For $1 \le i < k$ let t_i be the product of those primes p that divide r_i and r_k but no other r_j. Let $t_k = \prod_{i=1}^{k-1} t_i$, and for $1 \le i \le k$ let s_i be defined by the relation $r_i s_i = t_i$. Thus if $p | s_k$ then p divides r_k and at least two of $r_1, \dots, r_{k-1}$. Write

$$\rho_k = \sigma_k + \tau_k = \sigma_k + \tau_1 + \cdots + \tau_{k-1}$$

where $\sigma_k \in \mathcal{C}(s_k)$ and $\tau_i \in \mathcal{C}(t_i)$. This representation is unique, as $s_k, t_1, \dots, t_{k-1}$ are pairwise relatively prime. Put $s = [s_1, \dots, s_{k-1}] = r/t_k$, and similarly write

$$\rho = \sigma' + \tau'_1 + \cdots + \tau'_{k-1}$$

where $\sigma \in \mathcal{C}(s)$ and $\tau'_i \in \mathcal{C}(t_i)$ for $1 \le i < k$. Finally, for $1 \le i < k$ put $\sigma_i = \rho_i + \tau_i - \tau'_i$. The relation $\sum \rho_i = \rho \pmod 1$ implies that $\sigma_i \in \mathcal{C}(s_i)$. The condition $\sum \rho_i = \rho \pmod 1$ is equivalent to $\sum_{i=1}^{k-1} \sigma_i = \sigma \pmod 1$ where $\sigma = \sigma' - \sigma_k$. Thus the left hand side of (18) is

$$(20) \qquad \sum_{\sigma_k, \tau_k} G_k(\sigma_k + \tau_k) \sum_{\substack{\sigma_i \in \mathcal{C}(s_i) \\ 1 \le i < k \\ \sum_{i=1}^{k-1} \sigma_i = \sigma}} \prod_{i=1}^{k-1} G_i(\sigma_i - \tau_i + \tau'_i).$$

The numbers $s_1, \dots, s_{k-1}$ satisfy the relevant hypotheses, so by the inductive hypothesis the inner sum above is

$$\le \frac{t_k}{r} \prod_{i=1}^{k-1} \left(s_i \sum_{\sigma_i \in \mathcal{C}(s_i)} G(\sigma_i - \tau_i + \tau'_i)^2 \right)^{1/2}.$$

We insert this in (20) and apply Cauchy's inequality to see that the expression (20) is

$$\le \frac{t_k}{r} \left(\sum_{\sigma_k, \tau_k} G_k(\sigma_k + \tau_k)^2 \right)^{1/2} \left(\sum_{\sigma_k, \tau_k} \prod_{i=1}^{k-1} \left(s_i \sum_{\sigma_i \in \mathcal{C}(s_i)} G_i(\sigma_i - \tau_i + \tau'_i)^2 \right) \right)^{1/2}.$$

The first sum over σ_k, τ_k is

$$\sum_{\rho_k \in \mathcal{C}(r_k)} G_k(\rho_k)^2.$$

In the second sum over σ_k, τ_k, the summand is independent of σ_k. The sum over τ_k can be considered to be a sum over $\tau_1, \ldots, \tau_{k-1}$. Since the ith factor of the product depends only on τ_i, it follows that this second sum is

$$s_k \prod_{i=1}^{k-1} \left(s_i \sum_{\substack{\sigma_i \in \mathcal{C}(s_i) \\ \tau_i \in \mathcal{C}(t_i)}} G_i(\sigma_i - \tau_i + \tau_i')^2 \right) = s_k \prod_{i=1}^{k-1} \left(s_i \sum_{\rho_i \in \mathcal{C}(r_i)} G_i(\rho_i)^2 \right).$$

This gives (18), and thus the proof for squarefree r is complete.

Suppose that r has the canonical factorization $r = \prod p^{a(p)}$. We induct on $A(r) = \max_p a(p)$. We have established (18) when $A(r) = 1$. Now suppose that $A(r) > 1$ and write $r = st$ where s is the largest squarefree number dividing r. Similarly write $r_i = s_i t_i$ where s_i is the largest squarefree number dividing r_i. The relation $\rho_i = \sigma_i + \tau_i/s_i$ establishes a bijection between $\rho_i \in \mathcal{C}(r_i)$ and pairs $(\sigma_i, \tau_i) \in \mathcal{C}(s_i) \times \mathcal{C}(t_i)$. Similarly, we write $\rho = \sigma + \tau/s$. Put

$$\sigma' = \sigma'(\tau, \tau_1, \ldots, \tau_k) = \tau/s - \sum_{i=1}^{k} \tau_i/s_i.$$

The condition $\sum \rho_i = \rho \pmod 1$ is equivalent to the pair of conditions $\sigma' \in \mathcal{C}(s)$, $\sum \sigma_i = \sigma + \sigma' \pmod 1$. On putting $c_i = s/s_i$, we see that the first of these latter two conditions may be expressed as $\sum c_i \tau_i = \tau \pmod 1$. Thus the left hand side of (18) is

$$(21) \qquad \sum_{\substack{\tau_i \in \mathcal{C}(t_i) \\ \sum c_i \tau_i = \tau \,(\mathrm{mod}\ 1)}} \sum_{\substack{\sigma_i \in \mathcal{C}(s_i) \\ \sum \sigma_i = \sigma + \sigma' \,(\mathrm{mod}\ 1)}} \prod_{i=1}^{k} G_i(\sigma_i + \tau_i/s_i).$$

Since $s = [s_1, \ldots, s_k]$ is squarefree, from the preceding argument we see that the inner sum is

$$\leq \frac{1}{s} \prod_{i=1}^{k} H_i(\tau_i)$$

where

$$H_i(\tau_i) = \left(s_i \sum_{\sigma_i \in \mathcal{C}(s_i)} G_i(\sigma_i + \tau_i/s_i)^2 \right)^{1/2}.$$

These H_i also have period 1. Since $A(t) = A(r) - 1$, $t = [t_1, \ldots, t_k]$, and the t_i satisfy the relevant hypotheses, it follows from the inductive hypothesis with the side condition in the form (19) that

$$\sum_{\substack{\tau_i \in \mathcal{C}(t_i) \\ \sum c_i \tau_i = \tau \,(\mathrm{mod}\ 1)}} \prod_{i=1}^{k} H_i(\tau_i) \leq \frac{1}{t} \prod_{i=1}^{k} \left(t_i \sum_{\tau_i \in \mathcal{C}(t_i)} H_i(\tau_i)^2 \right)^{1/2}.$$

This gives the desired inequality.

5. Notes. Let

$$\delta(p) = \frac{(\log p)(\log \log p)(\log \log \log \log p)}{(\log \log \log p)^2}.$$

The best known lower bound in the direction of Cramér's conjecture is

$$(22) \qquad \limsup_{p_i \to \infty} \frac{p_{i+1} - p_i}{\delta(p_i)} \geq c > 0.$$

The first proof of (22) was by Rankin [**14**], with $c = e^\gamma$. The best known constant in (22) is now larger by a factor of 1.3; see Maier and Pomerance [**11**]. In the opposite direction our best upper bound for gaps between primes is much weaker, being of the form $p_{i+1} - p_i < p_i^{\theta+\epsilon}$ for $p > p_0(\epsilon)$. Recently Lou and Yao [**9**] showed that $\theta = 11/20$ is admissible, and R. C. Backer and G. Harman (to appear) have announced a proof that one may take $\theta = 15/28$.

The identity (7) is due to Hausman and Shapiro [**3**]. Our proof that (6) implies (4) for $\gamma < 1 + k/2$ follows Hooley [**5**]. That (6) holds for $\gamma = 2$ was conjectured by Erdős [**2**]. Montgomery and Vaughan [**12**] proved this conjecture by proving that (6) holds for all $k > 0$.

§2. For full details see §§5, 6 of Montgomery and Vaughan [**12**].

§3. For full details see §§3, 4 of Montgomery and Vaughan [**12**].

§4. The first form of the Fundamental Lemma originates in §2 of Montgomery and Vaughan [**12**]. The second form of the Fundamental Lemma is from Montgomery and Vaughan [**13**]. In this latter paper it is also shown that if the G_i are supported on the reduced residue classes (as was the case in the application of the Fundamental Lemma in §3), then the Fundamental Lemma admits to a small improvement:

$$(23) \qquad \left| \sum_{\substack{\rho_i \in \mathcal{R}(r_i) \\ 1 \leq i \leq k \\ \sum \rho_i = \rho \bmod 1}} \prod_{i=1}^{k} G_i(\rho_i) \right| \leq \frac{1}{\varphi(r)} \prod_{i=1}^{k} \left(\varphi(r_i) \sum_{\rho_i \in \mathcal{R}(r_i)} |G_i(\rho_i)|^2 \right)^{1/2}.$$

This is better than (18) if there is a prime that divides at least 3 of the r_i, but even then the improvement is so slight that it has no impact in the argument of §3. What is needed is a variant of the Fundamental Lemma that provides a greatly improved bound when the configuration is far from diagonal. Montgomery and Vaughan [**12**, Lemma 8] have taken a first step in this direction, but their attempt is very elaborate and the improvement is still rather small. Suppose that $k = 3$, $\rho = 0$, and that every prime divisor of r divides exactly two of the r_i. Then the sum on the left hand side of (18) can be written as

$$\sum_{\substack{\sigma_i \in \mathcal{C}(s_i) \\ 1 \leq i \leq 3}} G_1(\sigma_2 - \sigma_3) G_2(\sigma_3 - \sigma_1) G_3(\sigma_1 - \sigma_2).$$

where $s_1 = (r_2, r_3)$, $s_2 = (r_3, r_1)$, and $s_3 = (r_1, r_2)$. In the analogous analytic situation we ask for a bound for the integral

$$(24) \qquad \int_{\mathbb{T}^3} g_1(x_2 - x_3) g_2(x_3 - x_1) g_3(x_1 - x_2) \, \mathbf{dx}$$

where $g_i \in L^1(\mathbb{T})$. By mimicking the proof of the Fundamental Lemma we may show that this integral has modulus not exceeding

$$(25) \qquad \prod_{i=1}^{3} \|g_i\|_{L^2(\mathbb{T})}.$$

To assess this, suppose that the g_i have a peak at the origin, say

$$(26) \qquad g_i(x) = \begin{cases} 1 & \text{if } \|x\| \leq \delta \\ 0 & \text{otherwise.} \end{cases}$$

Then the integral (24) is $3\delta^2$ while the bound (25) is much larger: $(2\delta)^{3/2}$. On the other hand, by a judicious use of Hölder's inequality we may show that the integral (24) has modulus not exceeding

$$(27) \qquad \prod_{i=1}^{3} \|g_i\|_{L^{3/2}(\mathbb{T})}.$$

In the case of the peak functions (26), this expression is $4\delta^2$, which is the correct order of magnitude. Unfortunately, it seems that any hope of establishing something similar in the arithmetic situation is dashed by Example 2.

References

1. H. Cramér, *On the order of magnitude of the difference between consecutive prime numbers*, Acta Arith. **2** (1937), 147–153.

2. P. Erdős, *The difference of consecutive primes*, Duke Math. J. **6** (1940), 438–441.

3. M. Hausman and H. N. Shapiro, *On the mean square distribution of primitive roots of unity*, Comm. Pure App. Math. **26** (1973), 539–547.

4. A. Hildebrand and H. Maier, *Irregularities in the distribution of primes in short intervals*, J. Reine Angew. Math. **397** (1989), 162–193.

5. C. Hooley, *On the difference of consecutive numbers prime to n*, Acta Arith. **8** (1963), 343–347.

6. _____, *On the difference of consecutive numbers prime to n, II*, Publ. Math. Debrecen **12** (1965), 39–49.

7. _____, *On the difference of consecutive numbers prime to n, III*, Math. Zeit. **90** (1965), 355–364.

8. _____, *On the intervals between consecutive members of sequences*, Proc. Symposia Pure Math. 24, Amer. Math. Soc., Providence, 1973, pp. 129–140.

9. S. T. Lou and Q. Yao, *The number of primes in a short interval*, Hardy-Ramanujan J. **16** (1993), 21–43.

10. H. Maier, *Primes in short intervals*, Michigan Math. J. **32** (1985), 221–225.

11. H. Maier and C. Pomerance, *Unusually large gaps between consecutive primes*, Theorie des nombres (Quebec, 1987), de Gruyter, Berlin, 1989, pp. 625–632.

12. H. L. Montgomery and R. C. Vaughan, *On the distribution of reduced residues*, Ann. Math. **123** (1986), 311–333.

13. _____ , *A basic inequality*, Congress in Number Theory (Zarautz, 1984), Universidad del País Vasco, Bilbao, 1989.

14. R. A. Rankin, Proc. Edinburgh Math. Soc. (2) **13** (1962/63), 331–332.

Chapter 9. Zeros of L-Functions

1. Introduction. The *Riemann Hypothesis* (RH) asserts that all the non-trivial zeros of the Riemann zeta function lie on the critical line $\sigma = 1/2$, and the *Generalized Riemann Hypothesis* (GRH) asserts that the same holds for all Dirichlet L-functions. Assuming that these hypotheses are valid, one may speculate endlessly about how the truth will be revealed. On one hand, one could imagine finding a proof of GRH except for real zeros of L-functions of real characters. On the other hand, one could equally well imagine that the key lies in proving that $L(s, \chi) \neq 0$ for $\sigma > 1/2$ and real χ, and that then it will be relatively easy to extend the argument to yield GRH. In this chapter we leave such issues aside, and take an incremental approach. The classical zero-free region for L-functions, asserts that if $\rho = \beta + i\gamma$ is a zero of $L(s, \chi)$ then

$$(1) \qquad \beta < 1 - \frac{c}{\log q(|\gamma| + 2)}$$

unless $\gamma = 0$ and χ is a real character. First proved many years ago, this estimate has been improved since only in restricted cases. For example, the exponential sum methods discussed in Chapters 3 and 4 have been applied to give better upper bounds for $|\zeta(s)|$ when σ is near 1, and then a wider zero-free region can be derived for the zeta function. Such reasoning can be applied to L-functions, but it affects only the dependence of the zero-free region on $|\gamma|$, and has no impact on the dependence on q. In short, we have no workable q-analogue of our exponential sum techniques, except when q is very highly composite.

Suppose that we could replace the constant c in (1) by a function of q, tending to infinity with q. Such an improvement would have immediate arithmetic consequences. For example, we could deduce *Vinogradov's Hypothesis*, which asserts that if χ is a non-principal character modulo q then there is an integer n, $0 < n < q^\epsilon$, such that $\chi(n) \neq 1$, $\chi(n) \neq 0$. The derivation of this from an improvement of (1) is provided in §2, where we derive a precise upper bound for the least character non-residue from a hypothetical zero-free region. If such an improvement of (1) could be established for all $\chi \pmod{q}$, then one would also have an improved value of Linnik's constant: If $(a, q) = 1$ then there is a prime number p such that $p \equiv a \pmod{q}$ and $p < q^{12/5+\epsilon}$.

In §3 we show that if there is a zero of $L(s, \chi)$ near the edge of the classical zero-free region (1), then there must be many other zeros nearby. Our hope—

not yet realized—would be that such a situation could be proved impossible, perhaps by using ideas related to power sums or irregularities of distribution. To encourage such an approach, in §4 we employ a simple variant of our power sum ideas of Chapter 5, §6 to show that if an L-function of a real character has an exceptional zero (one that violates (1)), then the zero-free region (1) can be improved. This phenomenon was first noted by Deuring and Heilbronn.

2. Least Character Non-Residues. If χ is a nonprincipal Dirichlet character (mod q) then the *least character non-residue* of χ, denoted n_χ, is the least positive number n such that $\chi(n) \neq 1$ and $\chi(n) \neq 0$. We give an upper bound for n_χ in terms of the zeros of $L(s, \chi)$ near $s = 1$.

THEOREM 1. *Let χ be a non-principal Dirichlet character* (mod q), *and suppose that δ is chosen, $0 < \delta \leq 1/2$, so that $L(s, \chi) \neq 0$ when*

$$(2) \qquad\qquad \sigma > 1 - \delta, \qquad 0 < |t| \leq \delta^2 \log q.$$

Then there is an absolute constant A such that

$$(3) \qquad\qquad n_\chi < (A\delta \log q)^{1/\delta}.$$

If we write $\delta = \psi / \log q$, then the upper bound (3) takes the form $n_\chi < q^\epsilon$ with $\epsilon = \psi^{-1} \log(A\psi)$. Thus ϵ is small if ψ is large, and we see that Vinogradov's Hypothesis is true for χ provided that the distance from 1 to the nearest zero of $L(s, \chi)$ is large compared with $1/\log q$. By taking $\delta = 1/2$ we obtain

COROLLARY 1. *If χ is a non-principal character* (mod q), *and if all the non-trivial zeros of the function $L(s, \chi)$ lie on the critical line $\sigma = 1/2$, then*

$$(4) \qquad\qquad n_\chi \ll (\log q)^2.$$

PROOF OF THEOREM 1. If $\delta < 1/\log q$ then (3) is weaker than the trivial estimate $n_\chi < q$. Thus we may suppose that $\delta \geq 1/\log q$. Let x and y be real parameters, $1 < x < y$, to be chosen later, and put

$$(5) \qquad\qquad w(n) = \frac{1}{2\pi i} \int_{c-i\infty}^{c+i\infty} n^{-w} \left(\frac{y^w - x^w}{w} \right)^2 dw$$

where c is any constant. (The value of $w(n)$ is independent of c.) That is,

$$(6) \qquad\qquad w(n) = \begin{cases} 0 & \text{if } n \leq x^2, \\ \log n/x^2 & \text{if } x^2 \leq n \leq xy, \\ \log y^2/n & \text{if } xy \leq n \leq y^2, \\ 0 & \text{if } y^2 \leq n. \end{cases}$$

Take $c > 0$, multiply both sides of (5) by $\chi(n)\Lambda(n)/n$, and sum over all $n \geq 1$. The sum is uniformly convergent, so the integration and summation can be interchanged, and we find that

$$\sum_{n=1}^{\infty} w(n)\chi(n)\Lambda(n)/n = \frac{-1}{2\pi i} \int_{c-i\infty}^{c+i\infty} \frac{L'}{L}(w+1,\chi)\Big(\frac{y^w - x^w}{w}\Big)^2 dw.$$

On pulling the contour to the left we see that this is

$$\text{(7)} \qquad\qquad\qquad = -\sum_{\rho} \Big(\frac{y^{\rho-1} - x^{\rho-1}}{\rho - 1}\Big)^2.$$

Here the sum is over all zeros of $L(s,\chi)$. To analyze these zeros we must note that χ is not necessarily a primitive character. Suppose that χ^* (mod q^*) is the primitive character that induces χ. Then

$$\text{(8)} \qquad\qquad L(s,\chi) = L(s,\chi^*) \prod_{p|q/q^*} \Big(1 - \frac{\chi^*(p)}{p^s}\Big).$$

The zeros of $L(s,\chi^*)$ are of two types: the *non-trivial zeros* $\rho = \beta + i\gamma$, which lie in the *critical strip* $0 < \beta < 1$, and the *trivial zeros*, which are $-1, -3, -5, \ldots$ or $0, -2, -4, \ldots$, according as $\chi(-1) = -1$ or $\chi(-1) = 1$. Each factor of the product in (8) has an arithmetic progression of zeros on the imaginary axis, $\ll \log p$ zeros in any interval of length 1. Since $\sum_{p|q} \log p \le \log q$, it follows that $L(s,\chi)$ has $\ll \log q$ zeros in any interval of length 1 on the imaginary axis. The summand in (7) is

$$\ll \frac{x^{-2(1-\beta)}}{|\rho - 1|^2}$$

uniformly for $\beta \le 1$. Thus we see that the sum (7) is

$$\text{(9)} \qquad = -\sum_{\rho \in \mathbb{R}} \Big(\frac{y^{\rho-1} - x^{\rho-1}}{\rho - 1}\Big)^2 \; + O\Big(\sum_{\rho \notin \mathbb{R}} \frac{x^{-2(1-\beta)}}{|\rho - 1|^2}\Big) + O(x^{-2}\log q).$$

Here the sums are restricted to the non-trivial zeros (the real zeros and non-real zeros, respectively), and the last term reflects the contribution of the trivial zeros.

The size of the first error term in (9) depends on the number of zeros in various parts of the critical strip. Let $n_\chi(r,t)$ denote the number of zeros of $L(s,\chi)$ in the disk $|\rho - (1 + it)| \le r$. Put $\tau = |t| + 2$. We now demonstrate that

$$\text{(10)} \qquad\qquad\qquad n_\chi(r,t) \ll r \log q\tau$$

uniformly for $1/\log q\tau \le r \le 2$. To see this, recall that

$$\frac{L'}{L}(s,\chi) = {\sum_{\rho}}' \frac{1}{s - \rho} + O(\log q\tau)$$

uniformly for $-1 \leq \sigma \leq 2$, where $\sum'$ indicates that the sum is restricted to those zeros ρ of $L(s, \chi)$ for which $|t - \gamma| < 1$. (This is (5) in §16 of Davenport [5]). Take $s = 1 + r + it$. Since

$$\frac{L'}{L}(1 + r + it) \ll -\frac{\zeta'}{\zeta}(1 + r) \ll \frac{1}{r} \leq \log q,$$

it follows that

$$\sideset{}{'}\sum_{\rho} \frac{1}{1 + r + it - \rho} \ll \log q\tau.$$

Here each term has positive real part, and if $|\rho - (1 + it)| \leq r$ then the real part is $\geq 1/(2r)$. Thus there can be at most $\ll r \log q\tau$ such zeros.

With (10) in hand, we now estimate the first error term in (9). Cut the strip $1 - 2\delta \leq \sigma \leq 1 - \delta$ into squares of side length δ. By (10) we see that the contribution to (9) made by zeros in this strip is

$$\ll x^{-2\delta} \sum_{j=-\infty}^{\infty} \frac{\log q(|j\delta| + 2)}{(j^2 + 1)\delta} \ll x^{-2\delta}\delta^{-1}\log q.$$

On replacing δ by $2^k\delta$ we see that the contribution to the first error term in (9) made by zeros in the strip $1 - 2^{k+1}\delta \leq \sigma \leq 1 - 2^k\delta$ is

$$\ll x^{-2^{k+1}\delta}\delta^{-1}2^{-k}\log q.$$

On summing over $k = 0, 1, \ldots$, we deduce that the contribution to the sum first error term in (9) made by zeros for which $\beta \leq 1 - \delta$ is $\ll x^{-2\delta}\delta^{-1}\log q$. Now divide the strip $1 - \delta \leq \sigma \leq 1$ into squares. The zeros in the jth such square contribute an amount $\ll (j\delta)^{-2}$. Assuming that the first J such squares contain no zero, we sum over $j > J$ to see that these zeros contribute an amount $\ll \delta^{-1}J^{-1}\log q$.

Since the first term on the right hand side of (9) is negative, on combining our estimates we see that

$$(11) \qquad \Re \sum_{n=1}^{\infty} w(n)\chi(n)\Lambda(n)/n \leq Cx^{-2\delta}\delta^{-1}\log q + C\delta^{-1}J^{-1}\log q$$

where C is some absolute constant. Now suppose that $\chi(n) = 1$ or 0 for all n in the interval $x^2 \leq n \leq y^2$. By the prime number theorem we know that

$$\sum_{n=1}^{\infty} w(n)\Lambda(n)/n \sim (\log y/x)^2$$

when x and y are large with $y \geq 2x$. From this we must subtract the contribution made by the powers of the primes dividing q. Since the contribution of one such prime is $\ll x^{-2}(\log y/x)\log p$, it follows that the sum of such contributions is $\ll x^{-2}(\log y/x)\log q$. That is,

$$(12) \qquad \sum_{n} w(n)\chi_0(n)\Lambda(n)/n = (1 + o(1))(\log y/x)^2 + O(x^{-2}(\log y/x)\log q)$$

where χ_0 denotes the principal character $(\bmod\ q)$. The supposition that $\chi(n) = \chi_0(n)$ for all n in the range $x^2 \leq n \leq y^2$ implies that the left hand sides of (11) and (12) are equal, and consequently we see that

$$(\log y/x)^2 \ll x^{-2\delta}\delta^{-1}\log q + x^{-2}(\log y/x)\log q + \delta^{-1}J^{-1}\log q.$$

Taking $x^2 = (\delta \log q)^{1/\delta}$ and $y^2 = x^2 A^{1/\delta}$, we find that the above gives

$$(\log A)^2 \delta^{-2} \ll \delta^{-2} + (\log A)\delta^{-2}(\delta \log q)^{1-1/\delta} + \delta^{-1}J^{-1}\log q.$$

Since $\delta \log q \geq 1$ and $1 - 1/\delta < 0$, we see that the second term on the right is $\ll (\log A)\delta^{-2}$. On taking $J = [\delta \log q]$, the last term on the right is of the same order of magnitude as the first term on the right, and thus we have

$$(\log A)^2 \delta^{-2} \ll (\log A)\delta^{-2}.$$

But this inequality is false if A is a sufficiently large constant, and hence we deduce that the left hand sides of (11) and (12) are not equal. That is, there is an n, $x^2 \leq n \leq y^2 = (A\delta \log q)^{1/\delta}$ such that $\chi(n) \neq 1$ and $\chi(n) \neq 0$. This completes the proof.

Since n_χ is always a prime number, it is reasonable to ask for a similar bound for the least prime p such that $\chi(p) = 1$.

THEOREM 2. *Let χ be a Dirichlet character $(\bmod\ q)$ of order $K > 1$. Suppose that δ is chosen, $1/\log q \leq \delta \leq 1/2$, so that $L(s, \chi^k) \neq 0$ in the rectangle*

$$1 - \delta \leq \sigma \leq 1, \qquad |t| \leq K\delta^2 \log q,$$

for $0 < k < K$. Let ζ be any Kth root of unity. Then there is a prime number p such that $\chi(p) = \zeta$ and

(13) $$p < (AK\delta \log q)^{1/\delta}.$$

Here A is a suitable absolute constant.

PROOF. We note that

$$\frac{1}{K}\sum_{k=1}^{K} \chi(n)^k \zeta^{-k} = \begin{cases} 1 & \text{if } \chi(n) = \zeta, \\ 0 & \text{otherwise.} \end{cases}$$

It then suffices to apply the method used to prove Theorem 1, with $\chi(n)$ replaced by this linear combination of characters.

As in the case of Theorem 1, we note how this would read under GRH.

COROLLARY 2. *Let χ be a Dirichlet character $(\bmod\ q)$ of order $K > 1$. Suppose that all non-trivial zeros of $L(s, \chi^k)$ lie on the line $\sigma = 1/2$, for $0 < k < K$. Let ζ be any Kth root of unity. Then there is a prime number p such that $\chi(p) = \zeta$ and*

(14) $$p \ll K^2 (\log q)^2.$$

3.   Clumps of Zeros. For simplicity we express our results in terms of the zeta function, but our method applies equally to L-functions. By taking logarithmic derivatives in the Weierstrass product formula for the zeta function we find that (recall (8) in §12 of Davenport [**5**])

$$\Re\frac{\zeta'}{\zeta}(s) = -\Re\frac{1}{s-1} - \Re\frac{1}{s} + \frac{1}{2}\log\pi$$

$$+ \sum_\rho \Re\frac{1}{s-\rho} - \frac{1}{2}\Re\frac{\Gamma'}{\Gamma}(\frac{s}{2})$$

where $\sum_\rho$ runs over all non-trivial zeros of the zeta function. When $\sigma > 1$ we also have the option of logarithmically differentiating the Euler product formula for the zeta function, which yields the formula

$$-\frac{\zeta'}{\zeta}(s) = \sum_{n=1}^\infty \frac{\Lambda(n)}{n^s}.$$

For $\sigma > 1$ let

$$f(\sigma,t) = -\Re\frac{\zeta'}{\zeta}(\sigma+it)$$

$$= \sum_{n=1}^\infty \frac{\Lambda(n)}{n^s}\cos t\log n$$

(15)

$$= -\sum_\rho \frac{\sigma-\beta}{(\sigma-\beta)^2 + (t-\gamma)^2}$$

$$+ \frac{\sigma-\beta}{(\sigma-1)^2 + t^2} + \frac{\sigma}{\sigma^2+t^2}$$

$$+ \frac{1}{2}\Re\frac{\Gamma'}{\Gamma}((\sigma+it)/2) - \log\pi.$$

This is but one of many formulæ we have that link primes to zeros of the zeta function. We have a good understanding of the asymptotics of $f(\sigma,t)$ when $|t|$ is bounded, and we take advantage of the non-negativity of the coefficients $\Lambda(n)$. For example, from the inequality $|\cos\theta| \le 1$ we see that

$$|f(\sigma,t)| \le f(\sigma,0) \sim \frac{1}{\sigma-1}$$

uniformly for $1 < \sigma \le 2$. Put

$$F(\sigma,t) = 3f(\sigma,0) + 4f(\sigma,t) + f(\sigma,2t).$$

Since $3 + 4\cos\theta + \cos 2\theta \ge 0$ for all θ, it follows that $F(\sigma,t) \ge 0$ for all $\sigma > 1$ and all t. This relation is a standard part of the classical proof of the zero-free region. In (15) the contribution of each zero is negative; this is balanced by the gamma function, since

$$\Re\frac{\Gamma'}{\Gamma}((\sigma+it)/2) = \log|t| + O(1)$$

when $|t|$ is large. The difficulty we encounter when we try to use (15) to glean information concerning the distribution of zeros is that we have no way of telling whether the $-\frac{1}{2}\log|t|$ contributed by the zeros is due to $\approx \log|t|$ zeros at a distance ≈ 1 from s, as they would be if they were on the critical line, or whether we have a smaller number of zeros closer to s. Despite this, we are able to extract some partial information concerning the distribution of the zeros, assuming that there is a zero on the edge of the classical zero free region (1).

THEOREM 3. *Suppose that $\beta_0 + i\gamma_0$ is a zero of the Riemann zeta function with $0 < \beta_0 < 1$ and $\gamma_0 > 0$. Let $n(r,t)$ denote the number of zeros ρ of $\zeta(s)$ in the disk $|\rho - (1+it)| \le r$. If*

$$1 - \beta_0 \approx \frac{1}{\log\gamma_0}$$

then

(16) $$n(r,\gamma_0) + n(r,2\gamma_0) \approx r\log\gamma_0$$

uniformly for $1 - \beta_0 \le r \le 1$.

PROOF. The upper bound in (16) is immediate from (10). Thus it suffices to establish the lower bound. Let

$$G_\delta(\sigma, t) = F(\sigma, t) - F(\sigma + \delta, t).$$

Thus on one hand

$$G_\delta(\sigma, t) = \sum_{n=1}^{\infty} \frac{\Lambda(n)}{n^\sigma}(1 - n^{-\delta})(3 + 4\cos t\log n + \cos 2t\log n)$$

(17) $$\ge 0$$

for $\sigma > 1$, while on the other hand

(18)
$$G_\delta(\sigma, t) = 3w_\delta(\sigma - 1, 0) - 4\sum_\rho w_\delta(\sigma - \beta, t - \gamma)$$
$$- \sum_\rho w_\delta(\sigma - \beta, 2t - \gamma) \quad + O(\delta)$$

where

(19) $$w_\delta(x, y) = \frac{x}{x^2 + y^2} - \frac{x + \delta}{(x+\delta)^2 + y^2}.$$

The weights with which the zeros were formerly counted had the advantage of being non-negative (recall the derivation of (10) in the preceding section); the new weights w_δ are sometimes negative, but they are never *very* negative if δ is large compared with $\sigma - 1$, and they decay like an inverse square. Take

(20) $$\sigma = 1 + 27(1 - \beta_0), \qquad t = \gamma_0,$$

and suppose that

(21) $$\delta \geq 224(1 - \beta_0).$$

On the right hand side of (18), the pole of the zeta function contributes

$$3w_\delta(\sigma - 1, 0) \leq \frac{3}{\sigma - 1} = \frac{1}{9(1 - \beta_0)},$$

while in the first sum over ρ the term $\rho = \rho_0$ contributes

$$-4w_\delta(\sigma - \beta_0, 0) = \frac{-4}{\sigma - \beta_0} + \frac{4}{\sigma + \delta - \beta_0}$$
$$= \frac{-1}{7(1 - \beta_0)} + \frac{4}{28(1 - \beta_0) + \delta},$$

which by (20) is

$$\leq \frac{-1}{7(1 - \beta_0)} + \frac{4}{28(1 - \beta_0) + 224(1 - \beta_0)}$$
$$= \frac{-8}{63(1 - \beta_0)}.$$

Thus the combined contribution of these two terms is

(22) $$\leq -\frac{1}{63(1 - \beta_0)}.$$

To assess the contributions made by the remaining terms in (19) we first establish two useful inequalities concerning the weights w_δ. First,

(23) $$w_\delta(x, y) \geq \frac{-1}{\delta}$$

when $x \geq 0$, since

$$w_\delta(x, y) \geq -\frac{x + \delta}{(x + \delta)^2 + y^2} \geq -\frac{x + \delta}{(x + \delta)^2} = -\frac{1}{x + \delta} \geq \frac{-1}{\delta}.$$

Second,

(24) $$|w_\delta(x, y)| \leq \frac{\delta}{x^2 + y^2}$$

when $x \geq 0$. To see this it suffices to note that

$$w_\delta(x, y) = \frac{\delta}{x^2 + y^2} \cdot \frac{x^2 - y^2 + x\delta}{(x + \delta)^2 + y^2},$$

since the second factor on the right clearly has absolute value not exceeding 1.

By (23) we see that

(25) $$-4 \sum_{\substack{\rho \neq \rho_0 \\ |\rho - (1 + i\gamma_0)| \leq r}} w_\delta(\sigma - \beta, t - \gamma) \leq \frac{4n(r, \gamma_0)}{\delta},$$

and similarly that

$$(26) \qquad - \sum_{|\rho-(1+2i\gamma_0)|\le r} w_\delta(\sigma - \beta, 2t - \gamma) \le \frac{n(r, 2\gamma_0)}{\delta}.$$

On the other hand, by (24) we see that

$$-4 \sum_{|\rho-(1+i\gamma_0)|>r} w_\delta(\sigma - \beta, t - \gamma) \ll \delta \sum_{|\rho-(1+i\gamma_0)|>r} |\rho - (1 + i\gamma_0)|^{-2},$$

which by (10) and partial summation is

$$(27) \qquad \qquad \ll \frac{\delta \log \gamma_0}{r}.$$

Similarly,

$$(28) \qquad - \sum_{|\rho-(1+2i\gamma_0)|>r} w_\delta(\sigma - \beta, t - \gamma) \ll \frac{\delta \log \gamma_0}{r}.$$

On combining (17), (18), (22), and (25)–(28), we find that

$$\frac{4}{\delta}n(r, \gamma_0) + \frac{1}{\delta}n(r, 2\gamma_0) \ge \frac{1}{63(1 - \beta_0)} - O(\delta r^{-1} \log \gamma_0).$$

On taking $\delta = cr$ where c is a sufficiently small constant, it follows that

$$n(r, \gamma_0) + n(r, 2\gamma_0) \gg r \log \gamma_0$$

for $224c^{-1}(1-\beta_0) \le r \le 1$. For the remaining range $1-\beta_0 \le r \le 224c^{-1}(1-\beta_0)$, it suffices to note that

$$n(r, \gamma_0) + n(r, 2\gamma_0) \ge 1.$$

This completes the proof.

We now show that the zeros induced by ρ_0 lie more above or below ρ_0, rather than to the left of ρ_0.

THEOREM 4. *Suppose that $\beta_0 + i\gamma_0$ is a zero of the Riemann zeta function with $0 < \beta_0 < 1$ and $\gamma_0 > 0$, and that*

$$(29) \qquad \qquad 1 - \beta_0 \approx \frac{1}{\log \gamma_0}.$$

Then for any R, $2(1 - \beta_0) \le R \le 1$, there is an r, $\sqrt{R(1 - \beta_0)} \le r \le R$, such that there are $\gg r \log \gamma_0$ zeros ρ of $\zeta(s)$ such that

$$(30) \qquad \beta \ge 1 - \frac{Cr}{\log R/(1 - \beta_0)}, \qquad \min(|\gamma - \gamma_0|, |\gamma - 2\gamma_0|) \le r.$$

The constant C depends only on the constants implicit in the relation (29).

PROOF. Let $\sigma = 1 + 1/\log \gamma_0$. Then

$$\frac{\zeta'}{\zeta}(\sigma + i\gamma_0) + \frac{\zeta'}{\zeta}(\sigma + 2i\gamma_0) \ll \log \gamma_0,$$

and so by (10) it follows that

$$(31) \qquad \sum_{\rho} \frac{\sigma - \beta}{(\sigma - \beta)^2 + (\gamma - \gamma_0)^2} + \sum_{\rho} \frac{\sigma - \beta}{(\sigma - \beta)^2 + (\gamma - 2\gamma_0)^2} \ll \log \gamma_0.$$

Let δ be a parameter to be determined later, and write

$$n(r,t) = n_1(r,t) + n_2(r,t)$$

where a zero $\rho = \beta + i\gamma$ counted by $n(r,t)$ is counted by n_1 or n_2 according as $1 - \beta \geq \delta|\gamma - t|$ or not. Suppose that

$$(32) \qquad\qquad n_1(r, \gamma_0) + n_1(r, 2\gamma_0) \approx r \log \gamma_0$$

uniformly for $\sqrt{R(1 - \beta_0)} \leq r \leq R$. If ρ is a zero for which $1 - \beta \geq \delta|\gamma - \gamma_0|$ then ρ contributes an amount $\gg \delta/|\rho - (1 + i\gamma_0)|$ to the left hand side of (31), and the same applies if $1 - \beta \geq \delta|\gamma - 2\gamma_0|$. Hence by partial summation the left hand side of (31) is

$$(33) \qquad\qquad \gg \delta(\log \gamma_0) \log \frac{R}{(1 - \beta_0)}.$$

Now take $\delta = C/\log(R/(1-\beta_0))$ where C is chosen large enough so that (31) and (33) are inconsistent. Then (32) cannot hold uniformly in the specified range, and hence there is an r in this interval for which

$$n_2(r, \gamma_0) + n_2(r, 2\gamma_0) \approx r \log \gamma_0.$$

The zeros counted here all satisfy (30), so the proof is complete.

4. The Deuring-Heilbronn Phenomenon. We now show that if there is a real character χ_1 whose L-function $L(s, \chi_1)$ has an exceptional real zero β_1 then other zeros are "pushed back" from the 1-line.

THEOREM 5. (Linnik) *Suppose that $L(s, \chi_1)$ has an exceptional zero β_1, and that χ_1 is primitive* (mod q_1). *Put*

$$(34) \qquad\qquad A = \frac{1}{(1 - \beta_1) \log qq_1\tau}.$$

There is a (large) absolute constant C_1 and a (small) absolute constant c_2 such that if $A \geq C_1$ and χ is primitive (mod q) *then $L(s, \chi) \neq 0$ for*

$$\sigma > 1 - \frac{c_2 \log A}{\log qq_1\tau},$$

except for the original exceptional zero β_1 of $L(s, \chi_1)$.

Before embarking on the main body of the proof, we establish the requisite power-sum lemmas.

LEMMA 1. *Let*

$$P(r,\theta) = \sum_{k=1}^{K} \left(1 - \frac{k}{K+1}\right) r^k \cos k\theta.$$

If $0 \leq r \leq 1$ then $P(r,\theta) \geq -1/2$ for all θ. Also, $P(1,0) = K/2$, and $|P(r,\theta)| \leq 3r/2$ for $0 \leq r \leq 1/3$.

PROOF. Since $1 + 2P(1, 2\pi\theta) = \Delta_{K+1}(\theta)$ is Fejér's kernel, it is clear that $P(1,\theta) \geq -1/2$ for all θ. (Recall (16) in Chapter 1.) Let $z = re^{i\theta}$. Then $P(r,\theta)$ is a harmonic function of z, so its minimum on the disk is assumed on the boundary. The second assertion is obvious, since $\Delta_{K+1}(0) = K+1$. As for the third it suffices to note that

$$|P(r,\theta)| \leq \sum_{k=1}^{\infty} r^k \leq \tfrac{3}{2}r.$$

This completes the proof.

We now use the properties of $P(r,\theta)$ to establish a variant of Theorem 11 of Chapter 5.

LEMMA 2. *Let $s_\nu = \sum_n b_n z_n^\nu$ where the sum may have infinitely many summands. Suppose that $\sup_n |z_n| = |z_1|$, and that $b_n \geq 0$ for all those n for which $|z_n| \geq |z_1|/3$. Put*

$$L = \frac{1}{b_1|z_1|} \sum_n |b_n z_n|.$$

Then there is a ν, $1 \leq \nu \leq 24L$, such that

$$\Re s_\nu \geq \tfrac{1}{8} b_1 |z_1|^\nu.$$

PROOF. By homogeneity we may suppose that $|z_1| = 1$. Let $z_n = r_n e^{i\theta_n}$. In the notation of Lemma 1,

$$\sum_{\nu=1}^{K} \left(1 - \frac{\nu}{K+1}\right) (\Re s_\nu)(1 + \cos \nu\theta_1)$$

$$= \sum_n b_n \sum_{\nu=1}^{K} \left(1 - \frac{\nu}{K+1}\right) r_n^\nu (\cos \nu\theta_n)(1 + \cos \nu\theta_1)$$

$$= \sum_n b_n \left(P(r_n, \theta_n) + \frac{1}{2} P(r_n, \theta_n - \theta_1) + \frac{1}{2} P(r_n, \theta_n + \theta_1) \right).$$

The term from $n = 1$ contributes

$$\geq \left(\frac{K}{4} - \frac{3}{4}\right) b_1 > \left(\frac{K+1}{4} - 3r_1\right) b_1.$$

The terms for which $r_n > 1/3$ contribute $\geq -b_n \geq -3r_n b_n$ each. If $r_n \leq 1/3$ then the term is $\geq -3r_n|b_n|$. Thus

$$\sum_{\nu=1}^{K} \left(1 - \frac{\nu}{K+1}\right)(\Re s_\nu)(1 + \cos \nu \theta_1) \geq \frac{K+1}{4} b_1 - 3b_1 L.$$

Let $K = [24L]$. Then the right hand side is $\geq Kb_1/8$. But

$$\sum_{\nu=1}^{K} \left(1 - \frac{\nu}{K+1}\right)(1 + \cos \nu \theta_1) \leq 2P(1,0) = K,$$

and the summands are non-negative, so it follows that there is a $\nu \leq K$ such that $\Re s_\nu \geq b_1/8$. This completes the proof.

PROOF OF THEOREM 5. In this proof we employ an unusual convention: All sums and products over zeros are extended over all zeros of the function in question, *including the trivial zeros*.

Let χ be a character (mod q), $\chi \neq \chi_0$. We differentiate the partial fraction formula

$$\frac{L'}{L}(s, \chi) = B(\chi) + \sum_\rho \left(\frac{1}{s - \rho} + \frac{1}{\rho}\right)$$

$k - 1$ times to obtain the formula

$$(35) \qquad \frac{1}{(k-1)!} \sum_{n=1}^{\infty} \chi(n)\Lambda(n)(\log n)^{k-1} n^{-s} = -\sum_\rho \frac{1}{(s-\rho)^k},$$

for $\sigma > 1$, $k \geq 2$. If $\chi = \chi_0$ then $L(s, \chi)$ has a pole at $s = 1$, and the corresponding formula is

$$(36) \qquad \frac{1}{(k-1)!} \sum_{n=1}^{\infty} \chi_0(n)\Lambda(n)(\log n)^{k-1} n^{-s} = \frac{1}{(s-1)^k} - \sum_\rho \frac{1}{(s-\rho)^k},$$

for $\sigma > 1$ and $k \geq 2$. We now suppose that $L(s, \chi)$ has a zero $\rho_0 = \beta_0 + i\gamma_0$ with β_0 near 1. We distinguish several cases.

Case 1. $\chi \neq \chi_0$, $\chi \neq \chi_1$. We take $k = 2\nu$, $\sigma = 2$, $t = \gamma_0$, and form an appropriate linear combination of (35) and (36) to see that

$$(37) \quad \frac{1}{(2\nu-1)!} \sum_{n=1}^{\infty} \Lambda(n)n^{-2}(1 + \chi_1(n))(1 + \chi(n)n^{-i\gamma_0})(\log n)^{2\nu-1}$$

$$= 1 - \frac{1}{(2-\beta_1)^{2\nu}} - \sum_n b_n z_n^\nu,$$

where $b_n = 1$ for all n and the z_n are the numbers $(2 - \rho)^{-2}$ with ρ running over all zeros of

$$\zeta(s)L(s, \chi_1)L(s + i\gamma_0, \chi)L(s + i\gamma_0, \chi\chi_1)$$

except for the zero β_1 of $L(s, \chi_1)$, whose contribution has been written separately. The real part of the left hand side of (37) is non-negative, so that

$$(38) \qquad \Re \sum_n z_n^\nu \leq 1 - \frac{1}{(2 - \beta_1)^{2\nu}} \leq 2\nu(1 - \beta_1).$$

In the notation of Lemma 2 we have $|z_1| \geq (2 - \beta_0)^{-2}$, so that

$$L \leq (2 - \beta_0)^2 \sum_\rho |2 - \rho|^{-2} \ll \log qq_1\tau$$

by (10). By Lemma 2 there is a $\nu \leq 24L$ such that

$$\Re \sum_n z_n^\nu \geq \frac{1}{8}(2 - \beta_0)^{-2\nu} \geq \frac{1}{8} \exp\left(-2\nu(1 - \beta_0)\right).$$

On combining this with (38) we see that

$$\exp\left(2\nu(1 - \beta_0)\right) \geq \frac{1}{16\nu(1 - \beta_1)} \gg A.$$

This gives the result in this case.

Case 2. $\chi = \chi_0$. That is, $q = 1$ and $L(s, \chi) = \zeta(s)$. Then we have (37) as before, except that now the sum on the right includes an n for which $b_n = -1$, $z_n = (1 + i\gamma_0)^{-2}$. This term arises from the pole of $L(s + i\gamma_0, \chi)$ at $s = 1 - i\gamma_0$. Since we may assume that $|\gamma_0| \geq 2$, the hypotheses of Lemma 2 are still met, and the proof proceeds as before.

Case 3. $\chi = \chi_1$. We form the linear combination in (37) as before, but now we write the right hand side as

$$1 - \frac{1}{(2 - \beta_1)^{2\nu}} + (1 + i\gamma_0)^{-2\nu} - (2 - \beta_1 + i\gamma_0)^{-2\nu} - \sum_n b_n z_n^\nu$$

where the first four terms reflect the pole of $\zeta(s)$ at $s = 1$, the zero of $L(s, \chi_1)$ at β_1, the pole of $L(s + i\gamma_0, \chi\chi_1)$ at $s = 1 - i\gamma_0$, and the zero of $L(s + i\gamma_0, \chi)$ at $s = \beta_1 - i\gamma_0$. The difference of the first two terms is bounded as in (38). As for the third and fourth terms, we note that

$$(1 + i\gamma_0)^{-2\nu} - (2 - \beta_1 + i\gamma_0)^{-2\nu} = 2\nu \int_1^{2-\beta_1} (u + i\gamma_0)^{-2\nu-1} \, du,$$

from which we see that

$$\left|(1 + i\gamma_0)^{-2\nu} - (2 - \beta_1 + i\gamma_0)^{-2\nu}\right| \leq 2\nu(1 - \beta_1)|1 + i\gamma_0|^{-2\nu-1} \leq 2\nu(1 - \beta_1).$$

The net effect is that we still have (38), except that the coefficient 2 on the right must be replaced by 4. The remainder of the argument runs as before.

5. Notes. §1. For the Riemann zeta function, the classical zero-free region (1) was established in 1899 by de la Vallée Poussin. The full strength of this, with attention to dependence on q was established somewhat later by Gronwall [9] and Titchmarsh [30]. For the zeta function, the first improvement was given by Littlewood [21], who showed that $\zeta(s) \neq 0$ for $\sigma > 1 - c(\log \log \tau)/\log \tau$ where $\tau = |t| + 2$. Later, Chudakov [3, 4] used Vinogradov's exponential sum method to obtain a zero-free region of the shape $\sigma > 1 - c/(\log \tau)^\alpha$ with $\alpha < 1$. The value of α has been improved, the best result to date is that $\zeta(s) \neq 0$ for

$$\sigma > 1 - \frac{c}{(\log \tau)^{2/3}(\log \log \tau)^{1/3}};$$

This is due to Korobov [16, 17] and Vinogradov [31]. For Dirichlet L-functions we know similarly that $L(s, \chi) \neq 0$ if

$$\sigma > 1 - \frac{c}{\log q + (\log \tau)^{2/3}(\log \log \tau)^{1/3}}$$

except for the possibility of a real zero when χ is real. Postnikov [27], Rozin [29], and Gallagher [7] have given similar improvements in the dependence on q when q is a power of a fixed prime. Graham and Ringrose [8] have obtained a smaller improvement, analogous to that obtained by Littlewood, under the weaker hypothesis that q has many small prime divisors.

§2. Rodosskiĭ [28] showed that an improvement of (1) would yield Vinogradov's hypothesis; his upper bound for n_χ is an unspecified power of the bound (3) of Theorem 1. Our argument proceeds in the same spirit as Rodosskiĭ's, but with a simpler choice of the kernel. Theorem 1 is a special case of a more general result of Lagarias, Montgomery and Odlyzko [18], which was established by the same method. The Corollary of Theorem 1 was first proved for quadratic characters by Ankeny [1] by a complicated method, and then more simply by Montgomery [22, pp. 120–124]. The Corollary of Theorem 2 is Theorem 13.2 of Montgomery [22]. J.-P. Serre (private communication) has pointed out that the former publication of this result contains a serious misprint.

§3. The material in this section is based on Chapter 11 of Montgomery [22]. It seems that using differences offers an advantage over derivatives, as was done by Levinson [19].

§4. Deuring [6] and Heilbronn [11] noted the effect under discussion, but Theorem 5 is due to Linnik [20]. Linnik's proof was very complicated, but Knapowski [15] gave a simpler proof using Turán's method. Still further proofs have been given by Motohashi [23, 24], Jutila [12, 13], Pintz [25, 26], and Heath-Brown [10]. Bombieri [2, Théorème 14] has shown that if there is an exceptional zero then not only is the zero-free region wider, but zero-density estimates can be made stronger as well. His estimate of this kind implies our Theorem 5 as a corollary. In this connection see also Jutila [14]. The proof given here of Theorem 5 is previously unpublished. One may note that Siegel's theorem that $\beta < 1 - q^{-\epsilon}$ for $q > q_0(\epsilon)$ is a simple corollary of Theorem 5.

References

1. N. C. Ankeny, *The least quadratic non-residue*, Ann. of Math. **55** (1952), 65–72.

2. E. Bombieri, *Le grand crible dans la théorie analytique des nombres*, Astérisque 18, Société mathématique de France, Paris, 1974.

3. N. G. Chudakov, *On zeros of the function $\zeta(s)$*, Dokl. Akad. Nauk SSSR **1** (1936), 201–204.

4. _____, *On the functions $\zeta(s)$ and $\pi(x)$*, Dokl. Akad. Nauk SSSR **21**, 421–422.

5. H. Davenport, *Multiplicative Number Theory*, Springer-Verlag, New York, 1980.

6. M. Deuring, *Imaginäre quadratische Zahlkörper mit der Klassenzahl 1*, Math. Z. **37** (1933), 405–415.

7. P. X. Gallagher, *Primes in progressions to prime-power modulus*, Invent. Math. **16** (1972), 191–201.

8. S. W. Graham and C. Ringrose, *Lower bounds for least quadratic non-residues*, Analytic Number Theory (Allerton Park, IL, 1989), Birkhäuser, Boston, 1990, pp. 269–309.

9. T. H. Gronwall, *Sur les séries de Dirichlet correspondant à des caractères complexes*, Rend. Circ. Mat. Palermo **35** (1913), 145–159.

10. D. R. Heath-Brown, *Zero-free regions for Dirichlet L-functions, and the least prime in an arithmetic progression*, P. London Math. Soc. (3) **64** (1992), 265–338.

11. H. Heilbronn, *On the class-number in imaginary quadratic fields*, Quart. J. Math. Oxford **5** (1934), 150–160.

12. M. Jutila, *On two theorems of Linnik concerning the zeros of Dirichlet's L-functions*, Ann. Acad. Sci. Fenn. Ser. A I Math., no. 458 (1969), 32 pp.

13. _____, *On Linnik's constant*, Math. Scand. **41** (1977), 45–62.

14. _____, *Statistical Deuring-Heilbronn phenomenon*, Acta Arith. **37** (1980), 221–231.

15. S. Knapowski, *On Linnik's theorem concerning exceptional L-zeros*, Publ. Math. Debrecen **9** (1962), 168–178.

16. N. M. Korobov, *Weyl's estimates of sums and the distribution of primes*, Dokl. Akad. Nauk SSSR **123** (1958), 28–31.

17. _____, *Estimates of trigonometric sums and their applications*, Uspechi Mat. Nauk **13** (1958), 185–192.

18. J. C. Lagarias, H. L. Montgomery and A. M. Odlyzko, *A bound for the least prime ideal in the Chebotarev density theorem*, Invent. Math. **54** (1979), 271–296.

19. N. Levinson, *Zeros of the Riemann zeta-function near the 1-line*, J. Math. Anal. Appl. **25** (1969), 250–253.

20. Ju. V. Linnik, *On the least prime in an arithmetic progression, II. The Deuring-Heilbronn phenomenon*, Mat. Sb. N. S. **15(57)** (1944), 347–368.

21. J. E. Littlewood, *Researches in the theory of the Riemann ζ-function*, Proc. London Math. Soc. (2) **20** (1922), xxii–xxvii; Collected Papers of J. E. Littlewood, Vol II, Oxford University Press, Oxford, pp. 844–850; 935–938.

22. H. L. Montgomery, *Topics in Multiplicative Number Theory*, Lecture Notes 227, Springer-Verlag, Berlin, 1971.

23. Y. Motohashi, *On the Deuring-Heilbronn Phenomenon I*, Proc. Japan Acad. Ser. A Math. Sci. **53** (1977), 1–2.

24. _____, *On the Deuring-Heilbronn Phenomenon II*, Proc. Japan Acad. Ser. A Math. Sci. **53** (1977), 25–27.

25. J. Pintz, *Elementary methods in the theory of L-functions, III. The Deuring-phenomenon*, Acta Arith. **31** (1976), 295–306.

26. _____, *Elementary methods in the theory of L-functions, IV. The Heilbronn phenomenon*, Acta Arith. **31** (1976), 419–429.

27. A. G. Postnikov, *On Dirichlet L-series with the character modulus equal to the power of a prime number*, J. Indian Math. Soc. **20** (1956), 217–226.

28. K. A. Rodosskiĭ, *On non-residues and zeros of L-functions*, Izv. Akad. Nauk SSSR Ser. Mat. **20** (1956), 303–306.

29. S. M. Rozin, *On null Dirichlet L-series*, Izv. Akad. Nauk SSSR Ser. Mat. **23** (1959), 503–508.

30. E. C. Titchmarsh, *On a divisor problem*, Rend. Circ. Mat. Palermo **54** (1930), 414–429; **57** (1933), 478–479.

31. I. M. Vinogradov, *A new estimate for the function $\zeta(1+it)$*, Izv. Akad. Nauk SSSR Ser. Mat. **22** (1958), 161–164.

Chapter 10. Small Polynomials with Integral Coefficients

1. Introduction. Let

$$(1) \qquad P(x) = \sum_{n=0}^{N} a_n x^n$$

be a polynomial with integral coefficients, and put

$$(2) \qquad I(P) = \int_0^1 P(x)\,dx = \sum_{n=0}^{N} \frac{a_n}{n+1}.$$

Let d_N denote the least common multiple of the integers $1, 2, \ldots, N$. Then $I(P)$ is a rational number whose denominator divides d_{N+1}. Thus $I(P)d_{N+1}$ is an integer, and hence if $I(P) \neq 0$ then

$$(3) \qquad d_{N+1}|I(P)| \geq 1.$$

By using the fundamental theorem of arithmetic it is easy to see that $d_N = e^{\psi(N)}$ where $\psi(x)$ is the usual summatory function of the von Mangoldt Λ-function, familiar in the theory of prime numbers. This yields

THEOREM 1. *Let $P(x)$ be a polynomial with integral coefficients as in* (1), *and let $I(P)$ be defined as in* (2). *Then*

$$(4) \qquad \psi(N+1) \geq \log \frac{1}{|I(P)|}.$$

Since

$$\left(\frac{d_{N+1}}{1}, \frac{d_{N+1}}{2}, \ldots, \frac{d_{N+1}}{N+1} \right) = 1,$$

it follows that there exist integers $a_0, a_1, \ldots, a_N$ so that $I(P) = 1/d_{N+1}$, and hence equality can be achieved in (4), for any given N. However, it is more difficult to give an explicit construction of a good choice of the a_n. If we take $P(x) = x^m(1-x)^m$ then $0 < P(x) \leq 2^{-2m}$ for $0 < x < 1$, and hence $0 < I(P) < 2^{-2m}$, and (4) gives $\psi(2m+1) > 2m \log 2$. This is comparable to the simplest Chebyshev lower bound. Indeed, $I(P) = m!^2/(2m+1)!$, which is reminiscent of the use of binomial coefficients to derive Chebyshev estimates.

179

One strategy for making $|I(P)|$ small is to make $|P(x)|$ small, uniformly for $0 \leq x \leq 1$. Define r_N by the relation

(5)
$$r_N^{-N} = \min_{\substack{P \in \mathbb{Z}[x] \\ P \not\equiv 0 \\ \deg P \leq N}} \|P\|_{L^\infty[0,1]}.$$

If $P(x)$ is a polynomial for which this minimum is achieved, then $|I(P)| \leq r_N^{-N}$. On the other hand, there is nothing to prevent $I(P)$ from vanishing, so we consider instead $I(P^2)$. Since $0 < I(P^2) \leq r_N^{-2N}$, it follows from (4) that

(6)
$$\psi(2N + 1) \geq 2N \log r_N.$$

It would be nice if $r_N \to e$ as $N \to \infty$, since then one could obtain a new proof of the prime number theorem in this way, possibly with a good error term. Unfortunately, as we shall show below, r_N never gets this large. Nevertheless, we take upon ourselves the task of trying to determine the limiting behavior of r_N, and the nature of the extremal polynomials in (5).

In view of (6) and the prime number theorem, we see that $\limsup_{N \to \infty} r_N \leq e$. We now show that

(7)
$$r = \lim_{N \to \infty} r_N$$

exists. To this end, suppose that P is extremal of degree n. Write $N = nq + r$ with $0 \leq r < n$, by the division algorithm. Then $P^q x^r$ is an admissible polynomial of degree N, and hence

$$r_N^{-N} \leq \|P^q x^r\| \leq \|P\|^q = r_n^{-qn} = r_n^{-N+r} \leq r_n^{-N+n}.$$

Thus $r_N \geq r_n^{1-n/N}$, and it follows that $\liminf_{N \to \infty} r_N \geq r_n$. Now n may be chosen so that r_n is arbitrarily close to $\limsup r_N$. Hence $\liminf r_N \geq \limsup r_N$, so the limit (7) exists.

The first few values of r_N are easy to determine.

TABLE I. r_N for small N

N	r_N	$\log r_N$	extremal P
1	1	0.000000	x
2	2	0.693147	$x(1 - x)$
3	$2^{1/3}3^{1/2} = 2.182247$	0.780355	$x(1 - x)(2x - 1)$
4	2	0.693147	$x^2(1 - x)^2$
5	$\sqrt{5} = 2.236068$	0.804719	$x^2(1 - x)^2(2x - 1)$

When $N = 1$ or $N = 4$ there is more than one extremal polynomial, but when $N = 2$, $N = 3$, or $N = 5$ the extremal polynomial is unique. This is particularly easy to see in the case of $N = 2$. We note that $P(0) \in \mathbb{Z}$. Thus if $\|P\|_{L^\infty[0,1]} < 1$ then $P(0) = 0$, and similarly $P(1) = 0$. That is, $x(1 - x)|P(x)$. Thus the only extremal P of degree 2 is $P_2(x) = x(1-x)$. This polynomial takes its maximum at $x = 1/2$, so we consider the size of $P(1/2)$ for various possible P. Since $2^N P(1/2) \in \mathbb{Z}$, it follows that if $\|P\| < 2^{-N}$ then $P(1/2) = 0$, which is to say that $(2x - 1)|P$.

After $N = 2$, the value $N = 5$ is particularly interesting. Suppose that $\deg P = 5$ and that $\|P\| < 1/50$. We know that $x(1-x)(2x-1)|P$. The reasoning used to derive this can be taken a step further: The brothers Markov proved that if $P \in \mathbb{C}[x]$, $\deg P = N$ then

$$(8) \qquad \left\| \frac{P^{(j)}}{j!} \right\|_{L^\infty[0,1]} \leq \frac{N}{N+j} \binom{N+j}{2j} 4^j \|P\|_{L^\infty[0,1]}.$$

We note that if P has integral coefficients then so also does $P^{(j)}/j!$. Taking $N = 5$, $j = 1$, we see that $\|P'\| \leq 50\|P\|$. Thus if $\|P\| < 1/50$ then $\|P'\| < 1$. But $P'(0)$ and $P'(1)$ are integers, so it follows that $P'(0) = P'(1) = 0$. That is, $x^2(1-x)^2(2x-1)|P$. Hence the only polynomial P with integral coefficients, of degree 5, with $\|P\| < 1/50$ is $P_5 = x^2(1-x)^2(2x-1)$. To determine the value of $\|P_5\|$ we differentiate: $P_5'(x) = 2x(x-1)F(x)$ where

$$(9) \qquad F(x) = 5x^2 - 5x + 1 = 5\left(x - \frac{5+\sqrt{5}}{10}\right)\left(x - \frac{5-\sqrt{5}}{10}\right).$$

The roots of F lie in $[0,1]$, and P_5 attains its maximum modulus $5^{-5/2}$ at these two points. (Note that $5^{-5/2} < 1/50$.) The polynomial $F(x)$ arises in the same way that the polynomial $2x - 1$ arose when considering P_2. To show that the analogy continues, we recall the following simple result.

LEMMA. *Let $F(x) \in \mathbb{Z}[x]$, say*

$$F(x) = c_K x^K + \ldots + c_0 = c_K \prod_{k=1}^{K} (x - \beta_k).$$

If $P \in \mathbb{Z}[x]$, $\deg P = N$, then

$$(10) \qquad c_K^N \prod_{k=1}^{K} P(\beta_k) \in \mathbb{Z}.$$

If $P(x) = a_N \prod_{n=1}^{N} (x - \alpha_n)$ then the expression above may be written more symmetrically as

$$a_N^K c_K^N \prod_{\substack{1 \leq k \leq K \\ 1 \leq n \leq N}} (\beta_k - \alpha_n).$$

This is the *resultant* of F and P, denoted $R(F, P)$.

PROOF. The product in (10) is a symmetric polynomial in the β_k with integral coefficients. Hence by the fundamental theorem of symmetric functions it may be written as $Q(\sigma_1, \ldots, \sigma_K)$ where the σ_i are the elementary symmetric functions of the β_k. Moreover, Q has integral coefficients, and

$$\deg Q = \deg_{\beta_1} \prod_{k=1}^{K} P(\beta_k) = N.$$

Since $c_K \sigma_i \in \mathbb{Z}$ for all i, it follows that $c_K^N Q(\sigma_1, \ldots, \sigma_K) \in \mathbb{Z}$.

Returning to the polynomial F defined in (9), we see that $5^N P(\beta_1) P(\beta_2) \in \mathbb{Z}$. Hence if $\|P\| < 5^{-5/2}$ then $F \mid P$. This suggests that to find a better polynomial P we should search among polynomials of the form

$$(11) \qquad\qquad x^{a_1}(x-1)^{a_2}(2x-1)^{a_3}(5x^2-5x+1)^{a_4}.$$

Unfortunately, we have not yet been able to show that the pattern that has begun so promisingly continues beyond P_2 and P_5. Nevertheless, we see that the polynomials $2x - 1$ and $5x^2 - 5x + 1$ are of an interesting type: They have integral coefficients, their roots all lie in $[0,1]$, they are irreducible, and their leading coefficients are small. Let $\mathcal{F}$ denote the set of all polynomials $F \in \mathbb{Z}[x]$ that are irreducible over $\mathbb{Q}$ and have all their roots in $[0,1]$, and put

$$(12) \qquad\qquad s = \liminf_{\substack{F \in \mathcal{F} \\ \deg F = K}} c_K^{1/K}$$

where $c_K > 0$ is the leading coefficient of F. The polynomials $F \in \mathcal{F}$ form a barrier to forming good polynomials P in the following sense.

THEOREM 2. *Let r and s be defined as in (7) and (12). Then*

$$(13) \qquad\qquad r \le s.$$

PROOF. Let P be a non-zero polynomial with integral coefficients. Since P is divisible by at most finitely many $F \in \mathcal{F}$, it follows that the integer (10) is non-zero for all but finitely many F. Hence $\|P\| \ge c_K^{-N/K}$ for all but finitely many F, and consequently $\|P\| \ge s^{-N}$, which implies that $r_N \le s$ for all N.

We conjecture that $r = s$. Moreover, we expect that the extremal polynomials P_N are products of powers of $F \in \mathcal{F}$, at least for infinitely many N if not for all N. Let P_N denote an extremal polynomial of degree N, and suppose that $F \in \mathcal{F}$. Let $k = k(N, F)$ be the power of F dividing P, so that $F^k \| P$. Then we expect that $\lim_{N \to \infty} k/N$ exists; call it $\kappa(F)$. It may also be the case that $\prod_{F \in \mathcal{F}} F^{\kappa(F)}$ in some sense defines a measure on $[0,1]$. If so, it would be worthwhile to understand the support of this measure, associated extremal potentials, etc. It may be that proofs of these assertions will not be hard to construct, once one has gleaned a sufficiently detailed picture of the situation. Although our present knowledge falls far short of what we would like, we are nevertheless able to derive some interesting results, such as the following.

COROLLARY 1. *Let α be an algebraic integer of degree K over $\mathbb{Q}$, and suppose that α and all its conjugates lie in the interval $[1, \infty)$ on the real line. Then $N(\alpha) \geq (2.317)^K$ unless $\alpha = 1$, $\alpha = 2$, or $\alpha = (5 \pm \sqrt{5})/2$.*

PROOF. Let f be the minimal polynomial of α, and put $F(x) = x^K f(1/x)$. Then the roots β_k of F lie in $[0, 1]$. The leading coefficient c_K of F is $N(\alpha)$; suppose that $c_K < (2.317)^K$. In the Lemma take

$$P(x) = x^5(1 - x)^5(2x - 1)^2(5x^2 - 5x + 1).$$

This polynomial has degree $N = 14$, and critical points at $x = 0$, $1/2$, 1 and at the four points

$$\frac{1}{2} \pm \frac{\sqrt{35}}{70}\sqrt{8 \pm \sqrt{29}}.$$

Now $P(0) = P(1/2) = P(1) = 0$, while

$$P\left(\frac{1}{2} \pm \frac{\sqrt{35}}{70}\sqrt{8 + \sqrt{29}}\right) = \frac{-40923 + 1177574\sqrt{29}}{823543000000} = 7.6504895 \times 10^{-6}$$

and

$$P\left(\frac{1}{2} \pm \frac{\sqrt{35}}{70}\sqrt{8 - \sqrt{29}}\right) = \frac{-40923 - 1177574\sqrt{29}}{823543000000} = -7.7498722^{-6}.$$

Hence $\|P\| < 7.749873 \times 10^{-6} < 7.781001 \times 10^{-6} < (2.317)^{-14}$. Since $c_K^{14} < (2.317)^{14K}$, it follows that the expression (10) has absolute value < 1. Hence it is 0, so F is one of the polynomials $x - 1$, $2x - 1$, $5x^2 - 5x + 1$. Consequently α is one of the numbers 1, 2, or $(5 \pm \sqrt{5})/2$.

We now present a further sequence of polynomials, by means of which it may be seen that $s \leq 2.376842$. This also yields the best known upper bound for r.

2. The Gorškov-Wirsing Polynomials. Let $u(x)$ be the rational function

$$(14) \qquad u(x) = \frac{x(1 - x)}{1 - 3x(1 - x)}.$$

It is easy to see that $u(0) = u(1) = 0$, that $u(1/2) = 1$, that $u(x) = u(1 - x)$ for all x, that $u(x)$ is increasing in $[0, 1/2]$, and that $u(x)$ is decreasing in $[1/2, 1]$. Thus u takes the interval $[0, 1]$ to itself, as depicted in Figure 1. Consequently, if $f(x)$ is a polynomial of degree d with integral coefficients and d roots in $(0, 1)$ then

$$(15) \qquad F(x) = (1 - 3x + 3x^2)^d f(u(x))$$

is a polynomial of degree $2d$ with integral coefficients and $2d$ roots in $(0, 1)$. By iterating this construction we obtain a sequence of polynomials with all their roots in $(0, 1)$, and—as it turns out—relatively small leading coefficients. To expedite this approach, we first investigate the iterates of $u(x)$.

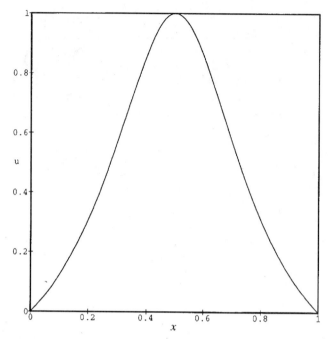

FIGURE 1.   The function $u(x)$ for $0 \leq x \leq 1$.

Let $u^{(k)}(x)$ denote the kth iterate of u. Here $u^{(k)}$ is also a rational function; to write it explicitly we introduce a sequence of polynomials $f_k(x)$ determined by the following relations:

(16)
$$f_0(x) = 2x - 1,$$
$$f_1(x) = 5x^2 - 5x + 1,$$
$$f_{k+1}(x) = f_k(x)^2 + f_k(x)f_{k-1}(x)^2 - f_{k-1}(x)^4.$$

Then

$$u(x) = \frac{f_0(x)^2 - f_1(x)}{2f_0(x)^2 - f_1(x)}.$$

Since $u^{(k+1)}(x) = u(u^{(k)}(x))$, we find by an easy induction that

(17)
$$u^{(k)}(x) = \frac{f_{k-1}(x)^2 - f_k(x)}{2f_{k-1}(x)^2 - f_k(x)} \qquad (k \geq 1).$$

As $u^{-1}\{0\} = \{0,1\}$, the zeros of $u^{(k+2)}$ are precisely the zeros of $u^{(k+1)}$ together with the roots of the equation $u^{(k+1)}(x) = 1$. By (17) we see that these x are the zeros of $f_k(x)$. Since $u^{(k+1)}(x) = 1$ has 2^k distinct solutions in $(0,1)$, it follows that $f_k(x)$ has at least 2^k distinct roots in $(0,1)$. On the other hand, by (16) it is clear that the degree of f_k is at most 2^k. On combining these two pieces of information, we deduce that $f_k(x)$ has degree exactly 2^k, that it has 2^k simple zeros in $(0,1)$, and that it has no other zeros. From (16) it is also clear that $f_k \in \mathbb{Z}[x]$. We show below that the f_k are irreducible over $\mathbb{Q}$, and hence it follows that $f_k \in \mathcal{F}$. For the present we merely observe that it is obvious that the irreducible factors of f_k lie in $\mathcal{F}$.

Although we have specified the f_k by means of the recurrence (16), these polynomials can also be generated by means of the procedure (15). More precisely,

$$(18) \qquad f_{k+1}(x) = (-1 + 3x - 3x^2)^{2^k} f_k(u(x))$$

for $k \geq 0$. We establish this by induction. The case $k = 0$ is clear from the definitions of u, f_0, and f_1 in (14) and (16). From (17) and the identity $u^{(k+1)}(x) = u^{(k)}(u(x))$ we see that

$$\frac{f_k(x)^2 - f_{k+1}(x)}{2f_k(x)^2 - f_{k+1}(x)} = \frac{f_{k-1}(u(x))^2 - f_k(u(x))}{2f_{k-1}(u(x))^2 - f_k(u(x))}.$$

By subtracting 1 from both sides we deduce that

$$\frac{-f_k(x)^2}{2f_k(x)^2 - f_{k+1}(x)} = \frac{-f_{k-1}(u(x))^2}{2f_{k-1}(u(x))^2 - f_k(u(x))}.$$

On the right hand side we multiply the numerator and denominator by $(-1 + 3x - 3x^2)^{2^k}$, and find that it is

$$= \frac{-\Big((-1 + 3x - 3x^2)^{2^{k-1}} f_{k-1}(u(x))\Big)^2}{2\Big((-1 + 3x - 3x^2)^{2^{k-1}} f_{k-1}(u(x))\Big)^2 - (-1 + 3x - 3x^2)^{2^k} f_k(u(x))}.$$

By the inductive hypothesis this is

$$= \frac{-f_k(x)^2}{2f_k(x)^2 - (-1 + 3x - 3x^2)^{2^k} f_k(u(x))}.$$

Here the numerator is the same as in the initial fraction; hence the corresponding denominators must be equal, so we have (18).

In order to derive an upper bound for s, we need to determine the leading coefficient of f_k. To this end, we first factor the numerator of u. From (16) we see that

$$f_{k-1}(x)^2 - f_k(x) = f_{k-2}(x)^2 \big(f_{k-2}(x)^2 - f_{k-1}(x)\big).$$

By using this inductively, we find that the above is

$$= \big(f_{k-2}(x) \cdots f_0(x)\big)^2 \\ \cdot \big(f_0(x)^2 - f_1(x)\big).$$

Here the last factor can be calculated by means of (16), and hence we see that the above is

$$(19) \qquad = \big(f_{k-2}(x) \cdots f_0(x)\big)^2 x(1 - x).$$

Put $g_0(x) \equiv 1$, and for $k > 0$ put $g_k(x) = f_0(x) \cdots f_{k-1}(x)$. Then (19) is equivalent to the identity $f_k(x) = f_{k-1}(x)^2 - x(1-x)g_{k-1}(x)^2$. Indeed, the polynomials f_k and g_k can be simultaneously generated by the identities

(20)
$$f_0(x) = 2x - 1,$$
$$g_0(x) = 1,$$
$$f_{k+1}(x) = f_k(x)^2 - x(1-x)g_k(x)^2 \qquad (k \geq 0),$$
$$g_{k+1}(x) = f_k(x)g_k(x) \qquad\qquad (k \geq 0).$$

By induction it is clear from these identities that $\deg f_k = 2^k$, and that $\deg g_k = 2^k - 1$. From the oscillatory nature of $u^{(k)}$ it is clear that the roots of $u^{(k)}(x) = 1$ interlace with those of $u^{(k)}(x) = 0$. That is, the zeros of $f_{k-1}(x)$ interlace with those of $x(1-x)g_{k-1}(x)$. Alternatively, from the interlacing of the zeros of $f_k(x)$ with those of $x(1-x)g_k(x)$, we see by (20) that the zeros of $f_{k+1}(x)$ and $x(1-x)g_{k+1}(x)$ interlace. In Figure 2 one can see that the zeros of f_3 interlace with those of $g_3 = f_0 f_1 f_2$. Consequently $(f_k, g_k) = 1$ for all k, and hence $(f_j, f_k) = 1$ whenever $j \neq k$.

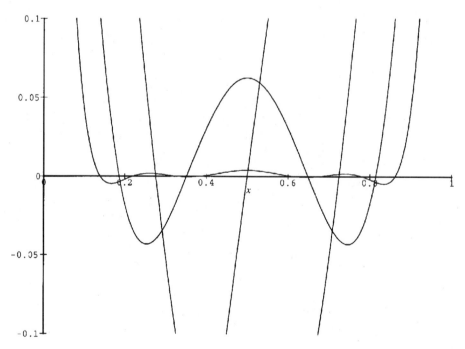

FIGURE 2. The polynomials f_0, f_1, f_2, f_3 for $0 \leq x \leq 1$.

Let a_k denote the leading coefficient of f_k, and let b_k be the leading coefficient of g_k. From (20) we see that

$$a_0 = 2,$$

(21)
$$b_0 = 1,$$
$$a_{k+1} = a_k^2 + b_k^2 \qquad (k \geq 0),$$
$$b_{k+1} = a_k b_k \qquad (k \geq 0).$$

Put $c_k = a_k/b_k$. Then

$$c_{k+1} = \frac{a_k^2 + b_k^2}{a_k b_k} = c_k + \frac{1}{c_k}.$$

That is, the sequence of rational numbers c_k can be generated by the relations

$$c_0 = 2,$$

(22)
$$c_{k+1} = c_k + \frac{1}{c_k} \qquad (k \geq 0).$$

Since $a_{k+1}/a_k^2 = 1 + 1/c_k^2$, it follows that

$$a_k^{1/2^k} = 2 \prod_{j=0}^{k-1} \left(1 + \frac{1}{c_j^2}\right)^{1/2^{j+1}}.$$

As $c_j \geq 2$ for all j, we see that the above increases with k and approaches a finite limit as $k \to \infty$. This yields the best-known upper bound for s.

THEOREM 3. (Gorškov) *Let the sequence* $\{c_k\}$ *be defined by* (22), *and put*

(23)
$$s_0 = 2 \prod_{j=0}^{\infty} \left(1 + \frac{1}{c_j^2}\right)^{1/2^{j+1}}.$$

Then $s \leq s_0$.

Numerically, $s_0 = 2.3768417062639 = \exp(0.86577259)$.

PROOF. We argue without using the irreducibility of the f_k. Choose $k > 0$. We note that f_k has degree 2^k and leading coefficient $a_k < s_0^{2^k}$. Hence f_k has at least one irreducible factor h whose leading coefficient is $< s_0^{\deg(h)}$. Among such irreducible factors of f_k choose one, say h_k. Clearly $h_k \in \mathcal{F}$. Also, the h_k are distinct, because $(f_j, f_k) = 1$ when $j \neq k$. Hence $s \leq s_0$.

It is useful to know that $f_k \in \mathcal{F}$ for all k. To establish this it remains only to prove

THEOREM 4. (Wirsing) *For* $k \geq 0$ *let* $f_k(x)$ *be defined as in* (16). *Then* $f_k(x)$ *is irreducible over* $\mathbb{Q}$.

PROOF. Clearly f_0 is irreducible over $\mathbb{Q}$. Suppose that f_k is irreducible but that f_{k+1} is reducible. In view of (18), a zero γ of f_{k+1} is a root of the equation

$u(x) = \beta$ where β is a zero of f_k. That is, γ is a root of

(24) $$x^2 - x + \frac{\beta}{1 + 3\beta} = 0.$$

This polynomial is reducible over $\mathbb{Q}(\beta)$, since otherwise γ would have degree 2^{k+1} and f_{k+1} would be irreducible. Thus $\gamma \in \mathbb{Q}(\beta)$, and hence $\gamma = q(\beta)$ for some polynomial $q(z) \in \mathbb{Q}[z]$. Let the conjugates of β be denoted β_i. Then the conjugates of γ are $\gamma_i = q(\beta_i)$. Let $r(x)$ be the minimal polynomial of the γ_i. In addition to γ, the equation (24) has the root $1 - \gamma$ with conjugates $1 - \gamma_i = 1 - q(\beta_i)$. These numbers have minimal polynomial $r(1 - x)$. The roots of $r(x)$ and of $r(1 - x)$ are distinct since we know that f_{k+1} has 2^{k+1} distinct roots. Hence over $\mathbb{Q}$ we have the factorization

$$f_{k+1}(x) = cr(x)r(1 - x).$$

By Gauss's lemma this factorization holds over the integers, and indeed c is a positive integer. By induction we see that $f_{k+1}(1) = 1$, and hence $c = 1$. Consequently $a_{k+1} = m^2$ where m is the leading coefficient of $r(x)$. However, by induction we see that $a_k \equiv -1 \pmod 3$ and that $b_k \equiv (-1)^k \pmod 3$ for all k. Hence a_k cannot be a perfect square. Thus we have a contradiction, and the proof is complete.

3. Notes. §1. The method for deriving a lower bound for $\psi(x)$ was invented in 1936 by A. O. Gelfond and L. G. Shnirelman (see Gelfond's editorial remarks in the 1944 edition of Chebyshev's Collected Works [**22**, pp. 287–288]). They employed the L^2 norm instead of the L^∞ norm, but the difference is immaterial, since by taking $j = 1$ in (8) it is easy to see that $N^{-1}\|P\|_\infty \ll \|P\|_2 \leq \|P\|_\infty$. Gelfond proposed that perhaps one could show that $\psi(x) \geq (1 + o(1))x$ in this way, but from Theorems 2 and 3 we see that this approach is incapable of showing that $\psi(x) \geq (0.87)x$, although it remains possible that a better constant could be obtained by considering polynomials in several variables. In contrast, Diamond and Erdős [**23**] used the prime number theorem to demonstrate that the parameters in Chebyshev's method can be chosen so as to show that $\psi(x) \geq cx$ and $\psi(x) \leq Cx$ with c and C arbitrarily close to 1. The Gelfond-Shnirelman approach was rediscovered by Nair [**39**, **40**], who also devised several other methods. Stimulated by Nair's work, in 1980 J. Mack and the author derived the material found in this section. We are grateful to P. Bundschuh pointing out that all this, and much more, had already been established by E. Aparicio [**3**–**20**].

For a discussion of the Markov inequality (8) see the survey article of Schaeffer [**43**]. This inequality is best possible, but for polynomials with the further property that $P^{(i)}(0) = P^{(i)}(1) = 0$ for $0 \leq i < I$, J. L. Ullman (unpublished) has given a better upper bound for $\|P^{(I)}\|$, namely

(25) $$\|P^{(I)}/I!\|_{L^\infty[0,1]} \leq \beta(I/N)^{(1+\epsilon)N}\|P\|_{L^\infty[0,1]}$$

where $\beta(v) = (v + 1/2)^{v+1/2}v^{-2v}(1/2 - v)^{v-1/2}$. In the interval $0 \le v \le 1/2$, this function takes its maximum value at $v = 2^{-3/2}$, where it attains the value

$$\beta_0 = \beta(2^{-3/2}) = 1 + \sqrt{2} = 2.414214.$$

The inequality (25) holds for all $P \in \mathbb{C}[x]$ with $\deg P = N$, but if the coefficients of P are integral then so also are the coefficients of $P^{(I)}/I!$. Hence $P^{(I)}(0)$ is an integer. Thus if $\|P\|_\infty < \beta_0^{-N}$ then by inducting on I we may deduce that $P^{(I)}(0) = P^{(I)}(1) = 0$ for all I, and hence $P \equiv 0$. Consequently, $r \le \beta_0$. This is not a very good upper bound for r, since Aparicio [10] had already given a simpler proof that $s \le 1 + \sqrt{2}$, but it raises a possibility of whether a sharper upper bound could be derived by using the fact that P must also vanish to high multiplicity at $1/2$, at $(5 \pm \sqrt{5})/10$, etc. It may be that the Julia set of $u(x)$ is relevant to further advances, perhaps as discussed by Barnsley, Geronimo, and Harrington [21].

The best possible base in Corollary 1 is $29^{1/4} = 2.320596$. Indeed, one can take the base to be 2.34, provided that the four algebraic integers

$$\frac{11}{4} \pm \frac{1}{4}\sqrt{5} + \frac{1}{4}\sqrt{19 \pm 7\sqrt{5}}, \qquad \frac{11}{4} \pm \frac{1}{4}\sqrt{5} - \frac{1}{4}\sqrt{19 \pm 7\sqrt{5}}$$

are added to the list of exceptions. These are the roots of the polynomial

$$x^4 - 11x^3 + 40x^2 - 58x + 29 = x^4 f_4(1/x).$$

§2. Our exposition follows the unpublished work of E. Wirsing, who was unaware of the earlier work of Gorškov [30]. The results of Wirsing were established in 1981, apart from Theorem 4, which he established in 1993 after reading a preliminary version of this chapter. Gorškov proceeded by observing that if $p(x)$ is a polynomial of degree d whose roots γ_i all lie in the interval $(0, +\infty)$ then one can define a polynomial $P(x)$ of degree $2d$ whose zeros are roots of the equations $x^2 - (2 + \gamma_i)x + 1 = 0$, all lying in $(0, +\infty)$. This led Gorškov to define polynomials $p_k(x)$, $q_k(x)$ by the recurrence

$$(26) \quad \begin{aligned} p_0(x) &= (x-1)^2, \\ q_0(x) &= -x, \\ p_{k+1}(x) &= (p_k(x) + q_k(x))^2, \\ q_{k+1}(x) &= p_k(x)q_k(x). \end{aligned}$$

This is equivalent to Wirsing's approach, since if γ_i is a root of p_k then $\beta_i = 1/(1 + \gamma_i)$ is the corresponding root of f_k.

It may be that $s = s_0$, but there certainly exist polynomials $F \in \mathbb{F}$ with leading coefficient $< s_0^{\deg F}$ other than the the polynomials f_k. This is exemplified by the polynomials

$$13x^3 - 19x^2 + 8x - 1,$$
$$31x^4 - 61x^3 + 41x^2 - 11x + 1,$$

whose roots are fixed points of $u^{(3)}$ and of $u^{(4)}$, respectively. Wirsing has studied the polynomials that arise in this way; the interested reader should contact him concerning the current state of his research.

By using the third formula in (20) one may establish the recurrences

$$(27) \qquad R(f_j, f_{j+1}) = \prod_{i=0}^{j-1} R(f_j, f_i)^2,$$

$$R(f_j, f_{k+1}) = R(f_j, f_k)^2 \qquad (k > j),$$

from which it may be deduced—by a double induction—that

$$(28) \qquad R(f_j, f_k) = 1$$

whenever $0 \leq j < k$.

References

1. G. D. Andria, *Approximation of continuous functions by polynomials with integral coefficients*, J. Approx. Theory **4** (1971), 357–362.

2. _____, *Convergence theorems for integral polynomial approximations*, J. Approx. Theory **7** (1973), 319–324.

3. E. Aparicio, *On some properties of polynomials with integral coefficients and on approximation of functions in the mean by polynomials with integral coefficients*, Izv. Akad. Nauk SSSR Ser. Mat. **19** (1955), 303–318.

4. _____, *On least deviation from zero of quasi-polynomials with integral algebraic coefficients*, Vestnik Moskov. Univ. Ser. I Mat. Meh. (1962), 21–32.

5. _____, *On the approximation of functions by polynomials with integer coefficients*, Proc. Eighth Annual Reunion of Spanish Mathematicians (Santiago, 1967), Publ. Inst. "Jorge Juan" Mat., Madrid, 1969, pp. 21–33.

6. _____, *Method of linear forms for obtaining bounds on the least deviations from zero of generalized polynomials with integer coefficients*, Proceedings of the First Conference of Portuguese and Spanish Mathematicians (Lisbon, 1972), Inst. "Jorge Juan" Mat. Inst., Madrid, 1973, pp. 133–143.

7. _____, *Generalization of a theorem of M. Fekete to polynomials with integer coefficients in several unknowns*, Rev. Mat. Hisp.-Amer. (4) **36** (1976), 105–124.

8. _____, *A general theorem in the theory of approximations of L^p functions by means of polynomials with integral coefficients*, Proceedings of the First Spanish-Portuguese Mathematical Conference (Madrid, 1973), Consejo Sup. Inv. Cient., Madrid, 1977, pp. 22–32.

9. _____, *Three theorems on approximation in the space L^p by means of polynomials with integer coefficients*, Collect. Math. **28** (1977), 217–234.

10. _____, *Methods for the approximate calculation of the minimum uniform Diophantine deviation from zero on a segment*, Rev. Mat. Hisp.-Amer. (4) **38** (1978), 259–270.

11. _____, *New bounds for uniform Diophantine deviation from zero in* $[0,1]$ *and* $[0,1/4]$, Rev. Univ. Santander (1979), No. 2, 289–291.

12. _____, *Diophantine approximations to zero of generalized complex polynomials over an imaginary quadratic field*, Publ. Sec. Mat. Univ. Autonoma Barcelona (1980), No. 21, 145–148.

13. _____, *On a system of algebraic integers of D. S. Gorshkov and its application*, Rev. Mat. Hispano-America **41** (1981), 3–17.

14. _____, *Generalization of a theorem of L. G. Shnirelman on the existence of limits in minimal Diophantine deviations from zero*, Proceedings of the twelfth annual conference of Spanish mathematicians (Malaga, 1976), Univ. Malaga, Malaga, 1983, pp. 159–164.

15. _____, *Some results in the problem of Diophantine approximations of functions by polynomials*, Trudy Mat. Inst. Steklov **163** (1984), 6–9; English transl. Proc. Steklov Inst. **4** (1985), 7–10.

16. _____, *Generalization of the theorem of L. G. Schnirelman*, J. Analyse Math. **48** (1987), 217–224.

17. _____, *On the asymptotic structure of the polynomials of minimal diophantic deviation from zero*, J. Approx. Theory **55** (1988), 270–278.

18. _____, *Diophantine approximations of functions by polynomials*, Congress of Number Theory (Zarautz, 1984), Univ. Pais Vasco, Bilbao, 1989, pp. 69–88.

19. _____, *Generalization of a theorem of Fekete to the case of generalized complex polynomials*, Litovskii Mat. Sb. **30** (1990), 645–650; English transl. in Lithuanian Math. J. **30** (1991), 291–295.

20. _____, *Polynomials of minimal Diophantic relative deviation from zero on the interval* $[0,1]$, New trends in probability and statistics, Vol. 2 (Palanga, 1991), VSP, Utrecht, 1992, pp. 3–7.

21. M. F. Barnsley, J. S. Geronimo, A. N. Harrington, *Orthogonal polynomials associated with invariant measures on Julia sets*, Bull. Amer. Math. Soc. (N.S.) **7** (1982), 381–384.

22. P. L. Chebyshev, *Collected Works, Vol. I, Theory of Numbers*, Akad. Nauk SSSR, Moscow, 1944.

23. H. Diamond and P. Erdős, *On sharp elementary prime number estimates*, Enseign. Math. (2) **26** (1980), 313–321.

24. M. Drmota, *Abschätzungen ganzzahliger Polynome auf dem Intervall* $[0,1]$, Elem. Math. **44** (1989), 57–63.

25. Le Baron O. Ferguson, *Approximation by polynomials with integral coefficients*, Math. Surveys 17, Amer. Math. Soc., Providence, 1980.

26. A. O. Gelfond, *On quasi-polynomials deviating least from zero on the segment* $[0,1]$, Izv. Akad. Nauk SSSR. Ser. Mat. **15** (1951), 9–16.

27. _____, *On polynomials deviating least from zero along with their derivatives*, Dokl. Akad. Nauk SSSR (N.S.) **96** (1954), 689–691.

28. _____, *On uniform approximations by polynomials with integral rational coefficients*, Uspechi Mat. Nauk **10** (1955), 41–65.

29. _____, *On approximation by polynomials with specially chosen coefficients*, Uspechi Mat. Nauk **21** (1966), 225–229.

30. D. S. Gorškov, *On the distance from zero on the interval* $[0, 1]$ *of polynomials with integral coefficients*, Proceedings of the Third All Union Mathematical Congress (Moscow, 1956), vol. 4, Akad. Nauk SSSR, Moscow, 1959, pp. 5–7.

31. E. Hewitt and H. Zuckerman, *Approximation by polynomials with integral coefficients, a reformulation of the Stone-Weierstrass theorem*, Duke Math. J. **26** (1959), 305–324.

32. M. A. Lachance, *Two extremal problems for polynomials with an interior constraint*, J. Approx. Theory **37** (1983), 224–237.

33. _____, *Bernstein and Markov inequalities for constrained polynomials*, Rational approximation and interpolation (Tampa, 1983), Springer-Verlag, Berlin, 1984, pp. 125–135.

34. M. A. Lachance and E. B. Saff, *Bounds for algebraic polynomials with zeros in an interval*, Second Edmonton conference on approximation theory (Edmonton, 1982), Amer. Math. Soc., Providence, 1983, pp. 227–237.

35. M. Lachance, E. B. Saff, and R. S. Varga, *Bounds for incomplete polynomials vanishing at both endpoints of an interval*, Constructive approaches to mathematical models (Pittsburgh, 1978), Academic Press, New York, 1979, pp. 421–437.

36. _____, *Inequalities for polynomials with a prescribed zero*, Math. Z. **168** (1979), 105–116.

37. F. Luquin, *Optimal bound of an approximation in* L^p *space by means of polynomials with integer coefficients*, Proceedings of the ninth conference of Portuguese and Spanish mathematicians, I (Salamanca, 1982), Univ. Salamanca, Salamanca, 1982, pp. 305–308.

38. _____, *Generalizatión a n variables de un teorema de A. O. Guelfond*, Actas VIII. Jornadas Luso Espanholas Matemáticas,Vol II, Univ. Coimbra, Coimbra, 1981, pp. 169–174.

39. M. Nair, *On Chebyshev-type inequalities for primes*, Amer. Math. Monthly **89** (1982), 126–129.

40. _____, *A new method in elementary prime number theory*, J. London Math. Soc. (2) **25** (1982), 385–391.

41. E. B. Saff, J. L. Ullman, and R. S. Varga, *Incomplete polynomials: an electrostatics approach*, Approximation theory, III (Austin, 1980), Academic Press, New York, 1980, pp. 769–782.

42. I. N. Sanov, *Functions with integral parameters, deviating the least from zero*, Leningrad. Gos. Univ. Uchen. Zap. Ser. Mat. Nauk **111** (1949), 32–46.

43. A. C. Schaeffer, *Inequalities of A. Markoff and S. Bernstein for polynomials and related functions*, Bull. Amer. Math. Soc. **47** (1941), 565–579.

44. R. M. Trigub, *Approximation of functions with a given modulus of smooth-*

ness on the exterior of a segment and on a half-axis, Dokl. Akad. Nauk SSSR **132** (1960), 303–306; English transl. Soviet Math. Dokl. **1** (1960), 568–572.

45. _____ , *Approximation of functions with a given modulus of smoothness on the exterior of a segment and semi-axis*, Studies of Modern Problems of Constructive Theory of Functions, Fizmatgiz, Moscow, 1961, pp. 47–51.

46. _____ , *Approximation of functions by polynomials with integral coefficients*, Dokl. Akad. Nauk SSSR **140** (1961), 773–775.

47. _____ , *Approximation of functions by polynomials with integer coefficients*, Izv. Akad. Nauk SSSR Ser. Mat. **26** (1962), 261–280.

48. _____ , *Approximation of functions with Diophantine conditions by polynomials with integral coefficients*, Metric questions of the theory of functions and mappings, No. 2, Izdat. "Naukova Dumka", Kiev, 1971, pp. 267–333.

49. _____ , *The approximation of functions by polynomials with special coefficients*, Izv. Vyss. Ucebn. Zaved. Mat. **1977, no. 1(176)**, 93–99; English transl. Soviet Math. Iz. VUZ **21** (1977), 77–82.

Appendix   Some Unsolved Problems

Most of these problems are old, and familiar in the folklore. Many of these problems seem unapproachable at the present time, but our desire to solve them exerts a strong motivating influence on current research. The problems are formulated here so that some of the long-term goals of the subject will be clearer to the newcomer.

A preliminary version of this list was circulated at the CBMS conference; this final form is greatly improved by the comments and contributions of the participants. Some of these problems were solved during or since the conference, and a few had been solved long before. Such problems have been retained, with references to the solution.

1. Uniform Distribution.

1. (Solved) *Can one construct an upper bound for $D(N)$ in terms of the $\widehat{U}_N(k)$ that is better than the Erdős-Turán inequality? Alternatively, show that*

$$E(N) = \min_K \left(\frac{N}{K} + \sum_{k=1}^{K} |\widehat{U}_N(k)|/k \right)$$

is the best possible upper bound for $D(N)$, using only upper bounds for $|\widehat{U}_N(k)|$.

As remarked in the Notes at the end of Chapter 1, this was solved by Ruzsa during or shortly after the conference. See Ruzsa [**54**]. In some delicate situations, such as in estimating the discrepancy of the sequence $\{n\omega\}$ where ω is badly approximable (i.e., the partial quotients in the continued fraction of ω are bounded), the bound $E(N)$ is larger than the truth by one logarithm. J. Beck (to appear) has devised a new method that starts with harmonic analysis, but saves that logarithm. See also Vaaler [**66**].

2. (Solved) *How much larger than $D(N)$ can $E(N)$ be? In particular, if $D(N) = O(1)$, how big can $E(N)$ be? By Theorem 1.2 we can deduce that $E(N) \ll N^{1/3}$, and it is not hard to construct examples in which $E(N) \gg N^{1/4}$.*

During the conference, Ruzsa [**55**] showed that one can have $D(N) \approx 1$ and $E(N) \approx N^{1/3}$.

2. van der Corput Sets.

3. *Let $\mathcal{H}_N = \{1^2, 2^2, \ldots, N^2\}$. Thus $\delta(\mathcal{H}_N) \to 0$ as $N \to \infty$, where δ is defined as on p. 20. How quickly does this quantity tend to 0 ?*

4. (Solved) *Put*

$$\eta(\mathcal{H}) = \sup_{\theta \in \mathbb{R}} \inf_{h \in \mathcal{H}} \|h\theta\|.$$

When $\mathcal{H}$ is the set of squares, we know that $\eta(\mathcal{H}) = 0$, by Heilbronn's theorem, and in general we call $\mathcal{H}$ a Heilbronn set if $\eta(\mathcal{H}) = 0$. In Theorem 2.9 we proved that $\eta(\mathcal{H}) \leq \delta(\mathcal{H})$. Thus any van der Corput set is a Heilbronn set. Is the converse true?

No, the converse is false; see the Notes at the end of Chapter 2.

5. *Let $\eta(\mathcal{H})$ be defined as above. Can one define a dual extremal quantity, and prove that it has the same value?*

6. *We know that $\beta_2^2 \leq \beta_\infty \leq \beta_2$. Is it true that $\beta_2 \ll \beta_\infty$?*

7. (Fürstenberg) *Let p and q be positive integers, not powers of the same number. Suppose that x is a real number, and let $\mathcal{S}_p$ be the set of fractional parts of the numbers $p^n x$. Similarly, let $\mathcal{S}_q$ be the set of fractional parts of the numbers $q^n x$. Show that if x is irrational then the sum of the Hausdorff dimensions of the closures of these sets is ≥ 1.*

From this it would follow that 2^n has a 7 in its base 10 expansion, for all large n.

8. *Show that for any real number θ and any $\epsilon > 0$ there is an $N_0(\epsilon)$ such that if $N > N_0(\epsilon)$ then there is an n, $1 \leq n \leq N$, such that $\|n^2\theta\| < N^{-1+\epsilon}$.*

Heilbronn [**31**] achieved the exponent $-1/2 + \epsilon$, and A. Zaharescu (to appear) recently improved this to $-4/7 + \epsilon$.

3. Weyl Sums.

8. *Show that if $P(x) = \sum_{j=1}^{k} \alpha_k x^k$, $|\alpha - a/q| \leq 1/q^2$, $(a, q) = 1$, then*

$$\sum_{n=1}^{N} e(P(n)) \ll_k N^{1+\epsilon} \left(\frac{1}{q} + \frac{q}{N^k} \right)^{1/k}.$$

Alternatively, construct examples that violate this. Even small improvements of existing bounds would be interesting. for example, when $k = 3$ and $q \approx N^{3/2}$, derive an upper bound that is $o(N^{3/4})$, say $O(N^\kappa)$ with $\kappa < 3/4$.

9. *Establish a best possible form of Vinogradov's Mean Value Theorem:*

$$\int_{\mathbb{T}^k} \left| \sum_{n=1}^{N} e\big(P(n,\boldsymbol{\alpha})\big) \right|^{2b} \mathbf{d}\boldsymbol{\alpha} \ll_{k,b} N^b + N^{2b-k(k+1)/2}$$

where $P(x,\boldsymbol{\alpha}) = \alpha_k x^k + \cdots + \alpha_0$ and $k > 2$.

The case $k = 2$ is settled, and indeed an extra factor of $\log N$ is required on the right hand side when $k = 2$, $b = 3$.

4. van der Corput's Method.

10. *Show that $(\epsilon, 1/2 + \epsilon)$ is an exponent pair, for every $\epsilon > 0$.*

11. *Give a sensible description of the boundary of the set of exponent pairs obtainable by using Processes A and B.*

5. Turán's Method.

12. *Improve on Halász's variant of Turán's First Main Theorem: Show that if $s_\nu = \sum_{n=1}^{N} b_n z_n^\nu$, $|z_n| \geq 1$ for all n, then*

$$\sum_{\nu=1}^{H} |s_\nu|^2 \gg |s_0|^2 e^{-N^2/H}$$

for $N \leq H \leq N^2$, and

$$\sum_{\nu=1}^{H} |s_\nu|^2 \gg |s_0|^2 H$$

for $H \geq N^2$.

This would allow one to replace the result of Halász and Montgomery [**30**] by a best possible result.

13. *Show that for any positive B there exist complex numbers $z_1, \ldots, z_N$ such that $|z_n| = 1$ for all n, and $s_\nu \ll_B N^{1/2}$ uniformly for $1 \leq \nu \leq N^B$.*

For $B < 2$ this is achieved in Example 5.6. See the Notes at the end of Chapter 5.

14. *Suppose that $|z_n| \geq 1$ for all n, and that $b_n \geq 0$ for all n. Prove that*

$$\max_{1 \leq \nu \leq 2N} |s_\nu| \gg \left(\sum_{n=1}^{N} |b_n|^2 \right)^{1/2},$$

or give a counter-example.

Under the stronger hypothesis that $|z_n| = 1$, this follows from Theorem 5.8.

6. Irregularities of Distribution.

15. *For any given positive integer k, show that there is a constant $c_k > 0$ such that if any N points are given in $\mathbb{T}^k$ then their discrepancy must be $>$ $c_k(\log N)^{k-1}$.*

This is known only for $k = 2$; see the Notes at the end of Chapter 6.

16. *Let N points be given in $\mathbb{T}^k$, and let $D(\boldsymbol{\alpha})$ denote the associated discrepancy function. Show that there is a constant $c_k > 0$ such that $\|D\|_1 > c_k(\log N)^{(k-1)/2}$.*

This is known only for $k = 2$; see the Notes at the end of Chapter 6.

17. (Komlós-Ruzsa) *Let $a_1, \ldots, a_N$ be distinct integers. Find a real number α so that the sequence $\{\alpha a_n\}$ is as close to uniform distribution (mod 1) as possible.*

This is several problems in one, depending on the interpretation given to the term "near."

(1) Minimize the discrepancy. It can be made $\ll (N \log N)^{1/2}$; is this best possible?

(2) Minimize the maximum gap between consecutive terms. Perhaps the correct order is $(\log N)/N$.

(3) Maximize the minimal distance. The order is N^{-2}; what is the best constant?

(4) Minimize the $1/N$-concentration defined by the quantity

$$Q = \max_{0 \leq x \leq 1} \operatorname{card}\{n : \|\alpha a_n - x\| < 1/N\}.$$

Komlós obtained $Q \ll N^{1/2}$ by estimating second moments. Ruzsa has given a more complicated proof that $Q \ll N^{1/3+\epsilon}$. Probably N^ϵ is the truth.

18. (Danzer) *Let $\mathcal{S}$ be a discrete set in the plane such that every rectangle in the plane of area 1 contains at least one point of the set. Let $N(R)$ denote the number of members of $\mathcal{S}$ in the disk of radius R centered at the origin. It is possible to have $N(R) \ll R^2$ as $R \to \infty$?*

It is easy to construct examples in which $N(R) \ll R^2 \log R$.

A large collection of unsolved problems concerning irregularities of distribution is provided in the book of Beck and Chen [**2**].

7. Mean and Large Values of Dirichlet Polynomials.

19. *Show that if $|a_n| \leq 1$ for all N then*

$$\int_0^T \left| \sum_{n=1}^N a_n n^{-it} \right|^{2p} dt \ll (T + N^p)N^{p+\epsilon}$$

uniformly for $1 \leq p \leq 2$.

This is given by (7.6) when $p = 2$ or $p = 4$. See §7.2 and the Notes at the end of Chapter 7.

20. *Show that if* $0 < t_1 < \ldots < t_R \leq T$ *with* $t_{r+1} - t_r \geq 1$ *for* $1 \leq r < R$, *and if* $|a_n| \leq 1$ *for all* n, *then*

$$\sum_{r=1}^{R} \left| \sum_{n=1}^{N} a_n n^{-it_r} \right|^2 \ll (N + R) N^{1+\epsilon}.$$

See §7.6 and the Notes at the end of Chapter 7.

21. *Let* $\lambda_1, \ldots, \lambda_N$ *be distinct real numbers, and put*

$$\delta_n = \min_{\substack{m \\ m \neq n}} |\lambda_m - \lambda_n|.$$

Determine the best constant in the inequality

$$\left| \sum_{\substack{m,n \\ m \neq n}} \frac{x_m \overline{x_n}}{\lambda_m - \lambda_n} \right| \leq c \sum_{n=1}^{N} |x_n|^2 / \delta_n.$$

Montgomery and Vaughan [**47**] proved this with $c = 3\pi/2$, and $c = \pi$ would be best possible. See §7.5 and the Notes at the end of Chapter 7.

22. *Show that there exists an absolute constant* C *such that if* $\mathcal{P}$ *is any finite set of prime numbers, and* a_p *are arbitrary complex numbers, then*

$$\sum_{\substack{p,q \in \mathcal{P} \\ p \neq q}} \frac{a_p \overline{a_q}}{|p - q|} \leq C \sum_{p \in \mathcal{P}} |a_p|^2.$$

Erdős asked for the special case of this in which $a_p = 1$ for all $p \in \mathcal{P}$, $a_p = 0$ otherwise. If it can be proved that the answer to Erdős's question is in the affirmative, would the more general inequality proposed above follow? Ruzsa has constructed a set $\mathcal{Q}$ of N integers such that the number of members of $\mathcal{Q}$ in any interval of length x is $\ll x/\log x$, but

$$\sum_{\substack{m,n \in \mathcal{Q} \\ m \neq n}} \frac{1}{|m - n|} \gg N \log \log N.$$

Ruzsa speculates that perhaps the following stronger information concerning the distribution of primes is the needed ingredient: Let $a_1, \ldots, a_K$ denote the number of primes in K consecutive intervals of length x. Then

$$\sum_{k=1}^{K} a_k^2 \ll \frac{K x^2}{(\log K x)^2}.$$

23. (Solved) *Show that*

$$\sum_{\substack{d|n \\ \delta|n \\ d\neq\delta}} \frac{1}{|d-\delta|} \ll d(n).$$

Proposed by Erdős, this was solved by Tenenbaum [**64**].

24. *Determine the best constant $C_1(a)$ such that if $a_n \geq 0$ for all n, and the λ_n are real numbers, then*

$$\int_{-a}^{a} \left| \sum_{n=1}^{N} a_n e(\lambda_n x) \right|^2 dx \leq C_1(a) \int_{-1}^{1} \left| \sum_{n=1}^{N} a_n e(\lambda_n x) \right|^2 dx.$$

See §7.3 and the Notes at the end of Chapter 7.

25. *Determine the best constant $C_2(a)$ such that if $|b_n| \leq a_n$ for all n, and the λ_n are real numbers, then*

$$\int_{-a}^{a} \left| \sum_{n=1}^{N} b_n e(\lambda_n x) \right|^2 dx \leq C_1(a) \int_{-1}^{1} \left| \sum_{n=1}^{N} a_n e(\lambda_n x) \right|^2 dx.$$

See §7.3 and the Notes at the end of Chapter 7.

26. (Halász) *Let $f(n)$ be a random unimodular multiplicative function. Is it true that $\sum_{n\leq x} f(n) \ll x^{1/2}$ almost surely?*

8. Reduced Residues in Short Intervals.

27. *Let $J(q)$ denote the maximum gap between consecutive reduced residue classes* (mod q). *Show that*

$$J(q) \ll (\log q) \log\log q,$$

and that

$$J(q) = \Omega\big((\log q) \log\log q\big).$$

The best known upper bound is due to Iwaniec; $J(q) \ll (\log q)^2$. In the opposite direction, it is known that there exist arbitrarily large q such that

$$J(q) > c \frac{(\log q)(\log\log q)(\log\log\log\log q)}{(\log\log\log q)^2}.$$

Erdős offers \$10,000 for a proof that one can replace the constant c above by a function tending to infinity with q.

28. (Erdős) *Let $\delta > 0$ be given, and let $J(q)$ denote the maximum gap between consecutive reduced residue classes* (mod q). *Is it true that $J(q) \ll_\delta \omega(q)$ when q is restricted to integers such that $\phi(q)/q > \delta$?*

29. (Erdős) *Let* $1 = a_1 < a_2 < \ldots$ *be the positive integers that are relatively prime to* q, *listed in increasing order. Put*

$$\delta_i = (a_{i+1} - a_i)\frac{\varphi(q)}{q}.$$

Show that there is an absolute constant $c > 0$ *such that*

$$\sum_{i=1}^{\varphi(q)} e^{c\delta_i} \ll \varphi(q).$$

9. Zeros of L-Functions.

30. *Prove the Generalized Riemann Hypothesis.*

31. *Prove the Riemann Hypothesis.*

32. *Prove that if* χ *is a quadratic character then* $L(s, \chi) > 0$ *for* $s > 0$.

33. *Prove that there is a positive constant* c *such that if* χ *is a quadratic character* (mod q) *then* $L(s, \chi) \neq 0$ *for* $s > 1 - c/\log q$.

34. *Show that there is a constant* $\kappa < 1/2$ *such that if* χ *is a quadratic character* (mod q), $q > q_0$, *then* $L(s, \chi) \neq 0$ *for* $s > 1 - q^{-\kappa}$. *Here* κ *and* q_0 *should be effectively computable.*

35. *Show that there is a function* $f(q)$ *with* $f(q) \to \infty$ *as* $q \to \infty$, *such that if* χ *is a character* (mod q) *then* $L(s, \chi) \neq 0$ *for* s *in the rectangle*

$$1 - f(q)/\log q \leq \Re s \leq 1, \qquad |\Im s| \leq 1.$$

10. Small Polynomials with Integral Coefficients.

36. *Let* $r = \lim_{N \to \infty} r_N$ *where*

$$r_N^{-N} = \min_{\substack{P \in \mathbb{Z}[x] \\ P \not\equiv 0 \\ \deg P \leq N}} \|P\|_{L^\infty[0,1]}.$$

Let $\mathcal{F}$ *denote the set of polynomials* $f \in \mathbb{Z}[x]$ *that are irreducible over* $\mathbb{Q}$ *and have all their roots in the interval* $[0, 1]$. *Let* s *be the least limit point of the set of numbers*

$$|c_f|^{1/\deg f}$$

as f *runs over all members of* $\mathcal{F}$; *here* c_f *denotes the leading coefficient of* f. *Show that* $r = s$. *Also, describe all* $f \in \mathcal{F}$ *such that* $|c_f| < s^{\deg f}$. *If* P *is of degree* N *and* $\|P\| = r_N^{-N}$, *does it follow that* P *is a product of powers of such* $f \in \mathcal{F}$?

11. Character Sums.

37. *Let $\mathcal{D}$ denote the set of fundamental quadratic discriminants. Show that*

$$\sum_{\substack{|d| \le D \\ d \in \mathcal{D}}} \left| \sum_{n=1}^{N} \mu(n)^2 a_n \left(\frac{d}{n} \right) \right|^2 \ll (N+D)D^\epsilon \sum_{n=1}^{N} |a_n|^2$$

for arbitrary complex numbers a_n.

The best known estimates are much weaker than this; see, for example, Lemmas 10 and 11 of Elliott [**26**], or Lemmas 5 and 6 of Montgomery and Vaughan [**48**].

38. (Fan Chung) *Let $\mathcal{S}$ be a set of Z residue classes* (mod p). *Show that*

$$\sum_{a,b \in \mathcal{S}} \left(\frac{a+b}{p} \right) = o(Z^2)$$

when $Z \approx \sqrt{p}$.

Friedlander and Iwaniec [**28**] have made some progress on this.

39. (Harvey Cohn) *If F is a finite field, $f : F \to \mathbb{C}$, $f(0) = 0$, $|f(a)| = 1$ for all $a \ne 0$, $f(1) = 1$, and*

$$\sum_{b \in F} f(a)\overline{f(a+b)} = -1$$

for all $a \ne 0$, does it follow that f is a character of F ?

12. Diophantine Approximation.

40. (Solved) *Does there exist a real number x that is normal to one base, but non-normal to another?*

Yes. Cassels [**8**] showed that there exists a real number x such that x is normal base 3, but x is non-normal to all bases that are not powers of 3. More generally, Schmidt [**58**] proved the following: Suppose that the integers $b > 1$ are partitioned into two classes $\mathcal{R}$ and $\mathcal{S}$, in such a way that all powers of b lie in the same class as b. Then there exist continuum many real numbers x that are normal to all bases $b \in \mathcal{R}$, and non-normal to all bases $b \in \mathcal{S}$.

41. (Littlewood) *Let $\|\theta\|$ denote the distance from θ to the nearest integer. Is it true that*

$$\liminf_{n \to \infty} n\|n\theta\|\|n\phi\| = 0$$

for any real numbers θ, ϕ ?

The late B. F. Skubenko [**59–61**] mounted an attack on this problem; some of his ideas may be useful.

42. *Let S be a set in $\mathbb{R}^n$. A lattice $\Lambda \subset \mathbb{R}^n$ is called* admissible *if $S \cap \Lambda = \emptyset$ or $S \cap \Lambda = \{\mathbf{0}\}$. The* lattice constant *of S, denoted $\Delta(S)$, is the infimum of the determinant of Λ over all admissible lattices. Construct a method (analytic, of course) to determine or estimate the size of the lattice constant $\Delta(S)$. Use it to determine whether the body*

$$(1) \qquad S = \{(x,y,z) \in \mathbb{R}^3 : |xyz| < 1\} \cup \{(x,y,z) \in \mathbb{R}^3 : |xy(y+z)| < 1\}$$

has a finite lattice constant.

Existing techniques are quite satisfactory for $n \leq 2$. The real problem begins with $n = 3$. By the work of Cassels and Swinnerton-Dyer [**9**], Littlewood's question (number 41 above) is equivalent to determining whether the lattice constant $\Delta(S)$ is finite, where S is defined in (1).

43. (Wirsing) *Let $k > 1$ be given. Does there exist a constant c_k such that for any real number $\theta \in [0,1]$ there exists a real algebraic number α whose degree over $\mathbb{Q}$ does not exceed k, such that*

$$|\theta - \alpha| < \frac{c_k}{H(\alpha)^{k+1}} \ ?$$

Here $H(\alpha)$ denotes the height of α.

For $k = 1$ this is Dirichlet's theorem. For $k > 1$ this was posed by Wirsing [**71**]. Davenport and Schmidt [**18**] settled the case $k = 2$, but the problem remains open for $k > 2$.

44. (Wills) *Show that if $1 \leq n_1 < n_2 < \ldots < n_K$ then*

$$\max_{\alpha \in \mathbb{R}} \min_{1 \leq k \leq K} \|n_k \alpha\| \geq \frac{1}{K+1}.$$

This would be best possible, since we may take $n_k = k$ for all k and $\alpha = 1/(K+1)$. This was originally conjectured by Wills [**69**]. See Weissbach [**68**], Cusick [**10**, **13**], Cusick and Pomerance [**16**], Dumir and Hans-Gill [**22–24**], and Dumir, Hans-Gill, and Wilker [**25**].

45. (Solved) *Find a normal number whose continued fraction coefficients are bounded.*

It may be that no specific such number has been exhibited, but certainly the existence of such numbers follows by combining the following three known theorems:

(1) (Jarník [**35**]) Let $\mathcal{F}_N$ denote the set of those real numbers whose continued fractions have coefficients lying entirely in the set $\{1, 2, \ldots, N\}$. Then the Hausdorff fractional dimension of $\mathcal{F}_N$ tends to 1 as $N \to \infty$.

(2) (Davenport, Erdős, and LeVeque [**17**]) If μ is a probability measure such that there is a constant $\eta > 0$ for which $\hat{\mu}(k) \ll |k|^{-\eta}$ for all $k > 0$, then μ-almost all real numbers are normal.

(3) (Kaufman [**38**]) If $\mathcal{S} \subseteq \mathbb{T}$ is a set of Hausdorff dimension $> 2/3$, then there is a probability measure μ supported on $\mathcal{S}$ such that $\widehat{\mu}(k) \ll |k|^{-\eta}$ for all $k > 0$, where $\eta > 0$ may depend on $\mathcal{S}$.

The observation that these three results can be combined to establish the existence of a normal number with bounded partial quotients was made by R. C. Baker (unpublished) when Kaufman's paper appeared. Hensley (to appear) has recently calculated the Hausdorff dimensions of the $\mathcal{F}_N$ to high precision. From his work we know that $\mathcal{F}_3$ satisfies Kaufman's hypothesis, but that $\mathcal{F}_2$ does not.

46. Let α be a real algebraic number of degree $k > 2$ over $\mathbb{Q}$. Show that the continued fraction coefficients of α are not bounded.

13. Metric Diophantine Approximation.

46. (Duffin-Schaeffer) *Let $\alpha(q)$ be an arbitrary non-negative arithmetic function. Show that if $\sum_{q=1}^{\infty} \alpha(q)\phi(q)/q = \infty$ then for almost all real numbers θ there exist infinitely many pairs a, q of relatively prime integers for which $|\theta - a/q| < \alpha(q)/q$.*

The converse is trivial, by the Borel-Cantelli lemma. The desired conclusion is known to follow if a suitable additional hypothesis is imposed. For example, by a result of Khintchin [**39**] we know that it is enough to assume that $q\alpha(q)$ is decreasing. Erdős [**27**] proved that it is enough to assume that for each q either $\alpha(q) = c/q$ or $\alpha(q) = 0$. Vaaler [**65**] improved on this by showing that it is enough to assume that $\alpha(q) \ll 1/q$, and Vilcinskiĭ [**67**] showed that it is enough to assume that $\alpha(q) \ll q^{-1} \exp\left(\exp(cq/\phi(q))\right)$ for some suitable $c > 0$. For any given function $\alpha(q)$, let $\mathcal{E}$ denote the set of those θ such that the inequality $|\theta - a/q| < \alpha(q)/q$ has infinitely many solutions with $(a, q) = 1$. Gallagher [**29**], using a method of Cassels [**7**], showed that the Lebesgue measure of $\mathcal{E}$ is either 0 or 1. R. C. Baker and G. Harman (unpublished) have shown that $\mathcal{E}$ has Hausdorff dimension 1 if $\sum \alpha(q)\phi(q)/q = \infty$. The problem was generalized to k dimensions by Sprindzhuk [**63**]. For $k > 1$ it was solved by Pollington and Vaughan [**52**], but the original problem (k = 1) remains open.

47. *Show that there is a positive constant C such that for any positive integer q there is a number a, $1 \le a \le q$, $(a, q) = 1$, such that the continued fraction coefficients of a/q are all $\le C$.*

See Cusick [**11**, **12**, **14**] and Hensley [**31**, **32**].

48. (Leo Moser(?)) *A weakening of the above: Show that there is a positive constant C such that for any positive integer q there is a number a, $1 \le a \le q$, $(a, q) = 1$, such that the sum of the continued fraction coefficients of a/q is $\le C \log q$.*

The work of Diamond and Vaaler [**19**] may be useful.

14. Algebraic Integers.

49. (Lehmer) *The* Mahler measure *of a polynomial* $P(x) = a_n x^n + \cdots + a_0 = a_n(x - \alpha_1) \cdots (x - \alpha_n)$ *is the quantity*

$$M(P) = |a_n| \prod_{i=1}^{n} \max(1, |\alpha_i|).$$

Show that there is a constant $c > 1$ such that if $P \in \mathbb{Z}[x]$ and $M(P) < c$ then P is a product of cyclotomic polynomials (i.e., $M(P) = 1$).

The least known value of $M(P) > 1$ was found by Lehmer [**43**] long ago, in an exhaustive search. Lehmer's polynomial

$$P(x) = x^{10} + x^9 - x^7 - x^6 - x^5 - x^4 - x^3 + x + 1$$

has arisen many times since; it achieves $M(P) = 1.1762808$. Let $\theta > 1$ satisfy $\theta^3 - \theta - 1$. Siegel proved that θ is the least PV number. Smyth [**62**] proved that if P is irreducible and $M(P) < \theta$ then P is a reciprocal polynomial. That is, $P(x) = x^n P(1/x)$. More recent numerical studies have been conducted by Boyd [**4**].

50. (Salem) *An algebraic integer $\alpha > 1$ is called a* Salem number *if all conjugates of α lie in the closed unit disk $|z| \le 1$, with at least one conjugate on the unit circle. Let S denote the set of all PV numbers, and T the set of all Salem numbers. Salem proved that every member of S is a limit of members of T. Does T have any other limit points? Prove that 1 is not a limit point of T. Prove that $S \cup T$ is closed.*

For basic properties of PV and Salem numbers, see Salem [**56**] or Bertin, Decomps-Guilloux, Grandet-Hugot, Pathiaux-Delefosse and Schreiber [**3**]. See also numerous papers of Boyd, and papers cited therein.

51. *Show that there is a constant $c > 0$ such that if an algebraic integer α and all its conjugates lie in the disk $|z| \le 1 + c/n$ then α is a root of unity.*

The best result in this direction thus far is due to Dobrowolski [**20**], who proved that there is a $c > 0$ such that if

$$M(\alpha) < 1 + c \left(\frac{\log \log n}{\log n} \right)^3$$

then α is a root of unity. The value of c has been improved, and the proof simplified, by Cantor and Straus [**6**], Rausch [**53**], and Louboutin [**44**].

52. (Boyd) *Let α be an algebraic integer that is not a PV number. Give a lower bound for the distance from α to the set S of PV numbers.*

15. Trigonometric Polynomials.

53. (Bohr) *Let $\Delta = \Delta(N)$ be chosen so that if $f(x) = \sum_{n=1}^{N} a_n e(k_n x)$ where the n_k form an increasing sequence of integers, then*

$$\max_M \left\| \sum_{n=1}^{M} a_n e(k_n x) \right\|_{L^\infty} \leq \Delta \|f\|_{L^\infty}.$$

How large is Δ as a function of N? That is, find

$$\Gamma = \limsup_{N \to \infty} \frac{\log \Delta(N)}{\log N}.$$

Clearly $\log N \ll \Delta \ll N^{1/2}$. Bohr showed that the value of Γ is related to a question concerning the abscissa of uniform convergence of generalized Dirichlet series.

54. (Bohr) *Let $\{k_n\}$ be an increasing sequence of integers. How small can*

$$\left\| \sum_{n=1}^{N} \sin 2\pi k_n x \right\|_{L^\infty}$$

be?

It is known that it can be as small as $cN^{2/3}$.

55. (Littlewood) *Can one choose coefficients $\epsilon_n = \pm 1$ in such a way that*

$$(2) \qquad \left| \sum_{n=1}^{N} \epsilon_n e(nx) \right| \approx \sqrt{N}$$

uniformly in x?

Kahane [**36**], building on work of Körner [**41**] and Byrnes [**5**], showed that for any $\epsilon > 0$ there is an $N_0(\epsilon)$ such that if $N > N_0$ then one can choose unimodular complex numbers $\epsilon_1, \ldots, \epsilon_N$ so that

$$(1 - \epsilon)\sqrt{N} \leq \left| \sum_{n=1}^{N} \epsilon_n e(nx) \right| \leq (1 + \epsilon)\sqrt{N}$$

uniformly in x. During the CBMS conference, Beck [**1**] showed that (2) can be achieved with coefficients such that $\epsilon_n^{400} = 1$ for all n.

56. (D. J. Newman) *Let $P(x) = \sum_{n=1}^{N} \epsilon_n e(nx)$ with $\epsilon_n = \pm 1$ for all n.*
   Strong Conjecture. *There is a constant $c < 1$ such that $\|P\|_{L^1(\mathbb{T})} \leq c\sqrt{N}$.*
   Weak Conjecture. *There is a constant $c > 0$ such that $\|P\|_{L^1(\mathbb{T})} \leq \sqrt{N} - c$.*

57. (Erdős) *Let $P(x) = \sum_{n=1}^{N} \epsilon_n e(nx)$ with $\epsilon_n = \pm 1$ for all n. Show that there is an absolute constant $c > 1$ such that $\sup_x |P(x)| \geq c\sqrt{N}$.*

By Hölder's inequality we see that the Strong Newman Conjecture implies this.

58. *Suppose that* $P(z) = \sum_{n=0}^{N} \epsilon_n z^n$ *where* $\epsilon_n = \pm 1$ *for all* n. *Define numbers* c_n *by the relation* $|P(e(t))|^2 = \sum_{n=-N}^{N} c_n e(nt)$. *Thus* $c_0 = N + 1$. *We call* $P(z)$ *a* Barker polynomial *if* $|c_n| \leq 1$ *for all* n.

Strong Conjecture. *There is no Barker polynomial of degree* $N \geq 12$.

Weak Conjecture. *There are only finitely many Barker polynomials.*

The Weak Newman Conjecture implies the weak conjecture above.

59. (D. J. Newman) *Let* $\epsilon_0, \epsilon_1, \ldots, \epsilon_N$ *be independent random variables with* $\mathbf{P}(\epsilon_n = 0) = \mathbf{P}(\epsilon_n = 1) = 1/2$. *Put* $K(z) = \sum_{n=0}^{N} \epsilon_n z^n$. *Show that there is an absolute constant* $c > 0$ *such that*

$$\mathbf{P}\left(\min_{|z|=1} |K(z)| < 1 \right) > c > 0.$$

Does there exist a choice of the $\epsilon_n \in \{0, 1\}$ *such that* $\min_{|z|=1} |K(z)| > c > 0$ *? What if* c *is replaced by* $c\sqrt{N}$ *?*

60. (Saffari) *Suppose that* $f(x) = \sum_{n=1}^{N} \epsilon_n e(nx)$ *where* $|\epsilon_n| = 1$ *for all* n. *Write* $f(x)^2 = \sum_{n=2}^{2N} d_n e(nx)$. *Is it true that* $\sum_{n=2}^{2N} |d_n|^2 \gg N^2$ *?*

It is obvious that $\sum_{n=2}^{2N} |d_n|^2 \gg N^2$.

61. (Hardy-Littlewood) *Suppose that* $f \in L^2(\mathbb{T})$, *and that* $\hat{f}(k) \neq 0$ *only when* k *is a perfect square. Does it follow that* $f \in L^p(\mathbb{T})$ *for all* $p < 4$ *?*

A. Córdoba (unpublished ?) has shown that the answer is in the affirmative if one assumes that the numbers $\hat{f}(k^2)$ are positive and monotonically decreasing.

62. (Hajela) *Let* $n_1, n_2, \ldots, n_K$ *be distinct positive integers. Show that*

$$\left\| \sum_{k=1}^{K} e(n_k^2 x) \right\|_{L^1(\mathbb{T})} \gg \left\| \sum_{k=1}^{K} e(k^2 x) \right\|_{L^1(\mathbb{T})}.$$

Hajela has noted that this would follow from an affirmative answer to the question of Hardy and Littlewood, above.

16. Miscellaneous.

63. (Erdős) *Can one walk to infinity on the Gaussian primes, taking steps of bounded length?*

It may be that the answer is no when the nth step has length $\ll (\log n)^c$ with $c < 1/2$, but yes when $c > 1/2$.

64. (Littlewood) *By elementary reasoning it is easy to show that every interval of the form $[x, x + 5x^{1/4}]$ contains a sum of two squares. Show that if $f(x)$ tends to 0 sufficiently slowly, then the interval $[x, x + f(x)x^{1/4}]$ suffices.*

65. (solved) *Let $\sum_{n=0}^{\infty} a_n z^n$ have radius of convergence 1. The set of z, $|z| = 1$, for which the series diverges is a $\mathcal{G}_{\delta\sigma}$ set. Given such a set of points on the circle, is there a power series for which it is precisely the set of divergence?*

Originally posed by Herzog and Piranian, this was solved in the negative by Lukasenko [45], following similar work of Körner [40] concerning Fourier series. For a general exposition see Körner [42], especially the unsolved problems on the last page.

66. (H. S. Shapiro) *Consider finite sums of the form $\sum a_n e^{\omega_n z}$. If two such entire functions have infinitely many zeros in common, must there exist a third such sum (with more than one term!) that divides them both?*

67. (Gelfond) *Let $w(n)$ denote the number of 1's in the binary expansion of n; this is called the* binary weight *of n. Show that $w(p)$ is odd for asymptotically half of the primes.*

Olivier [50, 51] attacked this problem by using Vinogradov's method of prime number sums, but it seems that the "Type II" sums were never estimated.

68. (Proth) *Given an initial sequence $\{u_n\}$ of integers, form a new sequence $\{v_n\}$ by taking the absolute value of the difference of two adjacent elements, $v_n = |u_{n+1} - u_n|$. Suppose that the initial sequence is the set of primes in increasing order, and that this operation is performed repeatedly. Do all the sequences formed have 1 as their initial term? What sort of gap or density property of an initial sequence would imply this property?*

2		3		5		7		11		13		17		19		23		29		31		$\ldots$
	1		2		2		4		2		4		2		4		6		2			$\ldots$
		1		0		2		2		2		2		2		2		4				$\ldots$
			1		2		0		0		0		0		0		2					$\ldots$
				1		2		0		0		0		0		2						$\ldots$

This problem is often known as Gilbreath's conjecture. Odlyzko [49] has constructed heuristics and extensive numerical evidence.

69. (Landau) *Four unattackable problems*:
  (1) *Goldbach's conjecture*;
  (2) *Twin Prime Conjecture*;
  (3) *For every n there is a prime p between n^2 and $(n+1)^2$*;
  (4) *There are infinitely many primes of the form $p = n^2 + 1$.*

70.   *Does there exist a continuous measure μ on $\mathbb{T}$ such that μ is invariant under $x \mapsto 2x$, and also under $x \mapsto 3x$, but μ is not Lebesgue measure?*

71. (Erdős) *The congruences*

$$x \equiv a_i \pmod{m_i} \qquad (1 \le i \le k)$$

are called covering congruences *if every integer satisfies at least one of these congruences, provided that the moduli m_i are distinct positive integers. Show that for any $C > 0$ there is a system of covering congruences with all moduli $> C$.*

Erdős offers \$1,000 for a proof of this.

72. *Let $\mathcal{C}$ denote a simple closed curve in the plane. A point $\mathbf{P}$ is called* equichordal *if every line through $\mathbf{P}$ meets the curve at two points that are a constant distance apart. Can a curve have two distinct equichordal points?*

Suppose that the constant distance in question is 1 and that the distance between the two equichordal points is c. This problem is now essentially solved since it has recently been shown that there can be at most finitely many c for which such a curve can exist. See Wirsing [**70**], Michelacci and Volcic [**46**], and Schäfke and Volkmer [**57**].

73. (Erdős) *Let $\mathcal{A}$ be an infinite set of positive integers, and let $r(n)$ be the number of ways of writing n as a sum of two members of $\mathcal{A}$. If $r(n) > 0$ for all n, does it follow that $\limsup_{n \to \infty} r(n) = +\infty$?*

74. (Veech) *Suppose that α is given, $0 < \alpha < 1/2$. Does there exist a function f, not identically 0, such that f has period 1, is even, $f(0) = 0$, $\sum_{a=1}^{q} f(a/q) = 0$ for every positive integer q, and $f \in \operatorname{Lip}(\alpha)$?*

75. *Let X_n be independent random variables with $\mathbf{P}(X_n = \theta^n) = \mathbf{P}(X_n = 0) = 1/2$. If $\theta = 1/2$ then the distribution function of $\sum_n X_n$ is Lebesgue measure. If $\theta < 1/2$ then the distribution is singular. What if $1/2 < \theta < 1$?*

76. (solved) *Let A denote a Banach algebra of functions $f \in L^1(\mathbb{T})$ whose Fourier coefficients are absolutely convergent. If $f \in A$ and $g \in C^\infty$, does it follow that $g(f) \in A$?*

A theorem of Wiener asserts that the answer is yes if g is analytic. However, the hypothesis $g \in C^\infty$ is too weak; see p. 239 of Katznelson [**37**].

77. (Erdős & Szekeres) *Does there exist a function $f(n)$ tending to infinity with n such that if $2 \le i \le j \le n - 2$ then $\gcd(\binom{n}{i}, \binom{n}{j}) \ge f(n)$?*

Roughly twenty years ago, Erdős and Szekeres proved that if $1 \le i \le j \le n-1$ then $\gcd(\binom{n}{i}, \binom{n}{j}) > 1$. The proof is easy, since $\binom{n}{j}\binom{j}{i} = \binom{n}{i}\binom{n-i}{j-i}$ and $\binom{n}{i} > \binom{j}{i}$. J. L. Selfridge has noted that it is not always true that $\gcd(n(n-1), \binom{n}{i}, \binom{n}{j}) > 1$; the triple $(n, i, j) = (46, 10, 23)$ is a counter-example.

78. (Erdős) *Let $P(n)$ denote the largest prime factor of n. Show that the set of n such that $P(n) > P(n+1)$ has asymptotic density $1/2$.*

79. (Erdős & Graham) *Suppose that the positive integers are partitioned into finitely many sets $\mathcal{S}_1, \ldots, \mathcal{S}_J$. Does there necessarily exist a j such that the equation*

$$\sum_{k=1}^{K} \frac{1}{n_k} = 1$$

is solvable for some K with all $n_k \in \mathcal{S}_j$?

References

1. J. Beck, *Flat polynomials on the unit circle—note on a problem of Little-wood*, Bull. London Math. Soc. **23** (1991), 269–277.
2. J. Beck and W. W. L. Chen, *Irregularities of Distribution*, Cambridge Tract 89, Cambridge University Press, Cambridge, 1987.
3. M. J. Bertin, A. Decomps-Guilloux, M. Grandet-Hugot, M. Pathiaux-Delefosse, and J. P. Schreiber, *Pisot and Salem Numbers*, Birkhäuser, Basel, 1992.
4. D. W. Boyd, *Reciprocal polynomials having small measure*, Math. Comp. **35** (1980), 1361–1377; *II* **53** (1989), 355–357, S1–S5.
5. J. S. Byrnes, *On polynomials with coefficients of modulus one*, Bull. London Math. Soc. **9** (1977), 171–176.
6. D. C. Cantor and E. G. Straus, *On a conjecture of D. H. Lehmer*, Acta Arith. **42** (1982/1983), 97–100.
7. J. W. S. Cassels, *Some metrical theorems in diophantine approximation*, Proc. Cambridge Philos. Soc. **46** (1950), 209-218.
8. _____, *On a problem of Steinhaus about normal numbers*, Colloq. Math. **7** (1959), 95–101.
9. J. W. S. Cassels and H. P. F. Swinnerton-Dyer, *On the product of three homogeneous linear forms and the indefinite ternary quadratic forms*, Philos. Trans. Roy. Soc. London Ser. A. **248** (1955), 73–96.
10. T. W. Cusick, *View-obstruction problems*, Aequationes Math. **9** (1973), 165–170.
11. _____, *Continuants with bounded digits*, Mathematika **24** (1977), 166–172.
12. _____, *Continuants with bounded digits, II*, Mathematika **25** (1978), 107–109.
13. _____, *View-obstruction problems, II*, Proc. Amer. Math. Soc. **84** (1982), 25–28.
14. _____, *Continuants with bounded digits, III*, Monatsh. Math. **99** (1985), 105–109.

15. _____, *Hausdorff dimension of sets of continued fraction*, Quart. J. Math. Oxford Ser. (2) **41** (1990), 277–286.

16. T. W. Cusick and C. Pomerance, *View-obstruction problems, III*, J. Number Theory **19** (1984), 131–139.

17. H. Davenport, P. Erdős, and W. J. LeVeque, *On Weyl's criterion for uniform distribution*, Michigan Math. J. **10** (1963), 311–314.

18. H. Davenport and W. M. Schmidt, *Dirichlet's theorem on diophantine approximation*, Symposia Mathematica, Vol. 4 (Rome, 1968), Academic Press, London, 1970, pp. 113–132.

19. H. G. Diamond and J. D. Vaaler, *Estimates for partial sums of continued fraction partial quotients*, Pacific J. Math. **122** (1986), 73–82.

20. E. Dobrowolski, *On a question of Lehmer and the number of irreducible factors of a polynomial*, Acta Arith. **34** (1979), 391–401.

21. R. J. Duffin and A. C. Schaeffer, *Khintchine's problem in metric Diophantine approximation*, Duke Math. J. **8** (1941), 243–255.

22. V. C. Dumir and R. Hans-Gill, *View-obstruction problem for 3-dimensional spheres*, Monatsh. Math. **101** (1986), 279–289.

23. _____, *The view obstruction problems for boxes*, J. Indian Math. Soc. (N.S.) **57**, 117–122.

24. _____, *Markoff type chain for the view obstruction problem for three-dimensional cubes*, J. Indian Math. Soc. (N.S.) **57** (1991), 123–141.

25. V. C. Dumir, R. J. Hans-Gill, and J. B. Wilker, *Contributions to a general theory of view-obstruction problems*, Canadian J. Math. **45** (1993), 517–536.

26. P. D. T. A. Elliott, *On the mean value of $f(p)$*, Proc. London Math. Soc. (3) **21** (1970), 28–96.

27. P. Erdős, *On the distribution of convergents of almost all real numbers*, J. Number Theory **2** (1970), 425–441.

28. J. Friedlander and H. Iwaniec, *Estimates of character sums*, Proc. Amer. Math. Soc. **119** (1993), 365–372.

29. P. X. Gallagher, *Approximation by reduced fractions*, J. Math. Soc. Japan **13** (1961), 342–345.

30. G. Halász and H. L. Montgomery, *Bernstein's inequality for finite intervals*, Conference on harmonic analysis in honor of Antoni Zygmund (Chicago, 1981), Wadsworth, Belmont, 1983, pp. 60–65.

31. H. Heilbronn, *On the distribution of the sequence θn^2 (mod 1)*, Quart. J. Math. (2) **19** (1948), 249–256.

32. D. Hensley, *The distribution of badly approximable numbers and continuants with bounded digits*, Théorie des nombres Quebec, 1987), de Gruyter, Berlin, 1989, pp. 371–385.

33. _____, *The distribution of badly approximable rationals and continuants with bounded digits, II*, J. Number Theory **34** (1990), 293–334.

34. _____, *Continued fraction Cantor sets, Hausdorff dimension, and functional analysis*, J. Number Theory **40** (1992), 336–358.

35. V. Jarník, *Zur metrischen Theorie der diophantishen Approximationen,* Prace Mat.-Fiz. **36** (1928), 91–1106.

36. J.-P. Kahane, *Sur les polynomes a coefficients unimodulaires,* Bull. London Math. Soc. **12** (1980), 321–342.

37. Y. Katznelson, *An Introduction to Harmonic Analysis,* 2nd Edition, Dover, New York, 1976.

38. R. Kaufman, *Continued fractions and Fourier transforms,* Mathematika **27** (1980), 262–267.

39. A. Khinchin, *Einige Sätze über Kettenbruche, mit Anwendungen auf die Theorie der Diophantischen Approximationen,* Math. Ann. **92** (1923), 115–125.

40. T. W. Körner, *Sets of divergence for Fourier series,* Bull. London Math. Soc. **3** (1971), 152–154.

41. _____ , *On a polynomial of Byrnes,* Bull. London Math. Soc. **12** (1980), 219–224.

42. _____ , *The behavior of power series on their circle of convergence,* Banach Spaces, Harmonic Analysis, and Probability Theory (Storrs, 1980/1981), Lecture Notes in Math. 995, Springer-Verlag, Berlin, 1983, pp. 56–94.

43. D. H. Lehmer, *Factorization of certain cyclotomic functions,* Ann. of Math. **34** (1933), 461–479.

44. R. Louboutin, *Sur la mesure de Mahler d'un nombre algébrique,* C. R. Acad. Sci. Paris Ser. I Math. **296** (1983), 707–708.

45. S. Ju. Lukasenko, *Set of divergence and nonsummability for trigonometric series,* Vestnik Moskov. Univ. Ser. I Mat. Mekh. (1978), 65–70; English transl. Moscov Univ. Math. Bull **33** (1978), 53–57.

46. G. Michelacci and A. Volcic, *A better bound for the excentricities not admitting the equichordal body,* Arch. Math. **55** (1990), 599–609.

47. H. L. Montgomery and R. C. Vaughan, *Hilbert's Inequality,* J. London Math. Soc. (2) **8** (1974), 73–82.

48. _____ , *Mean values of character sums,* Canadian J. Math. **31** (1979), 476–487.

49. A. M. Odlyzko, *Iterated absolute values of differences of consecutive primes,* Math. Comp. **61** (1993), 373–380.

50. M. Olivier, *Sur le developpement en base g des nombres premiers,* C. R. Acad. Sci. Paris Ser. A-B **272** (1971), A937–A939.

51. _____ , *Repartition des valeurs de la fonction "somme des chiffres",* Seminaire de Theorie des Nombres, 1970–1971, 7 pp.

52. A. D. Pollington and R. C. Vaughan, *The k-dimensional Duffin and Schaeffer conjecture,* Mathematika **37** (1990), 190–200.

53. U. Rausch, *On a theorem of Dobrowolski about the product of conjugate numbers,* Colloq. Math. **50** (1985), 137–142.

54. I. Z. Ruzsa, *On an inequality of Erdős and Turán concerning uniform distribution modulo one, I,* Sets, Graphs and Numbers (Budapest, 1991), Coll.

Math. Soc. J. Bolyai 60, 1992, pp. 621–630.

55. _____ , *On an inequality of Erdős and Turán concerning uniform distribution modulo one, II*, J. Number Theory (to appear).

56. R. Salem, *Algebraic numbers and Fourier analysis*, Wadsworth, Belmont, 1983.

57. R. Schäfke and H. Volkmer, *Asymptotic analysis of the equichordal problem*, J. Reine Angew. Math. **425** (1992), 9–60.

58. W. M. Schmidt, *Über die Normalität von Zahlen zu verschiedenen Basen*, Acta Arith. **7** (1961/1962), 299–309.

59. B. F. Skubenko, *Minima of a decomposable cubic form in three variables*, Zap. Nauchn. Sem. Leningrad. Otdel. Mat. Inst. Steklov. (LOMI) **168** (1988), 125–139, 189–190; J. Soviet Math. **53** (1991), 302–310.

60. _____ , *Minima of decomposable forms of degree n in n variables for n ≥ 3*, Zap. Nauchn. Sem. Leningrad. Otdel. Mat. Inst. Steklov. (LOMI) **183** (1990), 142–154, 166, 168.

61. _____ , *On a question of A. Woods and P. Bambah concerning codes of decomposable cubic forms*, Zap. Nauchn. Sem. S.-Peterburg. Otdel. Mat. Inst. Steklov. (POMI) **204** (1993), 90–92, 169.

62. C. J. Smyth, *On the product of the conjugates outside the unit circle of an algebraic integer*, Bull. London Math. Soc. **3** (1971), 169–175.

63. V. G. Sprindzhuk, *Metric theory of Diophantine approximation*, V. H. Winston and Sons, Washington, 1979.

64. G. Tenenbaum, *Une inégalité de Hilbert pour les diviseurs*, Indag. Math. (N.S.) **2** (1991), 105–114.

65. J. D. Vaaler, *On the metric theory of Diophantine approximation*, Pacific J. Math. **76** (1978), 527–539.

66. _____ , *Refinements of the Erdős-Turán inequality*, Number theory with an emphasis on the Markoff spectrum (Provo, 1991), Dekker, New York, 1993, pp. 263–269.

67. V. T. Vilcinskiĭ, *On simultaneous approximations by irreducible fractions*, Vestsi Akad. Navuk BSSR Ser. Fiz.-Mat. Navuk (1981), 41–47, 140.

68. B. Weissbach, *Zu einer Aufgabe von J. M. Wills*, Acta Math. Hungar. **48** (1986), 131–137.

69. J. M. Wills, *Zwei Sätze über inhomogene diophantische Approximation von Irrationalzahlen*, Monatsh. Math. **71** (1967), 263–269.

70. E. Wirsing, *Zur Analytizität von Doppelspeichenkurven*, Arch. Math. **9** (1958), 300–307.

71. _____ , *Approximation mit algebraischen Zahlen beschränkten Grades*, J. Reine Angew. Math. **206** (1960), 67–77.

Index

A boldface number indicates a principal reference, or a reference to a definition.

Other Titles in This Series

(Continued from the front of this publication)

(See the AMS catalog for earlier titles)